THE SPARTAN

by Caroline Dale Snedeker

TO MY MOTHER

WHO BY HER ENTHUSIASM FOR HELLAS AND THE GREEKS ENCOURAGED
MY CHILDHOOD DESIRE TO TELL THE STORY OF ARISTODEMOS

AND TO MY HUSBAND

WITHOUT WHOSE CRITICISM I COULD NOT HAVE
WRITTEN THE TALE

Reprinted
"in the Interest of Children,"
by American Home School
Publishing, LLC

First AHSP Printing, July, 2005
Printed in the United States of America
ISBN: **0-9667067-8-1**

PREFACE

The writer gratefully appreciates the welcome which this story has received from many men and periodicals whose judgments are of the greatest value. After living so long with Leonidas and Aristodemos, endeavoring to comprehend them, it was a delightful surprise on returning to find how many people of the twentieth century are interested in the life of those far off days—the most vital in all human history—and to realize again how keen, unspoiled and modern are the scholars who specialize in things Greek.

She wishes to acknowledge her debt to Mr. Martin L. D'Ooge of the University of Michigan, Mr. Charles B. Gulick of Harvard University, and Mr. Arthur G. Leacock of Phillips Exeter Academy, for encouragements and fundamental discussions. Also to Mr. Edward Delavan Perry of Columbia University, Mr. Milton W. Humphreys of the University of Virginia, Mr. Walter Miller of Tulane University, and Mr. Philip Van Ness Myers of College Hill, Ohio, for many careful criticisms of which she has availed herself in the present edition.

In the spelling of Greek names the aim has been to secure some slight sense of Greek sonorousness and strength as against the hissing of "C"s and the degrading of vowels with which we have become familiar through the Latin. This was not ventured in the case of very familiar names. The result is inconsistent and perhaps indefensible.

The new title of the book will be found a little less misleading than the former. One must perhaps know our hero well before "Coward of Thermopylæ" can become an affectionate paradox.

- Caroline Dale Snedeker, 1912.

CONTENTS

THE SPARTAN

CONTENTS

PROLOGUE

The Sacred Way

It is a wonderful road that leads from Athens north-west through the open country to Eleusis, a road of dim wood-spaces and gnarled olive orchards that still re-new their bloom. It has glimpses of sea, blue as sapphire, of islands with sharp crests against the sky, of temples asleep in the bright sunshine, and of tombs that crumble away with soft gray shadows. One of these covers the dust of a woman loved once beyond an empire's wealth.

It is a road of dreams, as fragrant of memories as a spice garden. It leads away and away, farther than Eleusis, into the dim-locked centuries of the past. And save for the past of Jerusalem it has the richest past in the world. For before it fell asleep it was "The Sacred Way" of the Eleusinian Mysteries—those rites of Demeter and Persephone that were the highest religious experience of the Greek, and survived as his latest comfort.

Here the great, keen heart of Hellas went longing and seeking. The deep hopes that stirred and troubled them they here sought out. One must almost weep in thinking how they came, so eager, so childlike, groping for the eternity that was not their lot to fathom. For their gods were happy gods who turned away with loathing from the death of men, and gave no promise of the bright sun to those who went down into the hollow earth. "Fare-well," says the dying Hippolytos to his delicate goddess, as she turns away from him. "How easily dost thou forego our lifelong friendship!"

Before setting out, the Mystics went down into the purifying sea. "To the sea! To the sea, ye Mystai!" was their call.

They came forth pure for the mysteries, men and women bearing with them the image of a nursing child, symbol of new life, and calling it by name, "Iac, O Iacchos! Iac, O Iacchos!"

They came dancing full to overflow with a discerning, penetrating life, a kind of genius given not to an individual but to a whole race. They hit with divine and childlike accident, what we still reach for with labouring fingers.

The distance to Eleusis might have been covered in four hours. But the Mystics progressed slowly, stopping now at a bridge, now at a tree or shrine. At each place they had some time-rich ritual to be said or danced or sung. Sometimes their religious ecstasy, rising like a fountain jet into the light, tumbled back again in sparkling laughter, riotous fun, peltings of flowers, rude jests uncontrolled.

After nightfall they came to the Temple precinct where the priests received them. Chantings and songs filled the air, torches flared in the darkness, or trailed backward with flame and smoke as the swift dancers bore them. Now there were haltings and callings in the dusk. All was life, bustle and happy confusion.

Then they passed within. The doors were shut, leaving the silent world and the sea. One heard now a muffled shout of surprise sounding out into the moonlight, now a fragment of song when some portal was opened and quickly closed again. The air became faintly fragrant as incense burned within. The very moonlight seemed to listen and expect.

But what the sacred secrets were, no one has told. Out of that careless seeming crowd, generations of such crowds, was not one babbler. The precious seal of silence was pressed down, and we stand without, wishing and questioning.

THE SPARTAN

CHAPTER ONE

An April Journey

It was an early April morning, four hundred and
ninety three years before Christ. At sunrise, the invari-
able starting time of the early rising Greek, two travellers, mother and son, passed out of Athens by the
Thriasian Gate, upon the Sacred Way. They were a
strangely mated pair. The mother, a Spartan: her high
borne head and wide, square set shoulders bespoke it.
Even her new widowhood, marked by her rough shorn
hair, could not wholly cloud the thought of the return to
Sparta, which gleamed in her eyes, a telltale joy.

The boy was all Athenian, with never a feature of
his mother save her golden hair. He was spare with the
thinness of ten years, but showing already the deftness
of step, and delicate control that Athenian training gave.
There was more of widowhood in his young face than in
his mother's. He had looked on death, he had lost his
own; and his eyes bore in them a look of inner awakening that does not often come to one so young.

They took their way, with their eight necessary
slaves, through the gray olive wood. Here the morning
air took on a certain drowsiness and mystery. A few
level sunbeams crept into the wood along the ground,
picking out now a spray of myrtle, now a fantastic root—
for the olives were old—and now pausing in irresolute
brightness upon a glistening bit of moss, wet with some
hidden spring. The leafy canopy seemed full of whis-

pers, and the boy was not without his prayer to the shy dryads that almost visibly haunted the place.

The travellers crossed the Kephissos, musical with its spring fullness. By the streamside a thousand violets opened their eyes, and gave to the bank a dim blue shining. They paused and washed hands before stepping into the stream. For then, happily, many things were sacred. Gradually they left the olive wood, and began to climb the arid slope of Aigaleos, a thistly place, where they had much ado to keep the brown donkey, that drew the mother in the little cart, from turning aside to his prickly repast. The road mounted narrow between two rocky walls until they stood isolated upon the height, with all Attica falling away below them. Here was the last sight of the city.

The boy looked back upon Athens, as has every traveller these countless generations since. It was a little Athens then, a few houses huddled at the base of the Acropolis—an Acropolis where no Parthenon yet smiled. But how he loved it! Oh, with all the rich racial love that the immortal Parthenon was some day to express! He could see Hymettos, mist-blue behind the bold cut crag of the Acropolis, and he recalled the wild thyme flavour of its, honey, his chief sweetmeat. All his life that fragrance was sweet to him. He saw on the low ground south of the city the massive, half finished columns of the Tyrant's temple to Zeus, looking almost as lonely and ruinous then as it does to-day.

He even caught a glimpse of his own gymnasium, Kynosarges, far beyond the eastern gate, dazzling in the morning light. Beyond that, a glint of the Euripos. And still beyond, shadowy against the sky, the Eubœan hills. His love was in his eyes as he looked. His mother, standing impatiently by him, the slaves, waiting with pathetic slave patience, could not but see the thoughts in his tender child face. Had he been two years older, his mother had never brought him thence.

He turned suddenly, his eyes blurred with tears, and went down the farther slope. All the way his young feet planted themselves stubbornly and his round golden head drooped in silence. But his sorrow was his own, and he gave no voice to it. There seemed to be in the child certain precious things that he would not share.

A full hour they walked in silence, only the slow shuffle of the slaves, the stepping of the donkey, the rattle of the little cart, breaking the morning quiet. At last, on a turn, the sea appeared. The boy caught his breath at the stretch of intense blue washing to its shore in lines of pearly surf. The Gulf of Salamis lay spread below them, island-locked, innocent yet of battles. Upon it the gay flock of Athenian shipping was busy with the opening of spring, the sails flying ever faster and faster as the wind freshened.

Later the little company stopped to drink and say a prayer beside the Sacred Fig Tree, that first of fig trees which Demeter herself gave to mortals. Over it pious hands had reared a light roof upon slender columns. Near by was an almond tree lifting its crooked branches amid a veil of pink blossoms. How it glowed in the sun! What a fragrance it shed about the place! It had scattered a rain of petals at its foot.

With quick impulse the boy buried his hand in these and flung them aloft. Then, with sudden ruth, he gathered them together, and offered them to the naiad of the spring. Standing, he made his prayer, lifting as in a cup the shattered blossoms. "The Naiad will be sorry and she will keep them alive on her bosom," he said as the petals floated on the surface of the pool. Indeed, the life of the boy himself was not unlike the life of the pool, quiet-seeming above, but ever fed and freshened secretly.

The road now skirted the shore. Here the untouched sand was smooth as satin, save for a bright shell here and there. As the afternoon light grew soft they passed a rude image of a sea-god stuck lonely, slanting, in the loose beach. It was scarcely more than a post roughly carven and hewn. But from it fluttered a net left there by some fishermen thankful for a safe return from his perilous harvesting. Then, in the evening coolness, they came to Eleusis itself, and, weary with the first day's journeying, stopped at the nearest inn.

"Eleusis!" The boy slept lightly with the thought of it. "Wonderful Eleusis!" He rose before the sun, threw on his short chiton and then his full himation, pulling the white folds over his shoulders modestly to hide his arms. Then he went forth. All the earth was still, save for a drowsy note now and then from a laurel thicket, and the steady, soft lapping of little gray waves waiting for the dawn. He washed in the tingling sea, and hastened on. The grim walls of the sacred precinct rose before him shutting him out from dear and wonderful secrets. His father had been a Mystes. Had he not come home with shining eyes from the autumn festival?

How still it was. The brown crag against which the temple stood rose ruggedly above the place. Over the wall he saw a cypress-tip waving almost imperceptibly in the gentle air as if moved by winds too faint for mortal sense. The akroteria that topped the temple roof began to gleam in the dawn, strange figures painted red, blue and gold; the blessed Demeter, Kore the maid, Demophon, the little child that the goddess sheltered in her bosom what time she walked the earth. To the imaginative boy they seemed to move with the glancing light.

"But they are alive," spoke the child aloud. "They step with their feet and their eyes see!"

"Do they?" said a kind voice at his side. And the boy started, seeing a young man, athletic, wholesome, with curling locks and wearing the short, tree dress of the torch-bearing priest.

"Hail to thee, Servant of holy Demeter!" said the boy.

The greeting was both reverent and gay, as if he had said, "All the glory of the rising sun be upon thee!" The man could not but smile. He looked the little figure up and down, from his white, upturned forehead to his light, sandalled feet.

"And who art thou that worshippest so early?"

"I am Aristodemos son of Lykos."

"Lykos of the tribe of Pandion?" asked the man eagerly. "I knew him well. He was high among the Mystai. Thou art indeed his son, and as like him as stars are alike!"

"Nay, but this star is among the living, and that one shines in the realms of the dead," said the boy quiveringly.

"Yes, yes. Who hath not known of his untimely going! Whom the gods love—" the priest mused. "But come, child. Thou canst not go within; but thou shalt walk with me, and afterward break thy fast by the Sacred Well."

They walked together past the temple precinct, around the curve of the bay, and into the fields of waving barley—those sacred fields where men first learned to plow. The boy was quiet at first, but gradually he talked, answering the torchbearer's questions, clinging to his hand and walking close to him. He talked of his father, of the boys at school, of his gymnasium, and even of his own shy ambitions there.

"But it takes many years, my father said, to make a man beautiful in all his acts, in the rim, the jump, the disk throw."

It was full day as they returned and stopped by the Sacred Well of Kallichoros, where the maids were wont to weave in a ring the sacred dance to Demeter. About the well was a circular pavement set for their flying feet. Near by in a shaded place a slave had set their morning meal.

"Now thou must keep without the gates," said the priest kindly. "But when thou art a man thou shalt be of the Mystai, and go within and see such wonders as the gods vouchsafe to men."

As they finished the meal a slave came running.

"The Spartan Makaria is searching everywhere for

her son. She is in haste to be off on her journey."

The boy looked into the torchbearer's face.

"Must I go?" he asked.

"I fear thou must, since thy mother sends for thee."

Aristodemos rose reluctantly from the small table, and slowly put aside the fig and little barley cake, half eaten. The priest thought it was of these he was thinking. But suddenly he lifted his bright head, crossed over to where the man sat, and threw his arms about his neck. He kissed him again and again, then turned and ran quickly down the road, not looking back at all.

And as the priest gazed after him he found his own eyes wet with sudden tears.

CHAPTER TWO

Aristodemos Meets a Hero

The second day's journey was easy and without event. They passed the so-called Flowery Well, where Demeter had sat so weary, looking for her lost Persephone, when the three damsels came, and fetched the goddess to their home as the nurse of their little brother.

All the country side was full of Demeter. Her august footsteps seemed but yesterday to have passed that way; her gentle presence was upon the land even now. For was not spring itself the blossoming of her joy? Every flower by the road, every field ripening for the harvest, was the utterance of the goddess's soul reanimate with gladness at the return of her daughter from the dead.

The road was in constant striving with the hills. Now they thrust it to the very edge of some wave-washed cape, now suffered it to hug close at their base. And now the hills themselves suffered invasion as the road climbed steeply up and wound among the headlands above the sea.

Makaria was more wearied in her jolting cart than the boy, whose eager interest kept him leaping the way. They arrived at Megara late in the afternoon, and Makaria went to rest. But Aristodemos hasted to bring sacrifice to Pandion, his tribal hero, who was buried there.

He went scornfully enough through the town. Megara was noted even in those fresh early years for the bigness of its private houses. "They build for themselves," said the Athenians, "as if they were to live for-ever, and eat as if they were to die to-morrow."

He ascended the bluff on which the grave of Pandion stood, carrying in his childish hands his gifts of sacrifice. They were simple enough—a bit of cedar wood for a flame and for sweet savour to the dead, two honey-cakes withheld from his midday meal, a measure of barley, and a wool fillet of costly purple dye, for he felt that one gift should be more than a day's treasuring. So he made his sacrifice, burning the sweet-smelling wood in the afternoon sunshine and scattering the bar-ley while he prayed and asked protection for the jour-ney that yet lay before him. As he turned away he noted the grave of Prokne, King Pandion's daughter. For af-ter all, this was but the family burying place of that an-cient king.

Thinking of Prokne, his ancestress, Aristodemos went quite into a dream. For Prokne had been turned into a nightingale, and through her he himself was blood related to the birds. Never a swallow twittered under the eaves, but he half expected it to speak plain. And once his father had watched him with reverent eyes as he left his hand and, creeping into the thicket, called softly to the nightingale singing there:

"Grieve not so, dear nightingale! I will be thy son!"

And now as he walked down the hill into the stranger city, he chanted softly an old Homer song, his accus-tomed hand lifting itself all unconsciously and plucking an imaginary lyre.

> "Even as when the daughter of Pandareos,
>   The brown bright nightingale,
> Sings sweet in the first season of spring
>   From her place in the thick leafage of trees,
> And with many a turn and trill
>   Pours forth her full voiced music,
> Bewailing her child, dear Itylos,
>   Whom on a time she slew with sword un-witting—

ARISTODEMUS MEETS A HERO

Even as her song,
My troubled soul sways to and fro."

Child that he was, what did he know of "troubled swaying of soul?" Yet he chanted very softly the song he had learned at school.

Next morning at break of day they started forth. And well might Aristodemos offer a prayer, for the hardest stage of the journey now lay before them. They left behind them the cart, because of the steepness of the way, and Makaria sat upon the donkey's back, not a little cross at the prospect of the toil.

The road still led them close to the sea, and among the tombs of Megara, famous tombs, some of them. But their thoughts were upon the Skironian Rocks, that difficult pass between the sea and the cliff. The unconscious donkey, plodding along with bent head and swaying ears, who could not "look before and after," was the only happy one of the party.

As for the old slave, Antiphon, who brought up the rear, his complaint was loud—not loud enough to reach Makaria, but poured into his little master's ear, with whom he had certain privileges. For in Athens Antiphon had been paidagogos to the boy, and had gone with him to school of mornings, carrying his lyre and his small wax writing tablets. From Antiphon's lips Aristodemos had heard the story of Prokne; aye, and many a tale of the gods that his father would ill have liked the boy to hear, so careful was Lykos to bring only the nobler stories to his son's hearing. But Antiphon babbled all; the story of Ion, of Hippoth, old superstitions, fragments of demon worship that had come down from the Pelasgians. Children were like to hear much in those days that is kept from them now.

"And to think," complained the old slave, as his staff clicked unceasingly upon the hard road, "to think that I should go to Sparta, and at my years! Thy father had never brought me this journey."

"That I believe," assented the boy, a thought sadly.

THE SPARTAN

"Sparta! Why, they treat the slaves like dogs there, even the good ones. Though I doubt they have good ones! Now thy father, he was ready with his jest. Many's the time he has set us all a-laughing. No sour looks from him—no sour looks!" And the old man shook his head dolefully. "But now—now in my age I shall be cuffed, beaten, burdened—"

The boy's eyes flamed.

"No!" he cried. "Thou shalt not be cuffed. Thou, art my slave, and I shall grow older, and then thou shalt be free."

"Yes, yes, little Master. And when thou growest older I shall be naught."

Antiphon laboured groaning up the rocky path. Slave though he was, Aristodemos could not resist giving him a tug up the steep incline. He felt very tender toward the old man, thinking on his present piteous unwillingness, and how obedient he had always been. But as the boy laid hold of the arm, so fragile under its rough sleeve, he began to look at Antiphon with a narrow, definite gaze, with a sudden clear consciousness of him, his crooked shoulders, slow legs and withered hands. Would he ever become like that, so helpless, so apart from loveliness and health? A thought almost of despising came over him—not of the old man but of his eld. Better almost to die as his father had died than to live so crooked, so numb to life. Involuntarily he ran ahead, and took pace by his mother's donkey.

The path became narrower and steeper. The sea fell away below them to the left while on their right the rocky wall rose precipitous, encroaching nearer upon the path, which finally hugged close against the cliff.

At noon they stopped to rest and eat in a steep wood, and then set out again, finding themselves indeed on the very Skironian Rocks. The thin pine forest seemed set edgewise upon the face of the cliff. The trees mounting upward hung finally above their heads, flinging out gaunt peen arms against the sky. Then even these gave place to the bare wall with the sun beating upon the tawny rock. Here and there a great mass had given way, leaving a staring white rent in the yellow cliff, obstructing the path with rubble. But the fallen bulk of it could be discerned below, far down by the sea's edge. A terror, as of a great gesture with which nature had broken silence, seemed in it yet. It gave to the immovable mountainside a menace not its own.

The travellers scarce dared to look out over the sea, so high were they above it. The very horizon seemed lifted with them. And to-day it was so blue, the blue of a low-burning flame Aristodemos thought, one far, intense level from which the eyes shrank back.

The slaves picked their way fearfully, and even the donkey lifted each foot with care lest he plant it on a rolling stone. Aristodemos, oppressed with the silence and awe of the place, began to sing.

"Best spend thy care in looking to the path," said his mother. "One false step would be thy last. We were fools not to go by sea!"

She had scarce spoken when there came a great shaking of a thicket, a scuffle on the stones, and suddenly, black before them, stood men—eight or ten of them—but they seemed an army. Like an avalanche they fell, so unlooked for, so impassable.

Makaria gave a sharp cry of despair. Shrewd enough in a possible outcome, she saw here no escape. The stout slaves shrank against the wall, hiding behind burdens, and old Antiphon, from whom the boy expected some faithfulness and spirit, crept with unwonted nimbleness over the cliff's edge and hid him on a shelf below.

It happened that Aristodemos was walking in advance. He looked the leader full in the face and spoke first.

"Art thou really a robber?"

The tone was not without pleasure. The man was a sight indeed for an imaginative boy. The heavy face, the eyes that peered from a matted black of locks, the squat body with its covering of skins, and above all the bright hoops of earrings that dangled viciously.

The man grunted and stopped, attracted by surprise like a dull animal. So dark and heavy he seemed over against the fair alertness of the child.

"And what dost thou want?" came the quick voice again.

"Thy goods and gold, little fool."

"But it is thou art foolish!" answered the child with merry triumph. "We have neither goods nor gold. Dost think we would bring treasures this way to leave them with thee? Not while the blessed Athena guides us!"

"Yes, but ye have them," returned the robber, with an impatience that boded ill.

"Yes, but we have them not," persisted the boy. "If we had, we had sent them by sea. But we be poor folk now. My dear father is dead, and ere he died all our fortune was lost through a trick."

The childish voice broke a little, and quavered off, especially as the man reached past him and seizing a bundle from the donkey's back, flung it on the ground, and tore it fiercely open. It was soon disclosed Makaria's robe and the chlamys or cloak of the boy, laid aside for the heat. With an oath the man kicked them over the edge. Down they tumbled, fluttering, catching on rock and bush, and one himation of scarlet floated with a putt, bellying, rippling out over the bright sea.

The pitifulness that was growing in the boy faded at the sight.

"What vile manners!" he said, almost with a laugh. "What was the use to do so?"

The man seized a second pack and went on with his work. But the boy bent over him, full of interest.

"Thou'rt a big robber," he said, "but canst not be a good robber this once?"

The man grunted, his hands among the cookery pots.

"—And oh!" said the boy, remembering old tales, "art thou Skiron's son, perchance?" For Skiron was the prince of robbers.

"Yes, I be." And the man rose and started forward. But the child placed his little body directly in his path. He had never been crossed or resisted, and hardly understood.

"Dost thou live here summers and winters too?"

The man paused and looked down.

"Well, ye be poor folk. But ye be not afeard."

"Why should I be afraid? Ye are country folk. I am an Athenian." And up went the slender chin.

"Will ye listen to that!" quoth the robber, bursting into laughter and turning to his men. The child's ignorance of danger amused him. He planted himself astride the path to play as a cat with a mouse.

"Why do ye live here in this wolfish place? Have ye never heard of Athens?"

"Never," said the man, with a backward wink.

"Poor man! Poor man! Hast never seen the Agora where men buy and sell, and where thou hearest the news?"

"No."

"Nor the Kerameikos?"

"No."

"Nor the olive branch—the first, first olive branch that Athena gave us?—And, oh, Harmodios and Aristogeiton! Has never seen them?"

The man still shook his head.

"They stand near the market place, and oh, so fair and new! And they will kill the tyrant. But they are of bronze, you know, and the cunning Antenor fashioned them. Ah, I wish thou mightest look upon them!"

"That do not I!" said the outlaw, significantly. "But thou must go!" the boy prattled on. "Then thou wilt sing that song—dost know it?" And he burst out with the little song so popular in Athens:

> "In a myrtle bough shall my sword be hid.
> Thus Harmodios and Aristogeiton did,
>   The day they struck the tyrant down
>   And made this Athens a freeman's town."

It was a catch full of rhythm. Out over the silent places the high boyish voice rang with merry sweetness, and his light feet tapped the tune. At Makaria's nod a slave stealthily brought a lyre and followed the melody with a twanging, all faint and thin in the open air, but enough to add spirit to the boy. Verse after verse he sang, for the skolion was endless, one of those melodies sung everywhere and added to at will. Faster and faster ran the lay. The boy now was the tyrant, now the patriot, and all in vivid acting.

> *"Ever their fame shall be and brighten,*
> *Dearest Harmodios and Aristogeiton,*
> *Because they put the tyrant down*
> *And made our Athens a freeman's town."*

He finished breathless.

"Now, wilt thou go to Athens?" he said, seizing the man with both his strong little hands.

But the man stood quite still, bending upon him a helpless look, half fear, half awe. Lives there a Greek who is not moved by music?

Presently he said, "I thank ye, little Master, for thus singing to me."

"Oh, I sang not for thee, Robber, but for the glory of dear Athens."

Then there was a quick turn of thought in the volatile mind, and the child took from one of the slaves a bundle, and opened it with eager fingers. Antiphon had wrapped it for him, and he trusted the old man to remember his especial delights.

"Here it is," he said at length. "Honey, my last, sweet piece of it. Take it, O Skiron. This is Hymettos honey. And when thou hast tasted, thou wilt surely go to Athens. Fate can not keep thee!"

The man took the gift in his great rough hand, and sucked one finger where the golden liquid ran, gazing the while at the eagerness in the child's gray eyes.

Then quite carefully he laid the honey down, and wrapping together the broken bundle, handed it to Makaria.

"Thou shalt go free," he said, and hugged the cliff for them to pass.

"An Athenian asks no passage from thee!" said the boy proudly. "Farewell, Skironides!" And as he went down the path he turned waving his hand at the rough, silent company.

"Farewell, farewell!" called the men.

"Farewell, Athenian! called the leader.

And thus, for the last time and from the lips of a rude outlaw, was Aristodemos called by the dear name of Athens.

CHAPTER THREE

Hollow Lacedæmon

The travellers wound quietly down the narrow ledge toward the level shore. It was characteristic of Makaria that she spoke no word of the robbers. She seemed to have forgotten the incident as soon as it was past. One of the slaves, drawing near the boy, caressed his arm timidly, as slaves will, and began to say: "Brave little Master, this day hast thou saved us alive."

No sooner were the words dropped from his lips than a sounding whack on the ear silenced him, and Makaria pointed him to the rear. She did not propose to have her little son spoiled by slave flattery. But she might have spared her pains, for the boy was more unconscious than she. He was living still in the skolion, humming it over, stepping lightly to the controlling rhythm. Indeed, the little fellow was at that moment forming a new stanza of his own. He looked up with quiet wonder at his mother's onslaught, and put it down in his mental catalogue as one of the vagaries of women.

The Isthmos which they were now traversing was a barren place. Presently they heard shoutings from afar, then coming nearer, groanings and creakings, sounds of dragging and of scraping over the rock. They were at the famous portage where the ships of prospering Corinth were dragged across from the Gulf, to be set free again in the Ægean. Truly the poor ship looked a prisoner, with her hull set heavily upon rollers, her painted dragon figurehead rearing high in the sunshine and grinning impotent sarcasm upon the toiling men. Now she quivered to her very mast as they bent to the ropes and hauled with chanting chorus, and she with another groan moved forward—she who had leaped so lightly on the sea, so responsive to every touch of the swift, invisible wind.

The boy laughed at the sight, little thinking that long years after this would be a very figure of his own life dragged through an element not his own.

They left behind the ship and the chanting, and came to the place of the Isthmian games, waiting in that far day for Pindar's songs. For Pindar had not yet sung here, though his heart was lifting and pulsing songs yet to be. Aristodemos, however, thought not of songs but of deeds. They came into the white, deserted stadion, in its pretty dell, with its empty seats and running place all fragrant with wild thyme. The whole place breathed of contests. One almost heard the whirr of the brazen diskos singing through the air from some young uplifted hand.

The boy's breath came quick. He took his mother's hand in one of those rare moments when he opened his heart to her.

"Mother, shall I ever come here and really be an agonist or maybe win the crown of pine?"

His heart was all on fire, wishing it.

"Yes, my son," answered Makaria. "I do think so. But for thee it is well not to think of the crown but of the struggle. Many days of ceaseless labour wilt thou give?"

"Yes, yes, Mother. I shall give them! I shall give them!"

"Perhaps thou wilt run. Thou hast good legs. Thy mother before thee was a runner in Sparta and won the prize." Makaria's face lighted as it had not lighted these years. Then she fell silent with thoughts of her girlhood.

In the precinct itself was an avenue leading to the temple. Here Aristodemos dropped his mother's hand, shrinking to himself with an instinct of joy in the place. On the right side of the way stood a dark procession of pines pluming their lofty tops against the blue. They were the sacred tree of the Isthmos. Darkness and contemplation breathed from them, and the boy felt deeply their mood of awe. But on the other side of the way all was life, for even then many victor statues had been set up, a row of slender, long-haired boys.

Was it the victor statues, the running place, the approach to Sparta? Something put into Makaria a sense of the past. As they now took the road leading westward to Corinth city, she refused to mount the donkey, but strode along with head set square, and with that stately gliding which girls use who bear brimming jars upon their heads from fountains. Thus Makaria shook off the bonds that

Athens had put upon her, and took again the free, athletic life of Sparta.

She would not pause at Corinth. Before dawn she started with her train upon the Argos road. They passed Mycenæ, stopping only at the tombs of Agamemnon and his father Atreus, dear to the hearts of those who love great deeds. There they saw the grave of Kassandra, the mad prophetess whom, all unwilling, the king brought from Troy to his own destruction. The tombs even then were hoary with age and rich of memory. But the simple travellers little recked, as they passed, of the treasure buried beneath their feet; gold fashioned with cunning fingers into every semblance of leaf and flower and delicate fish, handiwork of an era already locked into myth, whose doors have gone ajar these latter days, and we peep in and wonder at those bright children of a far distant past.

Upon the sixth day they came to Argos, pasture-land of horses. It was not a joyous place. And the boy fell back upon his inner thoughts, which dwelt ever with his father. As his mother freshened he seemed to droop. The lovely head with its clustering gold, cropped close in his father's memory, began to sink. The sandalled feet which had brought him so many miles seemed weary of the way.

"What ails thee, my son?" said Makaria. "What ails thee?" she asked again, for he had given no answer.

"My father, always my father!" The child turned away

and covered his face quickly with his garment.

Makaria was not quite impatient with the boy. Yet she seemed to brush aside every thought that kept her from what she had to say.

"Now is no time to grieve, as we near our journey's end," she said. "I have somewhat to say to thee."

Aristodemos nodded, and she went on.

"Thou didst well there on the rocks. Wast wiser with the robbers than thou knowest. But it is not right now that Athens be ever on thy tongue."

"But Athens is my own!" replied the boy, uncovering his face.

"No; Sparta is thy own. Art thou not thy mother's son? Thy father is dead. I am living."

The boy turned to her with a puzzled look, his face still wet with tears.

"Thy father left no wealth. For him, thou wouldst have been in poverty little better than a slave. So Athens served thee. Now comes Sparta. By the gracious gods my uncle is moved to send for thee. Dost thou understand?"

"It was for thee he sent," said the boy, remembering his mother's incoherent joy when the messenger arrived.

"No, for thee. Thy uncle has no child, and he is old. Two sons gave their lives in battle, and one is dead of plague. Unto thee the wealth shall come; the allotment of land, the goodly land with Helots tilling it. Not paltry gold such as Athens counts wealth. Therefore it behooveth thee not to speak of Athens. Set it behind thee in thy heart, even as thou hast upon the road."

The boy walked silently, and Makaria saw his hand clenched in the folds of his dress. The fire of anger had dried the tears and set the young face aflame.

"It may be that I shall be brought not to speak," he said at length. "But of dear Athens I shall think. Yes, I shall think, and shall dream at night. And my father— nay, he lives more than thou!" His voice rose to a ring of wrath, and he strode away at a distance. Not that day nor the next could his mother get word with him.

It was from Tégea that they set out for their last day's journey. Here a storm gathered out of the sunrise. The wind swooped down through the valley like a living creature, seized olive trees that lifted gray, affrighted hands, laid hold upon the little band and set their garments thrashing about their ears.

To Aristodemos the storm seemed good, something to struggle with as he could not struggle with unseen Fate. Even the thunder among the hills, the far borne voice of Zeus, did not affright him, though he wondered what the great Father might be saying up there in his lofty spaces. He did not see his mother's face alight with pride as she watched him stride along through the tempest, so strong, so uncomplaining, though the cloak lost over Skiron's cliff left him chill and wet.

It was a little after noon when Makaria cried out:

"Here! Here it is! See! Oh, at last!"

Upon the rugged slope stood a cairn of stone, and beside it a Hermes, "Guardian of Ways," half pillar and half man.

She flung herself at the pillar, her face a-rain with tears. She touched the image with her hands. She spoke to the god in words all broken with joy.

"Blessed Herm! My country! Oh, my country!" And upon her hands and knees, with wet garments wound close about her, she kissed the ground again and again. She had never so kissed her son's face, not at least since he could remember. This was her Lacedæmon. At last they stood upon its sacred soil.

All that afternoon, as they followed the road south down the bed of the river Oinous, Makaria seemed in a dream. No roughness of the way, no pools left by the rain through which they waded ankle deep, no tangle of fallen trees across the path—nothing could stay her. She put the branches away with a mighty hand. She strode the loose, slippery stones unpausing. Her long ten years of married exile were drawing to a close, and she would fain have crushed the last few hours into moments of time.

At last the road emerged. They clambered up a little hillside, and there, before them in the sunset light, lay the whole circle of hollow Lacedæmon, and Sparta in the midst, "Sparta, breeder of men."

Makaria gave a little sharp cry, then stood in seeming quiet. It was indeed a view to contemplate. Beyond the narrow plain Taÿgetos rose. First, lesser hills with shadow-purple gorges and flash of leaping streams, then the mighty slope, soft with its forest multitudes. Above, on the vast, bare cliffs hung the tired battalions of the storm, heavily purple in the golden light, casting shadows broad as counties over uplands and ravines. And above the clouds, at the sheer zenith edge, gleamed the perennial snows, peak upon peak, billowing away and away in upper air like a visible god-place unsullied by mortal tread. In such fashion do the awful hills o'ershadow Lacedæmon, and close her in from the world.

But it was not at the hills that the Spartan woman looked, not even at the plain with golden harvest breast high, where olives here and there flung lengthened shadows across the grain. She saw only the town itself. It looked to Aristodemos small and mean enough. But to her eyes its every roof was dear.

She marked on their little hills the separate villages of which Sparta was formed, Kynosoura, Mesoa, and Pitane where she herself was bred. In the midst the "Bronze House" gave back the sun from its metal plates—that ancient temple which had stood since Homer's day. This side the city shallow Eurotas wandered among his rushes, those rushes which Spartan boys were wont to gather for their beds. Down the river on the hither bank Therapne, burial place of kings, rose on a hill, with its temple to Spartan Helen.

Suddenly Makaria turned to her son.

"What thinkest thou?"

Aristodemos knew not what to reply.

"Nay—speak out! No fair-seeming walls? We have

a saying, 'The youths are Sparta's walls and their spear points her boundaries.' Come!"

Hand in hand, with slaves trailing after, they crossed the river by the little well-known bridge and made their way through the sweet-smelling wheat fields in the gathering night. They followed the street along the Acropolis, where the people stared curiously after them, passed through the Agora, and turned down a narrow way.

Aristodemos could hear his mother breathing in the dark as she paused before a low lighted door. She removed her veil and the aged porter howled with dismay.

"Blockhead!" said Makaria. "I am no ghost, but Makaria come home again. Go tell thy master."

Very stately she stepped over the threshold, folded her veil and laid it away in its old accustomed place, motioned the slaves to their quarters, opened a chest in the corner and looked carefully at the garments woven by the slaves, and inspected the carded wool, of which there was a plentiful supply. She took up the wonted household duties as though she had been gone but a day.

The boy stood shyly by the door, oppressed by the low, ill-lighted room. The home in Athens had been simple, but this was rough and not even clean! The house showed no place for leisure like his father's inner court with its font and altar.

A slow footfall approached and the uncle came in. At first he could not see in the light, and beetled his white brows at Makaria and the boy as he set his staff against the wall.

"Well," he said without greeting. "Thou'st come back to Sparta. Show me the boy."

Aristodemos stepped before him and stood blushing as the old man looked him, up and down.

"Fair enough," he said at length. "The hair is thine, Makaria. The boy is Spartan. I hope thy head's not full of nonsense. Hey, boy?"

Tears of pure shyness stood in Aristodemos's eyes.

He had never before been commented upon, and knew not what to reply.

"I have been taught of a good master," he faltered.

"Ay, the mischief's done, I'll be bound. Dost sing and twiddle at the lyre?"

"Nay," said Makaria, championing her son. "He is a good lad, Gylippos."

"Let him answer—let him answer!" growled the old man.

"I think it honour," said Aristodemos steadily, "to sing even as did my father."

"Thy father? I am now thy father. I never played the lyre. Not I!"

The boy looked up into the shrewd old face, but his voice quivered low as he said:

"Thou fatherest me with taunts, Gylippos. Thou knowest that I speak of Lykos of Pandion's tribe. My first dear father is he. Do ye of Sparta forget and dishonour your dead?"

"Do you young of Athens advise the aged?" retorted the old man, while Aristodemos hung his head in sudden shame. He had been wont to be silent before his elders. But Gylippos put his short, bony finger under the boy's chin and lifted up the blushing face.

"There, there! Thou hast well answered. Go and wait for me at the door." And before he realized what was doing Aristodemos stood without, the warm stars above him, and Taÿgetos impending like a great shadow in the sky.

A hand was laid upon his shoulder, a timid hand whose very trembling was familiar.

"Antiphon!" he said eagerly.

"Little Master, little Master!" and the timorous hand moved up and down the boy's arm. "Art thou in need this night?"

"No, Antiphon, not I," came the clear answer. But the boy moved closer to the form in the dark.

"Hast thou thought ill of me, Son of Lykos?"

"Of thee, Antiphon? And why?"

"That day upon Skiron's Rock, when I deserted thee and hid—"

"Nay, I thought not of it." Aristodemos spoke tenderly, as to a child. "Thou art old, and age is fearsome."

"No; not that, Master. It was this rather." Antiphon brought out a small bag. "I had this by me, and would save it for thee."

"But what is it? Honeycake or—"

"No, do not laugh that I give thee a gift," pleaded the, slave. "It is gold. Thou wilt need it."

"Not here in Sparta! But how hast thou gold, Antiphon?"

"In this way. Thy father was fain to let me buy my freedom, seeing I had been thy paidagogos. And every day I went a while to the Kerameikos and hired me to a potter and turned the wheel. Pots large and small grew under my hand. This is the price thereof."

He tried to force it into the boy's hands.

"Take it, little Master," he insisted. "It is thy father's gift. My hands that did the work were his."

But the boy quickly spoke as the master.

"No; slave earning I will not take. Thou shalt use my father's gift for thyself."

But the old man shook his head.

"All the journey this was a joy to me carried in my breast. I thought thou wouldest take it. But old Antiphon will bury it in the earth underneath his bed. And some day the little Master will ask for it, and old Antiphon will have it ready."

He turned away as the door darkened with the figure of Gylippos, who took the boy by the hand and walked him away without a word. They crossed the deserted Agora and turned down the Apheta Way. The old man gave no hint as to where they were going. He walked strongly, his bare feet making no sound on the beaten paths, his old woolen mantle flapping against the boy's arm and face. Aristodemos could scarcely believe him a rich man, still less a ruler of the state, as he really was.

Upon a stretch of level ground they came to a long, low building, lighted by a single smoking torch, as one might see through the open door, and from the glow atop, for there was no roof over the centre. Muffled sounds were heard within, a smothered laugh, a quick-vented vocal breath as at the break of effort; then scuffles, vigorous but guarded.

As they reached the door, a dodged missile, a bundle of rushes, hit Gylippos full in front.

"Ho, there!" he roared. "Who is our diskobolos?"

Whereat silence fell. Every boy scuttled to his place, and before the old man and his charge had passed the threshold the barrack was in order."

"A fine greeting to an Ephor of your city!" said Gylippos. "Wakeful nights make unsteady men. Rules are to obey!"

An older youth, one of the captains of companies, stood forth, taking the reprimand.

"The fault is mine, Father," he said. "I will take punishment for them."

"Come," interrupted Gylippos. "I have brought a boy for you to choose into a company."

Quite unnecessarily, it seemed to Aristodemos, the uncle pushed him forward. He stood, scarce knowing where to look. The Spartan boys, with a single swift step, formed into companies, each with its ilarch, a youth of nineteen or twenty, in front. Thin, sunbrowned boys they were, from ten to twelve years old, barefoot, bare-legged, wearing the single unbleached garment cut short above the knees. There was about them the trim swiftness of antelopes, and the shy lustre of the antelope look in their eyes.

The first ilarch put the vote to his little company of fifteen.

"Ayes!" he called in the heavy silence.

Then "Noes!" Upon which came a full, united shout. Aristodemos's heart gave a quick leap. A hot flush of shame shot over his whole body. His forehead grew wet, his hands cold.

Gylippos pushed him toward the next company.

A second time fell the sharp shout of "No!"

A third and then a fourth company rejected him.

Suddenly, with a fierce sob, he turned upon his uncle.

"No!" he cried. "The son of Lykos will not be scorned like a market slave! I will sleep in the street. And to-morrow I will—"

He started like a flash for the door, only to be caught and held fast by one of the strong young ilarchs. But Gylippos was speaking.

"The boy is right. He is my nephew and is come to be my son."

And while Aristodemos still struggled in the ilarch's arms the "Aye!" was shouted from a company down the line. Then the ilarch set him in their midst.

He looked up. His uncle was gone. His new comrades stood about him tittering at his flushed face and heaving chest. Then they lay down upon the small heaps of straw that were their beds and forgot him. Indeed, he might have stood there all night among the sleeping ones but for the ilarch of his company.

"Eurytos," he ordered, "bring that straw that Demonax threw."

A lithe, black haired boy leaped up and fetched it. "Lay it there."

Then, turning to Aristodemos and pointing to it in the corner, he said to him, "There is thy bed." Not a word of welcome, nor a "Good-night" to the lad who all his life had known the peculiar tenderness of an Athenian father.

Late in the night the ilarch sat up, roused by an unaccustomed sound. He was a faithful shepherd of the host. He rose and passed softly down the line of sleeping forms to where the new boy lay. But he lay quite still, curled close to keep warm, the pale moonlight on his face.

And the ilarch returned to his rest, wondering what it might have been.

CHAPTER FOUR

Whom Apollo Karneios Crowned

How came this boy to be so parented, at once of Sparta and of Athens? Sparta was not used to wed outside her borders, least of all with her growing rival state. His father Lykos would have explained it in a word. "He was born of a song." For to him it always seemed that the wistful beauty of his own youthful singing had gone into the boy and lived again. The child was indeed born of a great love impulse, one of those divine, unlooked for happenings that flash into life. Surely Kairos made him, that tip-toe god of golden opportunity or perhaps laughter loving Aphrodite who turneth upside down the plans of men.

It chanced that twelve years before Aristodemos's journeying to Sparta the young Lykos had travelled that same road. That was the year when Athens met the Bœotians by the Euripos and vanquished them, taking seven hundred captives. The city of the gray eyed goddess, freed at last from tyrants, was lifting her head and beginning with young joy her noble race, while Sparta looked on with jealous eyes, nursing the hatred that was finally to ruin Greece.

But at festival times all such jealousies were put aside in the common honour of the god. Especially was this true of the Karneia, at which lyrists and rhapsodists from all Hellas gathered in Sparta to sing in contest and win the laurel crown.

This year there came from Athens five men of noble race; Neokles, whose restless child Themistokles was then eight years old, young Xanthippos, Kleotes, and

Lykos, who brought with him Pindar, his dearest friend. Pindar was the Theban lad who was already astonishing his old master in Athens with his bold, youthful songs. Pindar was come a fledgeling, silent yet, to listen to the rest.

Lykos was the youngest of the singers, yet of them he alone was come to Sparta with a bit of statecraft in his heart. All through their journey he had times of silence when he would walk behind the others alone or grasping Pindar's willing hand. He would stride along thus, sometimes for hours, in deep absorption, his fine, low forehead puckered to a frown, his head bowed, twisting his ruddy nether lip between his thumb and finger. The boy Pindar would watch him with the trustful awe which the very youthful give to those they love. Then the mood would pass, and Lykos would shout ahead to his fellows some merry comment of the road that would set them all a-laughing. They were glad enough to get him with them again. Light hearted in his talk, deadly earnest in his scheme, nothing was farther from Lykos's thoughts than falling in love.

They arrived at Sparta the night before the feast and early in the morning were abroad, their bright flowing dresses showing gaily among Sparta's sober crowds. Athenians were of a curious nature, always prying and questioning like children into the least as into the greatest things. These men saw much and commented freely among themselves, while the Spartans scowled and set them down for chatterers.

It was a bright sunlit morning of Grecian midsummer, a morning when it was well to take the cool early hours, before Phœbus should reach his height and the heat begin. Above the little town slept the great mountain bulk, the morning clouds visibly whispering down its slopes, the far peaks gleaming with their remnant of winter's snow. In the busy city the Spartans passed them with the absorbed, unconscious smile of those who are hastening to pleasant sacrifice. Along the ways the young men were pitching tents of skins. For at the

Karneia the men of Sparta lived in tents as on the eve of battle, and all things were done in military order as the herald announced them. The Karneian Festival was War-in-Ritual.

The Athenians took their way southward through the busy Agora, and strolled down the Skian Road. Now they turned aside to see that exceeding ancient temple of bronze which dazzled in the sunlight, now stopped at the circular Skias where the Spartan assemblies were held. Here they saw hanging upon a pillar the lyre of Terpander, whom the Spartans had punished for adding new strings to the lyre.

"An thou wert Spartan, Pindar," said Lykos laughing, "we would soon see not thy lyre but thyself hung up by the toes. The Laconians could never bear thy free imaginings. "

"Hush," said the boy, pressing sensitively closer to his friend. "How that soldier scowls at us!"

"'Tis his hair that scowls," laughed his friend. "Don't let it fright thee. 'Twas doubtless combed for last year's festival. These Spartans in their roughness are as affected as our very coxcombs!" And he passed lightly on, carrying the others with him.

Soon they neared the god, Apollo Karneios, that ancient precious xoanon of wood. He was one of those statues upon whom is the mystery of great age. Doubtless from his place he had seen the bright haired Menelaos in his restless preparation when men were setting forth to Troy. He stood without temple, scarred with the passage of uncounted years, a rudely carved stiff figure beside the busy road. To his altar on this his day came all the sacrifice of Sparta—silent flocks pattering their little feet in the dust, cattle whose mellow lowings seemed to question what would soon befall.

Here the Athenians were as reverent as the Spartans. As they approached the altar, there met them full face a troop of barefoot maidens, calm creatures of the morning, full of life and strength. They wore the white Spartan shifts, girdled high and flowing softly to their lovely knees. On their heads were great shadowing baskets heaped brimful of flowers. They had been up among the hills in the dim hush of dawn visiting cool gorges and gathering iris, roses of second bloom and trailing vines.

Before the Apollo they halted. The foremost of them, raising her arms with an easy sweep, lifted lightly down the basket from her head and gave the sweet smelling blossoms to the god.

Then Lykos suddenly remembered that in Spartan streets noble virgins were wont to go unveiled.

The maiden stood bareheaded, crowned like a goddess with her golden hair, the rich colourful golden of the south. It parted rippling down her temples like the hair of Hera, was drawn softly back under a fillet into loose knot behind. It curled, glittered, fairly played with the sun, and gave to her whole figure a sense of lightness and of wings.

Lykos's soul suddenly went into his gazing eyes. All unconscious, absorbed in the girl's beauty, he actually spoke to her aloud.

"Daughter of golden haired, Menelaos, how fair art thou!"

She looked toward him, but not as if she saw him, her thoughts still busy with her prayer and sacrifice. Perhaps she was accustomed to such praise. Presently she lifted the great shallow basket to her head again, and swung easefully up the street.

"Come, Lykos, come!" said Kleotes, plucking the dreamer by the hand. "There are other sights in Sparta besides barefaced girls. Why, Lykos, thy hand is trembling. See here, old fellow!"

But Lykos turned his head away.

"The gods forbid! Thou are not in the snare of Aphrodite?"

"No—no," said Lykos confusedly. "I know not—" And to the amazement of his fellows he broke away in the direction the maid had taken.

He came up with her in the Agora, but he dared not

speak again. He watched her threading her way through the crowd, balancing with unconscious skill the basket on her head. Every motion of the fair child endeared her to him, so that as she walked he called down blessings on her head. He felt as if the gods themselves walked with her, unseen but keenly near.

She turned down a narrow street into the Pitane district, and like a foolish boy he trailed on after her. At her door, next to the ancient house of Menelaos, she stopped, lowered her basket and turning, was for the first time aware of Lykos. For a moment she looked, half in curiosity, half in scorn, at his delicate hands and long violet robe. Then suddenly she knew that he had followed her all the way and that he loved her. As who would not know, seeing that light in his eye?

With a laugh of new found power she bounded into the house. And oddly enough, all the brightness passed out of the sunshine at that moment, and all the pleasure out of the festive rites. Lykos had never in all his life felt so alone, so strangely melancholy. He stood irresolute in the narrow way, gazing at the door that had closed her away from him. Simple Lykos! For all his Athenian cleverness, it did not occur to him to look at the little upper window where the curtain stirred.

Later Lykos came upon his friends by the river. Pindar ran to meet him.

"Well, Lykos, dearest Lykos!" laughed Kleotes. "Hast really come back at last? Why, we have inspected all the relics in three temples!'

That day Lykos studiously followed his friends about the city. But he was not their careless laughing Lykos. He seemd to himself to be looking at the new sights through a veil that made them far away and altogether unimportant. Finally, he broke away from them, and in the late afternoon found himself on Colona Hill pacing up and down.

What had he to do with this foreign Spartan girl? Why so unable to control his thoughts? She was beautiful of course, beautiful as one of Antenor's new statues, beautiful as a flower or a boy—this was high praise from Lykos. But why had that virgin look so utterly confounded him? A Spartan girl indeed! He shook shoulders vigorously and hurried back to the town. But not to his friends.

He hurried to the little, narrow street again and stood looking at the wooden pillars of Menelaos's house. Suddenly with a rush of gladness he heard her voice in her home next door laughing and singing like a thrush.

"Makaria," came a voice of authority, "sing not so loud."

"But, Mother, it is festival time."

"The gods can hear, sing thou never so soft. Besides, there is a stranger in the street will hear."

"But, Mother, I have looked. There is no one there."

Something in the tone made him know that she had seen and that she was taunting him. He turned away red and furious. Yet it was he and no other who next day drew Pindar aside from his fellows and ran with him like a truant around the rocky corner of the Acropolis.

"Oh, Pindar, Pindar!" he said, throwing his arms about the astonished boy. "This woman, Pindar! Doth she not move like an Immortal? Was ever mortal head so crowned with sunshine? And Pindar, couldest thou but hear her laugh! The music of waters! Maidens do not laugh so in Athens. Speak to me, Pindar!"

"How can I speak, dear Lykos?" asked the breathless boy. "But I say yes! I believe I could love her myself."

"No," said Lykos with quick solicitude. "Do not thou love her, Pindar. Let no mere woman mar our vowed friendship!"

Pindar laughed, a merry boyish note.

"Oh, Lykos, Lykos, thou art surely Aphrodite's!"

"Do not laugh," pleaded Lykos. "No careless word this day!"

Pindar drew his friend's hand affectionately over his own shoulders.

"Lykos, hast thou forgot that to-day thou singest for

Athens's honour?"

"Yes, I had forgot," admitted Lykos blankly. "But I shall sing. I shall sing!"

For a while his earnest eyes looked straight ahead. Then he began to talk in low, hurried tones.

"Pindar, why do they not understand what is so plain—so plain? They laugh and feast who should be on their knees before the gods. The East will come upon us, boy. I have been in the Ionian Coasts and I know. Sparta must throw aside her jealousy and join hands with Athens. Even then we are but a handful to face the barbarian hordes."

In a moment the light hearted lover had vanished, and in his place stood the far seeing young statesman. He was prophesying long before its day the mighty struggle with Persia.

"I shall sing," he repeated. "And of a truth for Athens."

The singers' contest took place in that part of the Agora where the boys were wont to perform their daily choruses. The homely dressed Spartans gathered close about the choral ring and listened intently as each rhapsodist advanced and sang his song.

And now Lykos stood forth in the orchestra, his soft himation reaching to his feet, his bright lyre ready, his face keen with purpose. He sang:

> *"Why do ye hate fair Athens,*
> *The city by the sea?*
> *Whom the gods love, and most of all Athena*
> *The gray-eyed best loved goddess,*
> *Who goeth home to her own house*
> *On Athens's city hill.*
> *Whence is your hate toward her?*
> *Did not your own aged statesman,*
> *Hyakinthos the Spartan,*
> *Journeying to Athens long ago*
> *In obedience to oracles divine,*
> *Stay the dread plague of Athens,*

THE SPARTAN

*Sacrificing daughters twain upon the tomb of Cy-
clops,*
> *Saving our city from sorrowful death?*

*"There died the gentle Virgins,
Unwedded yielded up their dear loved breath
That Athens might be alive.
Therefore of us they are honoured,
The fair Spartan Maidens of Healing.*

*"And thou, great Sparta,
Shouldst also honour them,
Redeem their holy deed,
And take thy sister city by the hand!*

*"Behold a cloud ariseth in the East,
Dark to overwhelm us!
Pray ye the gods the Mede o'erwhelm us not!*

*"Let Hellas join, let Hellas join together.
And when the Mede doth come,
Drive him with shouts and with our glittering
spears
Beyond the wine-dark sea!"*

The song had begun in the Lydian mode and went
pleading on to the line "Take thy sister city by the hand,"
where it suddenly changed to the strength-giving Doric
and rose with ancient majesty, a clear toned gale of song
ending with a rhythm in which the very clash of spears
rang out.

The Theban boy stood tapping his feet in jubilant
impatience to embrace his friend. Not so the Spartans.

"Broken measures." "Not allowed." "Such freedom
goes to chaos." Then the cold silence of disapproval.

Lykos stood silent, his lyre trailing in his hand. He
was not the first in this slow world to see before his time
and to see alone. He dropped his head with a gesture
whose bitterness only the Theban understood.

WHOM APPOLLO KARNEIOS CROWNED

His eyes fell upon the crowd. He caught a glint of light—that golden head again, the maiden sacrificer of the morning. Taunting scorn was in her look. Lykos kindled at the challenge. The Athenian spirit is wont to leap up and snap fingers in the face of defeat. And when he lifted up his head and tossed back his hair, they all saw that Lykos would sing again.

This time it was an ancient nome of Terpander, a familiar modal melody which the Spartans had sung from mouth to mouth out of the hoary past. He flung it at them as if to say, "Then take this that ye can understand!" The old melody with its clear stately step rang new in the freshness and intelligence of his voice. He sang thereto a poem from his heart, created under stress with that easy creation which was possible when the world was young. He took the story of their own Spartan Penelope, when Odysseus came to take her away from Sparta to rocky Ithaca.

"Penelope was fair and young,
And lightly stood she in the chariot
Wherewith Odysseus was taking her away.
A veil was about her shoulders,
But hid not her head of gold,
A veil of the snow's whiteness
Which she herself had woven on the loom
Against her marriage day.

"For Penelope was the cunningest.
Weaver of mortal women,
Only the gods weave fairer,
And Arachne
The maiden who wove too well.

"Now her father Icarius loved her,
And he yet clamoured for her,
Clamoured and called her name.
He followed her running in the dust behind.

"Then Odysseus turned and spoke:

THE SPARTAN

'Penelope, wilt thou choose now
Whether thou wily have thy father,
The author of thy life,
Or whether me, thy lover?'

"To whom Penelope,
Being an honest maid and very shy,
Answered no word,
But in silence drew with her white hand
Her veil before her face,
And bowed her lovely head.

"In this wise told she him,
In this wise made her choice.
And Icarius gat him home.
But Odysseus took his bride to his own house.

"Now, therefore, is that place
To this day called in Sparta.
'The Maiden's Choice.'"

He closed with a long, sweet note, blended with the lyre tone sounding in unison. Then he was lost in the crowd.

"Victor! Victor!" clamoured the simple Spartans, quite won out of their stolidity by the character he had put into the ancient song. A young soldier pushed him forward all blushing and confused. One of the judges took a laurel wreath from the foot of the Agora Apollo and set it upon the bowed dark head.

Then Lykos rose, lifted the crown of sacred leaves from his brow and gave it back to the god. To the Greek it was honour enough to wear for a moment that divine leafage. The honour and privilege lay in giving to the god again his own. Then Lykos turned quickly from the crowd, seized Pindar by the hand, and hurried off.

When they were quite alone, he laid his late-crowned head upon the boy's shoulder and wept. No Spartan approval of his song could comfort him for his dear, great purpose, which had failed.

And the maiden, Makaria. Almost, she thought as she walked homeward, almost she could hate that young Athenian. Yet of what could she accuse him? Of his Athenian laughter and swift, too many words? No: it was rather a certain intensity of open expressiveness from which she shrank, as dumb things will. For she was of the silent, repressed life of Sparta, and that long, intent gaze of his had startled her. Yet, even so, why had she taunted him? That first song was not so ill sung. And the second—!

He had sung that song for her, there in the open square! Why else had he given Dame Penelope golden hair? Would the others know? she wondered. Her maiden comrades; would they tease her with it to-morrow?

"Why," she complained to her mother, "why do the Athenians come to our festival at all with their starings and their songs? It is Sparta's festival, and it is our own god we are honouring for the good of our own city. They have no part in it!"

Yet all that night the Penelope song ran with sweet insistence through her dreams.

The third afternoon of the festival, as the air grew cool and the great shadow of Taÿgetos began to creep over the dry, late summer fields, the maidens of Sparta gathered upon the Apheta Way to run their public race. Now the boys of Sparta were slenderer than boys of other states, worn down by the rigour of their discipline. But the girls, bred out of doors and exercised in the sunshine to become the lusty mothers of Laconia, bloomed with a vigorous beauty unknown among the veiled housed girls of Athens. They were a lovely company of wholesome wild roses, if roses could but chatter, laugh and move about with such restless eagerness.

They were slightly clad, as ready for their flight as birds might be. Their short Spartan tunics bared their knees, and were even slit at the sides to leave movement absolutely free. Arms and necks were bare and brown. Such dress the Spartan girls wore at all times, and with such simple fitness that even the Athenians who ridiculed could not but know that it served its modest purpose.

About this group of young creatures stood the matrons, veiled yet eager, inspiring the runners with references to their own early triumphs. The old men and rulers of the city ordered the crowds. The ranks of boys discussed eagerly the coming race.

"Orsobia will win!" clamoured some.

"Makaria!" said others.

But most spoke Argeia's name, their favourite runner.

Six girls were chosen. They stood a little apart, chatting with a certain anxious gaiety. In their midst, Makaria. Lykos recognized her with a quick leap of heart. She seemed so young for the great effort, the "agony" as the Greek called it, which she must put forth alone, in which none could help or further her. She seemed, too, a little apart from the gay mood of her fellows, silent, thinking on the race. Now he saw her lips move, praying to her god. He stood very near her in the crowd.

"Ei!" called out a Spartan boy. "Makaria never ran at Festival before. Look, she is afraid!"

Makaria turned defiantly, and as she turned, her eyes met full the gaze of the Athenian, praying with her, as it seemed, her own half-finished prayer. Her look softened, and she bowed her head to hide it. But as she did so she moved almost imperceptibly nearer to him for protection.

"Win, Makaria!" said Lykos, speaking low. "Maiden of the torchlike hair, bring thy torch to the goal!"

The herald called. The girls stood in tense silence, leaning forward, with unsandalled feet upon the line.

Then the signal!—and they sprang at once, as if six bows had twanged and let six arrows fly. They flashed past Lykos with a rush of wind and stroke of bare feet, creatures of glad effort and of flight. Then sped diminishing down the course.

WHOM APPOLLO KARNEIOS CROWNED

As for Makaria, she saved her breath and fixed her whole mind upon the goal. Just behind Orsobia she ran, feeling the wind in her face, the cool breeze kissing her neck beneath the flying locks.

Now she reached Orsobia, passed her with astonishing ease. What a thrill of joy! Could she win? The stranger's prayer—it was a prayer of power! Never had her feet been so light. The life within her seemed to lift and speed her unweighted flesh!

Ahead, Argeia strained, with glancing heel and fluttering garment. Foolishly she looked back at Makaria. Then the golden-haired shot up and ran breast-even with her.

Now they were at the Herm. They flashed around it turning sharp, Makaria getting the inner course.

Homeward they flew. They could hear each other's labouring breath. Greater, greater, grew the effort. Makaria felt her consciousness grow blurred, while her obedient legs kept pushing, pushing on mechanically toward the goal.

But why now was she less aware of Argeia at her side? Was some invisible hand pulling Argeia slowly backward despite the swift-flying feet and the eager, forward-striving body?

Makaria's heart leaped up. Keen thought came back. With a bound she put herself to the fore.

Then suddenly she felt herself free. No more in her nostrils the dust of the runners! Oh, the joy of the sweet evening wind, the clear track ahead, the ever fainter footfalls behind! And oh, the strength of victory, making her feel that she could never tire, though she ran the length of Hellas!

Lykos standing near the goal saw them come. Makaria running like a winged thing, eyes a-shine and sweet lips parted with the last supreme effort of the race. Now she made the finish, touching the goal with uplifted hands, breathing deep in her virgin bosom, quite speechless, but laughing in helpless joy at the praises sounding about her.

THE SPARTAN

"A new runner! Makaria! Makaria!" shouted the crowd.

"Oh, Pindar, Pindar!" whispered Lykos. "To see her run, so strong, so fair, so light! What a mother for a noble line!"

An elder laid the laurel crown of Apollo Karneios upon Makaria's brow, and all the people watched her reverently kneeling, praying beside the altar.

After the rejoicing Makaria eluded her friends and stole swiftly homeward. Across the darkling Agora she went, past the place where the stranger had sung, and into her own narrow street again, stepping lightly, looking this way and that, like a fawn in the forest alert for the hunter. Her cheeks still burned with exultation; her eyes were full of light. Hesitating, lovely, she came.

Surely that was only a shadow there in the portico of the Menelaos House. No. The stranger himself, his long violet cloak glimmering in the twilight! His head was bowed, yet he was looking at her with that long clear, tender gaze of his.

She stopped, with lips apart and eyes instantly wide. Lykos came gently toward her, as one might approach a bird fearing it would flyaway into heaven. Neither spoke. They were afraid of Aphrodite, in whose spell they knew themselves to be. The goddess was a fearful presence in the gloaming. They held their breath for joy.

And now Lykos lifted his hand and with reverent fingers touched her hair that he had so marvelled at from afar.

"My father toucheth my hair," said Makaria quite childishly, "but never as thou touchest."

"Then have I offended thee, thou lovely Victrix?" asked Lykos, almost with compassion for her tender, fleeting beauty.

"No," she answered, softly bowing her shy head. "Didst thou sing that song for me?"

"For thee and no other. Thou knowest."

She was trying to understand her own mood, trying

to make some excuse for him and for her own swift change of heart. Quite unexpectedly she lifted her head with a direct look into his eyes.

"Perhaps the gods willed it. Perhaps thou couldst not help loving me."

Never had boldness sat so fair upon a modest maid!

Lykos caught her in his arms, and kissed her ardently, cheek and brow and rosy mouth, holding her close until she broke away and with low, happy laughter lost herself in the shadow of her open door.

Lykos's mind was set. Had not Neokles married a foreigner? Was it so strange a thing to marry out of one's own city? He had thought of marriage as for offspring, a duty to the state, something which his friends might some day arrange for him, but which he rather dreaded as a drag upon his free public activities. He had never talked with a maid, nor had he ever seen maiden faces before, save at rare festivals. It had never crossed his mind that he might love as the gods love, or have actual speech with a woman before making her his bride.

And now, here upon his heart all unwilling, had come so rare a joy, so sweet a gift from the indulgent gods! Anakreon's strains and Psappha's ecstasy! They were all true, after all! He softly sang over the poet's words, wondering at their rich new meaning. No child of the myths reared by shy forest mother could ever be more taken by surprise than he.

He sought out the girl's father.

Yes, the old man said. Makaria was his youngest child. Yes, and the prettiest. Five daughters were too many, and hence he was a poor man. How much dower would the young man expect? Well, perhaps—yes, he could afford that. The young man was reasonable.

He could have her.

"And when," inquired the Athenian, "can the betrothal be? I am in haste to return to Athens.'"

"When? When?" repeated the old man. "Why, that's for thee! What unlucky words have escaped the door of thy mouth!" And he turned his back upon him. So Lykos saw that he must learn something of Spartan marriage customs.

He learned, to his astonishment, that there was no ceremony whatever; no feast nor torch-bearing, no epithalamion sung in the presence of the immortal gods, no sacrifices save private ones. Instead, he must go to her house by night and steal his bride away! It was an ancient custom to which the Spartans had clung long after the other Greeks had forgotten it.

At first this was a trial to Lykos, who so loved and honoured the dignified customs of Athens. But when all was arranged, and the next evening drew on, when the old kins-woman had prepared to receive them, and Makaria herself was ready—then the wild freedom of the symbol filled him with exultant joy.

The western fires went slowly down beyond the mountain. The evening star, like a bright shepherd of the flock, called his glittering multitudes into the evening sky. The night deepened and grew still.

Lykos stole down the narrow way, stood in the shadow of her house and gave the low signal. At once the door opened, and his beloved stood before him in the starlight. He kissed her in haste, swung her lightly to his shoulder, and ran with her like a deer down the empty street and away. He bore her swiftly across the silent Dromos, past the dark circle of Platanistous's sacred plane trees, past Colona's quiet hill where as a child she had so often gathered flowers and would gather them no more. Then before them glimmered her kinswoman's doorway. Ah, never for any race of her own had the maiden's breath so fluttered in her bosom!

Over the threshold Lykos lifted her and set her down, and with what tenderness lifted the matron's veil that hid for the first time her lovely face, and saw that deep content which he half feared to claim, lest the immortal gods looking on it should envy him his joy.

CHAPTER FIVE

An Ancient Childhood

Now Athens lay before the simple Spartan girl. To her the house of Lykos seemed wonderful. Simple though it was, it far surpassed the mean houses of Sparta. Instead of earth for a floor it had smooth clean stones set in cement. By the doorway burned at night a lamp of oil, clean and sweet, lighting the narrow passage. It had an open inner court where all the morning the sunlight lay upon the little altar of Apollo, and sparkled in the tiny stream of the fountain where they washed their faces upon rising. Here were planted two small laurel trees, as bringing down the very life of Apollo into the house. These were Makaria's especial care.

Very cool and fair seemed the rooms as she passed into them, very delicate the fountain that played so softly in the shadows. And above the stairs, the weaving room was cool and spacious. There were the distaffs waiting the ready hand, and heaps of wool like snow upon the floor.

She did not like the slaves' merry familiarity with their master, and reproved her husband for having left his household untrained. But Lykos only stroked her cheek and laughed at her. "Bless thee, wife," he said, "they are old in impudence, and I love them too well to change them now."

Makaria also found as she grew familiar with the new life that her Athens was practically bounded by the four walls of her home. She could not go forth, save with Lykos's consent; then only with a slave, and always with her himation drawn up over her head, concealing her face. Those pretty feet, accustomed to fly over the course, found the little courtyard but a scanty place for action. And the square bit of blue above it was but a poor exchange for soaring peaks and dizzy distances.

"But I can not let thee go forth without a reason," said the perplexed Lykos. "There, there—do not cry, dear wife! Wouldst not be thought a virtuous woman?"

"Yes!"

"Well, virtuous women are best unseen and at home."

"No, no, they are not!" wailed the wife. "Oh, I wish I were in Sparta, only to walk just once as far as I could wish!" Struggling, poor thing, like a bird in a cage.

Used as she was to free society and speech, she ill liked the withdrawing to her own rooms whenever Lykos brought friends to the house. The sitting at wool spinning, which the Athenian women enjoyed, she felt to be a confinement, and unbecoming a free born dame. The women themselves who slipped across the narrow streets to gossip with her when husbands were from home—what slack, pale-faced creatures they were, talking that half obsolete dialect which the men of Athens scarcely understood. She despised them, and was so proudly uncommunicative that they soon ceased to visit her. Then they left her alone with her slaves.

Lykos was generally busy with weighty matters of the city. No Athenian would have thought of spending his time at home with an unlettered girl. But he loved her, loved to sit beside her at the evening meal, loved to toy with her rich hair and call her his beautiful torch bearer. He was patient with her tears and even with her tempers, for he was too sensitive to fail of understanding what she felt.

"There, there, child," he would say with unfailing gentleness. "What a greeting is this for thy husband! But this new life is hard for thee, I know."

"And who maketh it hard but thou!" retorted Makaria. "Thou hast married a Spartan. Why not let her be a

Spartan?"

At which he would sigh and pass out of the house. Thus foolishly Makaria drove away her best comfort.

But as the year lengthened there came a great hope into the house of Lykos. Prayers and sacrifices were made to the household gods, and the laurels were kept green with even tenderer care. Makaria, absorbed in the new hope, forgot her childish lamentations and lifted her head with a new, solitary pride. Lykos, coming home, would find her stitting silent in the sunlit court, a dreaming, intimate look in her eyes. Again he reverently felt the veiled presence of the gods about her, as on that first day of seeing her in Sparta.

Then, coming one evening from his grain fields near Prasiai, Lykos saw fastened to his own door post the olive branch, token that a male child was added to the city. He ran in with throbbing heart. At the threshold his old slave nurse met him, and laid in his arms the hour-old boy.

Makaria, lying in her darkened room, heard his quick cry of joy, then his strong step as he came swiftly across the court, holding his first born in his arms. He stood beside her, bent over her, looking at her with greater gentleness than she had ever seen.

"Makaria, thou hast well done!" he said. "Hast indeed borne me a fair son!"

Makaria felt that she should never again be sorrowful, nor tread the common ways of life now that she had brought into the world a perfect man child.

On the third day the old nurse ran with the little one around the family hearth, putting him forever under the care of the household gods. On the tenth day Lykos claimed him formally as his own son, and named him Aristodemos after the Spartan hero, in honour of his mother.

"But he shall be an Athenian," Lykos said joyously to those who feasted with him. And an Athenian he was indeed, even to the day when glorious death overtook him, and he left the paths of men.

THE SPARTAN

Each year added some new sweetness to the child, some delicate charm. A little creature of joy with fair perfect body and a cloud of golden hair. Now he played in the fountain, now tossed the snowy wool above his head so that his mother punished him, now climbed the roof to watch Athena's mysterious owls that sat so silent there among the earthen pots set at the edge to frighten them away.

All the joy of the household centred about his comings and goings. The slaves were foolish over him, and Lykos's face lighted and softened at the sight of him. When he began to prattle and walk, Lykos kept him always at his hand. Makaria only kept discipline.

Her old desire for the open never returned with its first heat after she bore her child. She grew matronly with a certain self-contained practical wisdom that Lykos found good to depend on. She even seemed older than Lykos. Under her rule the household ordered itself like a little state in which there was no sedition. The slaves obeyed her to point of fear, and the boy found a rein upon his impulse which otherwise he would have lacked.

Now began the sweet, undimmed childhood of Aristodemos—a half open rose, flowering in that far away ancient spring over which the heavy centuries have closed. Even his own after years shut so suddenly and completely over it that it remained to him a precious thing apart, fragrant and ever young.

One of his memories from the faint, shadowy years was of waking in the early evening and seeing from the window one of the runners of the Lampadedromia, naked, helmeted, carrying a shield, bearing aloft a lighted torch, and skillfully guarding the sacred flame even in his flight. It was but an instant. The child saw the shine of the fresh-oiled body, the flash of the polished shield, the streaming flame, and the quick turn around the narrow corner.

The boy lay long awake, looking out into the starlight, possessed with the joy of that sight. All his life through he felt the symbolism of that altar-lighted flame, so carried and so cared for.

It was a pleasure of disobedience to steal out of bed, to which he was always sent too early, and find his way down the narrow stair to the locked door of the men's apartments. There, in the andron, Lykos often gathered his friends, not for the elaborate symposia of a later fashion, but for a simpler meal begun with the ancient grace of wine poured out to the gods, a simple opportunity for the companionship that gathered round the board.

Here great matters were discussed—the rebellion against the Persians, spreading then like a conflagration along the Ionian coast, the sending of the twenty Athenian ships to aid their kinsmen. This Lykos urged passionately and himself commanded one of the ships that went. Here upon his return they discussed the burning of Sardis and the anger of the Persian king; all the hopes, fears and heart stirrings that were abroad in a world growing ripe for Marathon.

These things the child could not comprehend, and he would finally slip away, sleepy and disappointed. But when they cast off care, and like the children they were sang joyous and holy songs, the lyre passing from hand to hand, then the child stayed kneeling in the dark, his ear against the door. How his soul drank in the sound! Now some booming passage of Homer in his father's manly tones—Hector with legs set wide, hurling the huge rock against the Danaan gates and leaping in with face like sudden night, Achilles, the dear loved hero weeping over the warrior maiden whom his own spear had laid low. Now he heard a new ode of Pindar, in Pindar's own clarion voice. Again, some tender, melting strain of Psappha, those songs which the Greeks likened to roses for delicate loveliness.

> *"As the sweet-apple blushes at the end of the topmost bough,*
> *The very end of the bough,*
> *Which the pluckers forgot somehow —"*

These words Makaria heard the child lisping at his play, and boxed him soundly without warning. She was always prompt at punishment. She guessed what he had been doing. But Lykos never knew that the boy had been listening in the dark while he sang so joyously.

When Aristodemos came to his sixth year, and his father took him to the little neighbouring school, Lykos was surprised to find the boy able to sing whole passages of Homer and almost all the odes that Pindar had yet composed. His fitting of metre to musical tones, a delicate matter in Greek music, was often wrong; but his voice had an angelic, high sweetness that struck Lykos with something like fear and made him say as he walked back to the quiet house, now first deserted of its fledgeling:

"Makaria, the gods are in it! The Nine Sacred Ones will have their way with our child!"

Aristodemos was not left to Antiphon as fully as most boys were left to their paidagogoi. As in his babyhood, his father had carried him before the altars of the gods, kissing his face and rosy body, so now he took him on happy expeditions about the little city, holding the warm, childish hand, telling him the stories of heroes.

Many a time they toiled up the steep Acropolis, called in those days, "The City." For then it was not so far back to the time when the city had been all contained on that abrupt crag, and timorous herdsmen still drove up their flocks at twilight within its protecting walls. The two looked down over the beloved land. It was rather a bare land even then, but clothed upon with the peculiar transparent haze of Attica through which the hills shone purple, rose and rusty gold, while olive groves lay upon the slopes like violet shadows. And they looked out to the islanded sea where it crisped in the morning breeze, or lay sapphire under a sapphire sky.

The Acropolis of those days was a gentle, pious place approached by rock-cut steps. Atop it was uneven, crossed by many paths, smooth trod of countless generations. Wild flowers nodded in the crevices, and the sacred olive tree, given by the beloved gray-eyed goddess herself, flourished in its sanctuary and was tended by fair young priestesses. The old Pelasgic wall still surrounded the place, and there, upon a peak which was afterward levelled, still frowned the hated palace-fortress of Pisistratos, ruinous now, since Athens was made free.

It was a place to stir the heart of a boy. He saw the ancient house of Erechtheus with its trident-mark where Poseidon struck when he and Athena were contending for the city. He saw the archaic statue of Athena herself striding forward wonderfully with spear and shield. "Athena Promachos" they called her—a trustful phrase "Athena-fighting-for-us."

Many altars stood there open to the breeze. From one to another the father and son went devoutly. And Aristodemos keenly felt his father's priesthood, as he brushed aside the ashes of former sacrifice, and offered his own with libations.

They went into the rich coloured, many columned temple of Athena, the Hecatompedon. How it glowed in the sunshine, topped with its flying akroteria! In the pediment Herakles contended with the Hydra. Was ever such a serpent! What joy and terror in his rich coils of blue and green extending down into the very comer of the triangle, and in his high head upreared! How manfully did young Herakles fight him!

Beyond the temple was the carven bull set upon by lions. Aristodemos always shrank closer to his father as they passed by. The poor bull crouched with head bent under, the lions with ruinous claws tearing his body and pulling his tail at great length behind while the red blood flowed. Everywhere were multitudes of painted living statues looking out upon the boy from jewelled eyes and smiling that strange archaic smile. There were girl priestesses who had served the virgin goddess, and then passed below, leaving these memorials. One of them, with full red lips and golden hair, looked like his mother. Another he liked for the delicate way she lifted her knitted tunic and stepped forward.

And there were young Apollos standing stiffly enough, though here a graceful shoulder there an out-stretched arm or modelled chest showed the glory of sculpture yet to be. Men were still dealing childishly with the stone, fumbling like children with their tools. Yet in every statue rude or skilled, glowed thought and love of truth and appreciation of the body's beauty. No wonder the boy loved to go there, and felt afterward as though he had walked with the gods.

Twice during his childhood his father took him to the Agora, where in the early morning all the citizens congregated to buy and talk, a place usually thought unfit for boys. In after years he always remembered the bustle and talk, the cries of venders, the rows of Hermes statues standing so silent in the midst, and the colon-nade where the more serious minded turned aside to talk in private. And he remembered the ringing of the hasty bell, when everybody stampeded to the fish mar-ket beyond. His father showed him the hill and the build-ing where the Athenians gathered to vote, told him how the idle would often loiter at the booths instead of going promptly to the voting, and how the guards would sweep a dirty rope up the place and drive the multitude along.

"What would you think, my son, of men who had to be driven to their voting?"

"I would think," answered the boy, "that they had the hearts of swine and the eyes of moles." Which wise observation the proud father quoted many a day.

In those years the Dionysiac dance was lifting itself to the borderland of drama. As the two passed through the precincts of the Lenaian Dionysos they would often hear the rhythmic shouting and the beat of dancing feet. Then they would hasten and join the crowd that stood about the primitive orchestra, a simple circle drawn upon the ground. Once his father lifted him up into a poplar tree to see the play, a favourite viewing place among the simple, happy folk.

What merry mimicry it was! What leaping of satyrs clad in rough goatskin; what music of wild pipes! The boy tingled with the joy of it. And when the mimetic chorus took up the tale with song, gesture and concordant movement, he quite forgot where he was and almost fell from his perch in the poplar.

About this time the theatre itself was building, and the boy, sitting among the high, unfinished seats with his mother, saw the dramas of Phrynichos. He even saw a tragedy by the young new writer, Æschylus, against whom there was so much complaint for his changing the ancient dramatic rite. "What has this to do with Dionysos?" they complained. The saying became a proverb. And, "Whither will this young Eleusinian lead us?"

Whither indeed!

It was the joyous Dionysiac festival, an early April morning. The wet dew was still upon the rocky-seats, the fragrance of the sea blowing across the theatre. All the spectators were crowned with flowers and sat expectant. They had brought baskets of nuts, figs and barley cakes for their noonday meal. For the dramas lasted the day.

The pageant began. The great story grew before them, terrible and lofty. The people sat breathless. Then suddenly they would burst into loud acclaim and fill the air, and the orchestra with the flowers they threw. And the boy always remembered the choral dancers, moving in a swift ring about the lighted altar, their bright enveloping robes rhythmic in the sunshine, their bare feet lightly treading. The ever swifter movement of the Dionysiac enthusiasm filled his heart. And yet, behind the childish excitement, he had always a vague overpowering sense of the tragedy, the mighty wrong, and the mighty suffering beyond his childish grasp. And when at dusk they took their homeward way his father's look was never to be forgotten.

Æschylus! Who shall recall the surprise of his first

world-utterance, his mastery as he came new upon a sensitive and story loving world? Oh, glorious youthtime of Hellas! How much it meant to be a part of that growing life!

These were city pleasures. There were also pleasures of the land beyond the walls. One day they walked down the beaten road to Phaleron, passing through open fields to the harbour itself. Here the waves came crashing up the beach like white-maned steeds and as they broke drew backward as if the mighty sea had reined them in. Then was a soft tinkle among the million wet pebbles quivering in the foam, and the boy, shouting, chased the breakers back and dug delighted fingers into the glistening sands.

They walked along the margin hand in hand, father and little son, and came to a still cove where two worn-out galleys lay drowsing in perpetual quiet, their ribs whitening in the sun.

"Look at them," said Lykos with true seaman's trim instinct. "Think how they once leaped the wave visiting the busy ports of men. Now those whom they served have cast them aside, worn hulks drowning here in solitude. So it often is, my son, with age."

And the child, awed by the words, forgot his play and they walked homeward in silence.

The father did not often sadden him thus. His companionship, like that of most Athenian fathers, was almost childlike. He was a father whom a child would delight to honour, so young himself, so quick of laughter, so free, yet full of dignity. His personal beauty drew the child. On his face the growing thoughtfulness of Greece had set a wonderful manly gentleness. The black locks hung about his ears graceful as the curling vine of grapes with which they were often crowned. They took the motion of his walk, giving spring to his movement. Men knew his bearing from afar, and would call him to hear his speech or have some jest of his to carry with them through the day.

All his life Aristodemos remembered as though it

still rang in his ears his father's voice in the Agora persuading the people to justice or rousing them to the love of state. Yet even in moments of highest passion, when the truth drove hot upon him, when his eyes widened and his head shook back the locks, there was upon the face of Lykos no excess, and his dress, falling in folds about his shoulders and feet, was not disturbed. He mounted his height as a god does, hasteless and controlling.

And the son remembered those quiet hours when the father came from talking with those great "lovers-of-wisdom" from Ionia sojourners in Athens, and sat long in quiet, a deep thoughtful light in his eyes. Then would he talk of things the child could little understand; the mystery of beginnings, those strange new thoughts that men across the sea were pondering, turning for the first time from the mere joy of living to the meaning of life itself.

Lykos searched his own spirit for the first principle of Nature, that clue which the Greek panted for with a passion that we moderns can little understand. Oh, that he might gather the All into the One, find all in the one great cause, air, heaven, growing earth, the heart of man, the very gods, even the nothingness of death!

As he spoke of death he would take the child quickly into his arms and hold him with a kind of fear that was not ignoble.

"Live thou!" he would say passionately. "It is not long ere a man goes down into the silent ways of death. But if his son live and his seed survive he shall have life upon the earth, remembrance still in the light of day, and sacrifice to the deathless gods in his behalf!"

Most of all was Lykos glorious in his singing—a singer first before all else, though he knew it not. For in those days men thought not of the song nor of the statue nor of the speech. They looked beyond them. The song was for Apollo, or maybe for some lesser god. The statue was a gift to Athena, and the honey-sweet speech was for the saving of the state. And just because they thought not of these gifts as their own they had them so abundantly. For the song is mortal and comes from mortal lips that to-morrow may be silent. But the god makes beautiful the gifts that to him go, and gives to them immortal character beyond the singer's own.

It was Lykos's habit each afternoon to go to the gymnasium for that full exercise of body which was deemed the duty of every Hellene. The Lyceum of those days was a shady grove watered by the Ilissos. It had been newly ornamented by Pisistratos. It had its fountain of Panops and its peristyle for resting after toil. Like all scenes of Athenian activity it was a sacred place. It was dedicated to Apollo.

Here Lykos came one warm afternoon in March, a wholesome, joyous figure, with his little oil flask in his hand. He greeted his friends with smile and ready words, stripped his sunbrowned body and bound his hair more closely in its fillet. What a sense of life there was in this free moment before activity!

He engaged Xanthippos and Neokles in a race, which was always his favourite exercise. They ran swiftly down the course and back again, Lykos in the lead. As they neared the goal a certain Arkesilaos, a clumsy fellow who was always breaking rules, dove across the stadium before the runners. He had been practising the Pyrrhic dance and still had his spear and bore his shield upon his arm. Lykos crashed full into him, and the other runners with great momentum plunged down upon the two. When the mass was disentangled, shield, spear and men, Lykos lay as dead upon the sand.

They raised him tenderly, and bore him to the covered portico where they laved his face with water and rubbed him vigorously.

Presently he opened his eyes with his own bright smile and sat up.

"It is nothing," he said, passing his hand across his forehead. "I shall have bruises to-morrow, but I can enjoy to-day." So he went on with his exercise, and later took his way home with his friends.

AN ANCIENT CHILDHOOD

He sat rather quietly at the evening meal, and went early to bed. Old Antiphon going in for the last services to his master found him in a deep sleep, his arms and legs twitching strangely. Antiphon looked him over lovingly, but with a slave's instinctive timidity did not awaken him.

Next morning the sleep had deepened into full unconsciousness. All day he lay so. The physician seemed helpless and said that Lykos would never rise again, perhaps not even waken. Aristodemos sat by his father too bewildered with terror to be aware of grief.

On the second morning the beautiful dark head began to turn from side to side upon the pillow. Then the sufferer began a low incessant moaning that hurt the very heart of the boy. Toward evening, Lykos opened his eyes with a dim, eloquent look upon them all. Makaria began to wail and beat her breast and pull her hair down over her face.

"Do not so—do not so," said Lykos feebly. And they drew her thence, still loudly wailing. Aristodemos with great effort held himself steady for fear of like banishment.

Now his father looked at him, a long, loving look.

"Kiss me, my dear son," he said very slowly. Aristodemos bent over him.

"No, upon my mouth." And the child kissed the cold lips again and again.

Presently, looking still into his face, Lykos asked:

"Aristodemos, where art thou?"

"I am here—here!" cried the boy piteously frightened.

"Yes? Then kiss me that I may not so forget."

Aristodemos wound his arms about his father's neck and kissed him fervently.

"Forget—forget—" repeated the faint voice. He seemed trying to form a thought upon the word. His flickering consciousness caught—then—dropped it again.

At last, pleading with voice, and look, he whispered:

THE SPARTAN

"Thou wilt—not forget—forget me—my son?"

"Oh, never, never!" sobbed Aristodemos breathlessly, now raining tears upon his father's face.

Lykos did not close his eyes again, but fixed them upon his son as if, out of all the rich world that had been his, he alone remained to him. As he lay so, a sudden pain passed across his features, and with a movement unutterably pathetic he caught the covering and drew it up over his face. It was the delicate last act of the Greek, hiding from the living the face of death. So, with a long, tired sigh, the bright soul of Lykos fared forth into the place of shadows.

He lay upon his couch in the andron, silent where he had once filled the place with song, his head crowned with the myrtle, his feet, once so light, set toward the door whence he was to go forth for the last time. Looking at him so, the child could not think him dead, though strangely far away.

As night deepened the great reality began to possess the boy with pity and longing. He had heard of the dead. They were like bats, chattering in the dark abyss, or fluttering up against the closed gates of life—futilely, for to them there was no light of the sun nor joy of growing things.

When, in weariness he began to sink to sleep he wondered if his father had felt so, dying—and then he was broad awake again. Finally, toward morning he fell into heavy sleep.

Before daybreak they were up and about their sad duties, for the sun must not be polluted by looking upon the dead. They washed hands in the lustral water by the door and went out into the dusk. They trod the crooked pathlike streets a sorrowful procession, the shrouded dead in their midst borne by loving hands. The people looked out of windows as they passed, awakened by Makaria's lamentations for her dead. But Aristodemos, walking in advance as became the head of the house, was quite silent and looked forward with awed and tearless eyes.

AN ANCIENT CHILDHOOD

Now and then he caught a glimpse above the houses of the familiar Acropolis cliffs where the two were never to walk again—cliffs touched with the faint white of earliest dawn. As they passed out of the city the larks sprang from the wet grass and circled up into the abyss of sky, where stars still shone through the dewy azure. By the side of Aristodemos walked his father's young friend Pindar. They came to the tomb in the rocky hillside and stopped in awed silence, set down the dear burden, and sacrificed to the dead a bird, symbol of the flying soul. They placed upon the tomb a rude image of Hermes, conductor of the dead, archaic, made of wood.

Aristodemos wondered at it with vague pain in his heart, thinking how his father had loved the beautiful new images of the gods. Could he see this one, this mere block of wood? Would it pain him to have it there continually above his narrow house?

Something in Aristodemos's eyes as they turned away struck his father's poet friend. He took the boy's hand quickly and walked awhile in silence. Then he said:

"Thou art thinking of death, child?"

"Yes."

"And thou so young! Canst thou not wait? Oh, boy, it is too difficult for thee!"

"I must," said Aristodemos, with stifled voice. "My father is dead. I must think of him."

"I too must think of him," the poet repeated musingly. "And I have thought long years, and know nothing as yet. All lies on the knees of the gods."

"But that does not help!" cried the boy pitifully.

"That does not help! Dost thou know that indeed so early?" And the young man gazed down into his eyes with infinite pity.

"My child," he said gravely, "listen to one who has thought much upon the gods. There be many evil tales of Zeus, evil tales even of Apollo. Fling such tales from thee. To speak evil of the gods is pitiful wisdom. We mortals do not understand. But believe not evil of the gods! Now it is thine to sacrifice in thy father's stead. Do it gladly unto all the gods, but especially unto Apollo, who keepeth men pure. And remember that thy father was of Eleusis, and of the Mystai we may say:

> *"Blessed is the man who hath seen these things*
> *Before he goeth under the hollow earth.*
> *He knoweth the end of life,*
> *And he knoweth its god-given origin."*

The boy listened so thirstily to those words that Pindar, motioning the others on, turned aside into a grove of olives. And there, not upon the breast of his mother but in the arms of the gentle Pindar the boy wept out his grief.

CHAPTER SIX

The Hunt in Taÿgetos

Aristodemos awoke in the Spartan barrack with the white dawn in the east, the wet dew on his hair. The lank brown boys were up and scuffling about him throwing on their garments. Their toilet was neither long nor careful, and Aristodemos had to make haste to get on his own white chiton, a service he had never done for himself, and to fasten his worn sandals beneath his feet.

Now like a flock of noisy birds they were off. They ran across fields to the Eurotas. Here they flung off garments again and one and all jumped shouting into the stream, Aristodemos with the rest. They frolicked wildly in the running water. The sun rose and glistened upon their backs, and far up the sky the snowy mountain ridge took fire.

"Hey, there," cried one. "Did ye ever see a diving fish? He's marked gold on the head and thinks he's better than all the fish of the sea."

"Where is he? Where is he?" called the others. "Here he is!" And with a sudden turn, the boy grabbed Aristodemos by the back of the neck and pushed him under.

But Aristodemos had been a swimmer from three years old and had buffeted with surf before now. Quick as a frog he kicked the boy off and, opening his eyes under water, turned and caught his tormentor's ankle. He came up puffing, but dragging his enemy sputtering and impotent behind him.

"Here's a lobster," he shouted. "See him come backward!" Then, before the boy could catch him he dived away, and came up almost across the stream.

The boys laughed uproariously.

"Oh, Demonax! Ducked by the little stranger! Ha, ha! At him! At him again!"

But Demonax was still blowing and shaking his ears.

And now the boys scrambled noisily out. They flung on their tunics with no attempt at drying. And Aristodemos missed his own white tunic among the soiled gray ones of his fellows. There was a dirty Spartan shift in its place, and when the boys were dressed no one was left naked. So he rightly judged that his own had been changed by authority. He pulled it on over his wet skin with scorn and trooped off with the rest. So he was lost among them, only the glint of his golden hair distinguishing him in the Spartan crowd.

They came back to quarters. The tables had been set each for its company of sixteen. The boys took their places in silence under their commanders. Then, at a sign, they all began to chant, with strong, foot beaten rhythm, the Lycurgus Laws:

> *"When ye have builded a temple to Zeus,*
> *To Syllanian Zeus and Syllanian Athena.*
> *Divided the folk into tribes and clans,*
> *And established a Senate of thirty persona,*
> *Including the two Kings,*
> *Ye shall summon the folk to a stated assembly*
> *Between Babrike and Krannon,*
> *And these shall have the deciding voice."*

and so on through the whole seventy-two laws.

Music and law were well enough, but Aristodemos was wonderfully hungry. He thought he could have eaten a whole sheep of sacrifice. Yet when the singing was done, only scanty portions of barley bread were brought in, with bowls of steaming broth, the black-blood Spartan soup. Aristodemos took the first mouthful hungrily. But not the second. Bah! It was vile with vinegar and salt.

He pushed it aside, famished as he was, and betook himself to bread of which he tried to get a sufficient quantity to appease his hunger.

After breakfast the boys marched to the field where all the youth of Sparta were assembled. The companies took their positions, Aristodemos, wondering, among them. The sharp commands in the harsh Doric dialect came down the line of officers from mouth to mouth. With a great united movement the drill began.

Aristodemos was familiar with the Pyrrhic or weapon dance, as practised by the Athenian boys. But this did not help him to understand the military drill and battle evolutions, or to take turn and step with the others. Again and again he was flung out of line or left in the rear by a sudden shift. The disharmony of his movements hurt him as much as the sharp reproof. He had never in his life been awkward. He turned scarlet and felt like to die of sheer chagrin.

At last it was over, and the boys, with many a covert jeer at him, were marched away to the Dromos. Here they were put to gymnastics, running, leaping, spear flinging, wrestling, while the old men looked on leaning upon their staves, correcting, directing and approving; Here Aristodemos was better matched. He flung his disk to a good distance and leaped as far as the rest.

He thought he caught a sight of his mother standing near Gylippos and watching him. But when he looked that way again she was not there. It gave him a great homesickness.

Long before the noonday meal he was hungry again, and when at last it came it was but an unsatisfying affair of broth and figs. He had heard of "man taming Sparta."

"Easy enough to tame men by starving!" he thought.

After dinner was a half hour's rest. Then, to his almost terror, drill once more. In the afternoon the boys were turned loose and Aristodemos's company with its young ilarch strolled out toward Colona Hill. One of the boys slapped Aristodemos on the shoulder. Athenian boys never handled each other, and Aristodemos turned

THE SPARTAN

upon him in displeasure.

"What sayest thou, Frog," said Philammon. "Shall we go hunting? Thou'rt hungry?"

"Oh, no," returned the polite Athenian. "I have well dined."

"Well, this is free Sparta, and lying is free. But I saw thee turn up thy nose at the soup."

"Yes, come," said the ilarch. "He who hunts may eat. I'm for a good supper."

Spears and short swords were found, and unshod and unhatted as they were they set out. One of the boys held a leash of Laconian hounds, thin wolflike brutes, coarse haired and savage. Aristodemos had never hunted before. That was sport for men! And he almost felt himself a man as he stalked along with the others.

They were boar hunting! Stories of Meleager flashed through his mind—the famous Kalydonian hunt in which Admetos joined, with Jason, Idas, Castor and Pollux, Nestor—all those great names which but to speak brings up a host of glorious deeds. He remembered how the boar was brought to bay at last, and how Atalante, the beautiful swift huntress, had got the first stroke.

Oh, if only the boys at the Athens school could but see him now! What if he himself should strike the boar first with the spear which the ilarch had given him, and so get the hide! Involuntarily he brandished his spear and smiled to himself. The ilarch smiled too, and found himself hoping that the boys might not notice the child or spoil his sport.

They mounted the foot-hills, scrambling over rocks, swinging across chasms by hanging vines, or wading the streams that leaped and sang downward towards the valley. Athenian boys, though merry enough, were reasonably decorous at all times; but these Spartans, silent as statues before their elders, broke all bounds when they were alone. Aristodemos caught the contagion, and yelled and leaped with the rest.

THE HUNT IN TAŸGETOS

"Quiet!" called the ilarch. The dogs had caught a scent. Then in a flash they were all dogs together for stealth and keenness and swift running. Just ahead the hounds sniffed the ground with short, excited yelps. Now they grew uncertain. Now, with united cry they caught the trail again and scrambled ever higher up the steep. Aristodemos followed, tingling, breathless.

Suddenly Eurytos was at his elbow.

"This way," he whispered. "A short cut."

Aristodemos turned after him.

"We'll get there first," said Eurytos confidently. "But the dogs—shall we not need them?"

"Why? Art afraid?"

"No, by the Twin Gods!" returned Aristodemos. They ran for some time in silence, the baying of the hounds sounding ever farther off and fainter.

"What wilt thou do?" asked Aristodemos, as at length they slackened their pace for want of breath and Eurytos began to creep with caution.

"Do thou go first and spear him well. Then I come up, and plunge my sword, so—"

"Good! Good!" said Aristodemos. "But it's my first boar!"

"I'll warrant it," responded Eurytos with a short laugh.

They came out upon a ledge. Just below them was a little field flat enough for grain. There the Perioikoi, or Spartan serfs, were beginning the harvest. Far down below the rim of the field they could see the plain of Sparta, and narrow Eurotas winding to the Laconic Gulf, and still beyond, even a glimpse of Aphrodite's Cythera, gleaming far off, white like silver in the blue waves.

"Slaves!" muttered Eurytos, shaking his sword at the harvesters, with that curious hereditary hatred of the Spartan toward the serf which, of course, Aristodemos could not understand. "Keep to your work a bit, and we'll—"

"Now, Aristodemos," he said a few moments later, "do as I say, and no questions."

"Yes, yes!"

THE SPARTAN

Eurytos wound his way skillfully through the wood without the cracking of a twig or the moving of a branch. Presently he dropped almost upon his knees, so that the low underbrush quite hid him, and Aristodemos had much ado to keep him in sight. Had Meleager approached his boar in such a fashion? thought the puzzled boy. But perhaps this was the Spartan way.

Then on a sudden they came upon a poor little stone hut, and a barn, also of rough piled stone. Eurytos held up a warning finger and looked at him with such fierce earnestness that Aristodemos asked no question.

They glided back of the hut, through the garden, pitifully small, guarded by its tiny deity, a rude phallic Priapos, god of fertility. They approached the barn from the side, so as not to be seen from within. Still more cautiously they entered. No one was there.

Hanging from the roof beam was a side of mutton, fresh killed. Against the wall lay a small bag of barley meal, evidently the last saving from the old year, with which the Perioikoi hoped to tide over the interval to the approaching harvest.

Eurytos seized this bag, swung it to Aristodemos's shoulder, then, cutting down the mutton and throwing it upon his own back, he pushed Aristodemos out of the door before him.

"To the left, where we came! Quick, fool!" he whispered, running ahead of Aristodemos.

Aristodemos was too dazed for a moment to comprehend what it all meant. But Eurytos's retreating figure was too plainly that of a thief to leave him long in doubt. He dropped the bag as if it burned him, and with cheeks on fire with shame rushed after him. He quickly caught the burdened Eurytos. With a blow he sent the mutton flying, then faced him in front, for he scorned to attack him in the rear, and crying, "Thief! Thief!" flung himself bodily upon the boy.

Eurytos reeled backward before the sudden rush, but he grappled Aristodemos so that they both rolled together upon the ground. For quickness they were about equally matched, but Eurytos was older and stronger. Fortunately Aristodemos was on top and by watchfulness and quick blows he kept his antagonist under. Eurytos fought silently, but Aristodemos filled the air with passionate cries.

Suddenly, as if the very ground gave them forth, appeared the boys, and a moment later the ilarch, with questioning looks. Then the frightened serfs came running from the fields weeping and wringing their hands.

"Take that, and that!" cried the outraged Aristodemos. "Thief! Robber! Stealing the food of miserable slaves! Oh, how I hate thee!"

Here with a quick twist Eurytos screwed himself out, and fixing his teeth in Aristodemos's arm turned him over and pinned him down.

"Now—now!" he muttered, and began to beat the golden head mercilessly upon the ground. Aristodemos closed his eyes in faintness. He felt as if black death had leaped upon him.

Then the weight was lifted. He was free, breathing. Over him the ilarch was holding back the still raging boy.

"Back, back, I say!" And quelled by the authority of the ilarch's tone, Eurytos stood up, a sorry sight with his bloody head and dirt-covered face.

But Aristodemos was awake now. "No, no!" he cried, jumping up. "I will fight him still! Don't hold him!"

"Fool!" said the ilarch. "He would have killed thee."

"Yes, yes! But he won! The thief won! I can't have it so!" wailed Aristodemos, making at him.

The ilarch shook him roughly. "Hast never learned to obey?" he thundered. "Stand still!"

He caught Aristodemos in his arms and held him firmly. But there was a tenderness in his tone as he said, "Dost not see that he is bigger than thou? Thou canst not beat him."

"But he will remember that he has beaten me, and he is a thief! I will fight him. I will!"

The ilarch did not answer.

"Come, I will wash thy wound in the spring. That

was an ugly bite."

"It's a dog's way, to bite," said the boy, in disgust.

"It is a Spartan's way too. Hadst best practise it thyself."

"I never will!"

The young man was now holding the tender bleeding arm over the spring, the water supply of the farm, and bathing it thoroughly.

"Get a wound clean," he said. "A clean wound goes to sleep. I did not know," he added quietly, "that the boys meant to try thee in the hills."

Having bathed the wound to his satisfaction the ilarch motioned the boys to move ahead. The serfs were casting wondering glances at the golden haired child who seemed to have been defending them. And timorously, as if afraid to claim their own, they carried back their mutton to the barn.

As the company went down the mountain with the lofty peaks towering dizzily behind him, the ilarch kept close to Aristodemos, to prevent him, so the boy thought, from righting himself with Eurytos, who limped ahead.

That evening in the barrack Aristodemos heard the sound of a stoutly wielded whip outside—but no cries.

"What is that?" he asked Demonax.

"Eurytos getting his thrashing."

"For stealing or for fighting?" questioned Aristodems again.

"Neither, simpleton! For getting caught!"

CHAPTER SEVEN

The Escape

The new boy is quick," said the old Polemarch one day to Aristodemos's captain.

"Yes, he is quick enough," replied the young man, "but he is not like our boys. When I command him he seems to weigh and decide his acts. I always feel that he might decide to disobey me. I'm frank to say that he baffles me."

"He can be transferred," said the Polemarch respectfully.

"No—oh, no," said the ilarch with quick energy. "I would rather master him myself!"

The boys were drilling for the Gymnopædia, "Feast of Naked Youths." Every morning they marched to the field and danced in ranks the glorious movements of the festival. They wrestled in pairs, with pauses now and again to manifest some beautiful crisis attitude. They swayed forward, backward, like wind-bent grain in June. They stretched to full height, flashing up a thousand thin young arms. So light they were, these young creatures of health, they seemed able to leap full free of earth.

In all this routine there was an undercurrent of excited expectancy. "'Platanistous—Platanistous," the boys kept whispering to one another.

"What is Platanistous?" asked Aristodemos. But the boys did not answer his question.

Each day the excitement grew. At last one morning the boy battalions were marched out of the city down the southeastern road. All Sparta followed. Aristodemos was full of excited curiosity. They soon reached a sunny meadow in the district of Kynosoura. There was a little circular island-like place surrounded by canals and about the canals the circle of tall plane trees which gave the name "Platanistous" to the place. Two opposite bridges led across to the island, each with its guardian statues which Aristodemos recognized as Herakles and Lycurgus. Surely this was some fine festival. Aristodemos lifted himself on tiptoe to see.

He saw two companies of boys, naked and unarmed, march across the bridges to the island. There fell a great silence. The two bands stood facing each other with a strange, growing fierceness.   Plainly it was a contest.

Then, with a great battle shout, the companies rushed at each other, struggling, trying to force each other off the island. It was a splendid contest. Aristodemos's blood tingled to be in the midst of it. Now the two leaders were wrestling. He saw them sway in the equal struggle. But suddenly, with a thud, the Heraklean fell, and the Lycurgians pushed in a mass over him, trampling and tearing his body. Blood frenzy seized them. They raged like hungry wolves, mad boars. They used fists, feet, teeth, nails. They gouged eyes, tore faces. Whoever weakened was trampled down. Their eyes grew terrible, their voices hoarse with hate. All the vaunted self-control of the Spartan youth was gone. The brute beast raged unchecked.

Aristodemos turned sick and hid his face. It was not for the bloodshed, not even for the killing. It was rather for the bestial uncontrol. "Oh! Oh!" he moaned. In a horror of disgust he broke away. But quickly he felt his shoulders seized. He looked up. The stern face of the ilarch was over him.

"Stand! Look!" he commanded. "Learn to despise death!" And he dragged him back into the sight of that degrading madness, into the hearing of that bestial din.

Several of the boys died next day. "Best so," said the old men, "the true Spartans survive."

THE ESCAPE

But it was not even Platanistous that made Sparta so loathsome to the Athens bred boy. It was the deadly monotony of the days that followed. They were so alike—like pease rolling out of a pot. Drill, dance, exercise! Exercise, dance, drill! Even the Spartans said, "Sparta at peace is a sword rusting in its scabbard."

The boy recalled his bright Athenian tasks, the learning of the old stirring Homer-poems, with their thrilling hazards. He repeated them softly after he had lain down at night, with a kind of fear lest he lose them and with them lose all connection with the world he had known.

The Spartan boys had no such songs. Their only whetstone of wit was uncouth riddles. The old men gathered about at rest hour and badgered the boy with these, trying to win terse answers. The riddles were grim, and the laughter they provoked grimmer still. Spartan training was all suppression.

A sense of stifling grew upon the boy. The thoughts he was not to express, the songs he must not sing, the affection which had no outlet—it all maddened and fevered him. He seemed sunk away from light to some sodden level far away from his proper atmosphere. He grew listless, pale. Even his mother, passing him in the street, noted the change.

"Art ill, son?" she asked. "Hast pain anywhere?"

"No. Only I am so tired."

Makaria went to Gylippos.

"Uncle," she said, "perhaps the discipline is too severe—thus—at once. Perhaps—"

"Perhaps he is a weakling," growled the old man. "Hast thou too grown soft in Athens, Makaria?"

"No, not I."

But strangely, that word of his mother fired the boy's heart. It was light to a ready torch. Unspeakable Sparta! He could not bear it. He would run away. Why had he not run away before? This very night he would run away!

He did not know that to leave Sparta was to incur death. Sparta was an armed camp; departure was desertion. He did know that the way to Athens had a hundred perils for a boy alone. But his whole body brightened with the hope. He began to plan. It would be impossible to go penniless. Antiphon's gold—yes, he would take it of the old man. Now it was the price of his own freedom.

That afternoon he said:

"Captain, may I go for an hour to talk with my mother?"

The captain's face went blank. "With thy mother?"

The boys broke into a loud laugh.

"Why, yes—no doubt," said the ilarch quietly. "Belike she hath thy swaddling clothes for thee from Athens."

The boys yelled in derision. Aristodemos was scarlet. "Thou couldst deny me without insult, thou Spartan lout!" he said hotly, and turned away.

There was breathless silence. What would happen to the new boy now? But to the boys' amazement the ilarch turned scarlet too, scowling and biting his lips.

"Go to barracks, Aristodemos," he said at length.

Aristodemos walked away, too disappointed to care for the awful disciplining that must surely be in reserve for him. Plainly there was no way to get at the gold. Well, then he would go empty handed.

That night he kept awake, a difficult task after the long day's work. Sleep seemed to steal upon him and deceive him making all things unprecious save itself. Fight as he would he found himself several times upon the edge of dreams. Then he heard the boys about him breathing deep. This woke him tense and clear.

Aristodemos sat up. All about him they were lying lax and still on their rush beds. The barrack was aflood with revealing moonlight, but along the wall there was a deep shadow. If only he could creep into that shadow! The ilarch was not in his usual place. That was fortunate.

The boy was intensely awake. His throat was so full and choked that he could not swallow, but his brain was clear. He waited yet longer, peering at each sleeper, especially at the other ilarchs who lay with their companies. At length it seemed safe.

But now he heard the sentinel's approaching tramp, tramp in the distance. Aristodemos lay down again. The steps drew nearer, coming up the street. Now the steps sounded flat. The sentinel was coming by the blank wall of the barrack, the click of his short sword in its scabbard hitting against his thigh, the folding and re-folding of his metal skirt—all these little noises, unnoted in day-time, sounded out distinct as if analyzed by the stillness of the night. He cleared his throat. What a sudden dispersal of the silence. But no one was roused, not even to the point of turning over or taking a deeper breath. Then the footsteps died away, and the deep silence closed again.

Aristodemos would not venture to sit up again. Roll-ing over upon his belly, he crept flat off the rushes and slowly, slowly along the aisle between the sleepers gain-ing at last the shore of shadow, where suddenly he re-alized that he was breathing again. Then on, on in the darkness. Oh, how far away was that square of green-ish light that marked the doorway! But he came nearer. Now he lifted himself upon his straight arms to look out.

He almost cried aloud.

Across the threshold lay his ilarch. He was stirring, too. Aristodemos dropped prone in the shadow, saw him sit up and shade his eyes with his hand, look over the sleeping companies, handle his sword and compose himself, his head upon his arm. So he sank again into light sleep.

But Aristodemos knew it was useless to try to pass him there, so wakeful, so ready.

An hour the boy lay motionless, not daring even to go back. But when the moon had sunk below the wall, he crept to his own bed again and there curled up, his teeth chattering as if with cold, his heart aching with the disappointment.

Next morning the boys wondered why Aristodemos overslept and had to be dragged out by the heels. His face looked pale and pinched as he ate his broth with the rest. At drill his shoulders drooped, and he blundered and forgot.

"Art going back to first days?" said the ilarch sternly.

The boy bowed his head dully and did not even flush at the reproof. Every time he looked up he met the ilarch's eye—serious, anxious, watchful. Aristodemos was sure of one fact now. The ilarch suspected him! This gave the boy a terrified sense of Sparta's omniscient guarding. Had anyone ever escaped Sparta? Puzzle as he would Aristodemos saw no smallest chance ahead. He lost his hope and with it his boyish courage.

At the rest hour the boys went down the Apheta Way, where long ago Makaria had won her merry race. They stopped by the river near the Royal Tombs, and dropped down in the grass. East of the Eurotas rose the height of Therapne, with its temple to Menelaos and Helen and its strange grave of her brothers, Castor and Pollux, inhabited by them on alternate days.

Aristodemos found a place a little apart from the others, and sat down, elbows on knees, chin in his hands. Truth to tell, the boy's heart was breaking for his father, yet with a dull sorrow that did not move his tears. After all, what use to go to Athens with no dear face of Lykos to greet him there? Mechanically he broke off one of the reeds of the river, cut it short with his sword and began to blow into it. He cut it shorter and blew again. Why should the note be higher, he wondered dully. Then he tossed the reed over his shoulder. Doing so, he glanced toward the boys. They were lying flat in the grass drowsing in the sunshine. The ilarch was asleep, weary no doubt with last night's watching.

Aristodemos's heart gave a great bound. For a moment he was afraid even to move. Then softly stepping among the reeds he cut another whistle, blew it lower and lower. He peered back through the canes. Not one had stirred. And oh, the reeds were blessedly tall and thick! He began to steal unseen among them along the river bank.

THE ESCAPE

At a narrowing of the stream he stopped. His mind lifted a moment to his goddess. "Pallas," he whispered, "Virgin Pallas!" But he could not form his prayer. He slipped into the stream, leaned forward, and sleek as an otter was across. At the farther bank he crept once more into the concealing rushes, there shook his wet head, wrung out his narrow skirt. There was not much about a Greek boy for wetting.

Then he ran like a deer. In a meadow he took an instant's breath, and with furious haste made an armful of daisies. He might meet visitors to the temple. He must have some gift. Then he began to clamber the hill. Pushing through the underbrush he came upon a deserted path, hesitated a moment, then hoping to make better speed leaped into it and began to run again.

He had not gone far when the path took a steep turn, and rounding it, Aristodemos saw above him stumping down the hill two old Spartan Ephors. Ah, he had done well to prepare a gift! He dared not turn. Breathless, but with a cunning new to him, the boy straightened shoulders and marched up toward them.

They scowled upon him.

"Who goes there?"

"Euagoras, son of Lysander," answered Aristodemos unblushing.

"Whither?"

"To the grave of Castor and Pollux."

"Why?"

"To bring gifts. My mother this morning gave birth to twins. One has died. But the other she wishes to preserve. I go to pray and offer gifts to the Twin Gods."

He answered without pause. His brain was as clear as the air. The shrewd Athena was surely helping her lying son.

"Didst thou see the babes brought this morning for inspection?" asked the old man, turning to the other.

Aristodemos's heart rose in his throat, but he kept an unquivering face.

"Yes. Two. One was weak and we rejected it. The

other we kept. But they were not twins."

Aristodemos made ready to break and run. But the other answered:

"Yes, Tisander, I think they were. One nurse brought both."

"Go on, my son," said the old Spartan. Aristodemos bowed his head and walked with a terrible self-compelling slowly up the hill.

Once out of sight he leaped again into the brush and fled on and on, breaking and snapping the twigs, straight away from the temple. On a jutting edge of hill he had a chance to look down upon the river, so calm and clear in its valley. Ei, what was that parting the ripples? Some animal? The flash of an arm—a dark head. The ilarch! O—oh! Pursuing him!

Aristodemos cried out, a poor, thin cry like a hunted creature's, and in a few mad bounds made the hill top. He ran pounding down the farther slope. His breath began to fail. He began to stumble among the stones. He fell headlong, and scrambled up again with bruised knee and dizzied head. Then, even in his madness, he began to reflect how good a start he had. The place now, too, was wild and partly forested. He began to go more slowly, as indeed he must with that fierce stitch in his side.

Crossing a little stream, he paused for a thirsty mouthful, and much refreshed took on a steadier gait through the wood. His delicate face was set with a new intensity. He had taken full heart again when he began to hear shouting from afar—his own name, calling, calling. His eyes went wide with fear. The ilarch must have taken a short cut through the hills. Aristodemos knew that steady glorious speed of his. He had seen him run in the Dromos. The boy could now no more keep ahead of him than could a toddling child.

He thought of turning in his track; but that was foolish with the man almost in sight. He ran on whimpering with bewilderment and came upon a great rock in the wood, grown thick with tangle. Aristodemos dropped near it, crawled into the laurels and to his joy found a tiny hollow. Truly the gods were kind! He lay there swallowing his sobs, stilling his breath, while wonderfully soon the ilarch himself came bounding past, eagle swift, with flying hair, a terrible pursuer.

Aristodemos waited. Thoughts of his father flashed upon him. What would he think to see his son hiding like a hunted thing? He was about to creep out again when something—hearing or a sense beyond it—gave him pause. Then through the wood he heard indeed the ilarch returning, saw him coming slowly looking about him even into the trees, and to the boy's terror, beating the thicket about the cliff.

Not many rods from the boy's hiding he sat down and dropped his head in his hands. Breathless, Aristodemos watched the man. He seemed weary with running and deeply troubled.

Suddenly there was a scurry in the bushes that set Aristodemos throbbing from head to toes. But it was only the ilarch's dog, who now came thrusting his black sharp nose between the ilarch's hands, settling down upon his haunches with the confidence of welcome.

The ilarch patted his black side. Aristodemos could hear him talking to the dog, familiarly, as he did not talk to human beings.

"Well, old fellow, we've made a' mess of it. We've failed." He rested his cheek, with its short, soft beard, against the dog's head.

"Thy master is a fool—a fool, Phialo," he said. "With the company we could have caught him. But we couldn't let the boys come, could we Phialo?"

Even while he feared the young man, Aristodemos could not help noticing the noble slope of his shoulders, and his strong neck bowed in disappointment. How different he seemed now, alone with his dog, from the strong young captain that ruled the company. He began to finger some arrows he had in his hunting quiver with his bow.

"Why could I not shoot?" he mused. "A wound would

have stopped him. Ah, the hills have him now."

Aristodemos shuddered. A little breeze sprang up, stirring the bushes and cooling the boy's face.

Instantly the dog was intent. He lifted his quivering, black nose, sniffing audibly. He began to bark with short, quick, eager yelps, and dashed into the bushes.

"Hares, hares?" said the ilarch indulgently. "Must always be thinking of hares!" But he followed the dog, parting the bushes with his hands.

And there before him, wild eyed and pale, crouched Aristodemos.

The boy leaped up, but the ilarch caught his wrists. He struggled and turned his face away. He expected—he knew not what. Perhaps death.

But the ilarch only said, "Boy! Boy!" in a grave way, looking at him.

"Yes, yes, strike if thou wilt!" cried Aristodemos, unable to endure this pause before the storm. "Thou art bigger! Oh, why dost thou play the hound?" he added passionately. "What is it to thee that I run away?"

"What is it to me?" replied the ilarch. "Thou wouldst perish on the road alone."

"I am perishing in Sparta. It is all one!"

Suddenly the young man's look changed.

"Dost thou so hate Sparta, Aristodemos? And me as well?" he added in a low voice.

Aristodemos looked at him in amazement. And truthfully came the answer.

"No. I hate Sparta. But thee I do not hate—at least, not now."

"Do not hate me, now or any time. For my heart is warm toward thee."

He drew the boy gently out of the bushes.

"I would not harm thee, not a hair of thy head. It was to save thee I came."

The young man seemed half awed at this break in his own reserve. He was almost shy before the boy.

"In Sparta," he continued hurriedly, "they deride me because I have no boy friend as the others have no

THE ESCAPE

bosom comrade to teach and help and take with me to battle. They choose friends easily. But I—I can not. And when thou camest, thou wert hardly Spartan. But at once I loved thee—when I gave thee thy bed, when thou foughtest Eurytos for thine own foolish reasons— even when thou fleddest Platanistous.

"But why didst thou flee Platanistous?" he asked, looking up. He was sitting on a fallen tree, holding Aristodemos at his knee.

"Because they were fighting like brutish beasts, and not like thinking men."

"Yes; thou hast always a reason. And fear is not of thee. For these things I love thee Aristodemos!"

If a god had suddenly spoken the boy could not have been more astonished than at this abrupt taking away of the mask that had hid a friend. He gazed at the man, scarce credulous. He had been so full of the ache of loneliness that at this unexpected balm he began to sob childishly, stretched his arms and clasped the ilarch close about the neck.

"Friend, friend—my friend!" he cried in a choking voice. Even so in olden days had the lad Patroklos returned from Death to clasp the great hearted Achilles. Aristodemos clung to the man, hiding his face against his breast, while the dog leaped about them barking with delight. The man caressed the curly head.

"Hast had rough days," he said tenderly. "Very rough—and wert so little and alone!"

"But not—alone—now. Not now!" whispered the boy.

Later the young man bent back the boy's face, looking into it as fondly as his own father had done.

"Thou hast much to learn," he said, "and I will teach thee all."

"Wilt thou teach me many, many songs—and Homer?" asked Aristodemos, looking full into his eyes.

"I am no singer," said the man humbly.

"The little temples of Sparta, then, and the shrines— wilt thou teach me all their stories?"

"Yes, yes—gladly." The man's lips parted in an amused smile.

"And oh, my ilarch," said the boy, "speak to me in whole sentences—long ones. I am so tired of Laconic saws."

"Yes. I will tell thee in twice the necessary words, thou foolish boy. But call me not ilarch. To thee I am—Leonidas."

"Leonidas!" repeated the boy, using for the first time the name that afterward became so dear.

"I am brother to Kleomenes, the elder king," said the man quietly.

"Brother to the King! The boys did not tell me. And wilt thou be king some day thyself?"

"No, probably not. My brother Dorieus is next in succession. Thou wilt never see me king."

"But I shall love thee, whether king or soldier."

"We shall be soldiers together," said Leonidas with shining, eyes. "Thou my defender and I thine, and only swift death shall part us!"

He took his short sword from its scabbard, pricked his own right arm, then that of the boy, and let the blood drop, mingled, into the earth. It was the ancient covenant of brotherhood.

"The gods have seen it," he said. "We are brothers now."

Taking the boy's hand he led him toward Sparta. And there, where law never could have held him, love easily led Aristodemos back.

CHAPTER EIGHT

And Sparta Has Her Say

Next day, at the last leap of the choral dance, the ilarch turned, walked directly through the deep breathing ranks to Aristodemos, took his hand and walked away with him.

It was an explicit act, and the eyes of the company followed him.

"The Twins be gracious!" gasped Demonax. "And Leonidas hath chosen him a friend at last!"

"He was long enough at it to have done better!" sneered Eurytos who had not forgotten his flogging over the mutton stealing.

The boys ran to the corner of the Agora looking down the Apheta Way whither the two had walked. They were as curious as a flock of village girls when a swain begins to show favour.

Aristodemos looked up with questioning eyes at the friend who walked silently beside him.

Leonidas answered his look.

"Did I not tell thee that I would show thee the shrines of Sparta?"

They were both of them excited, keenly alive. The morning sky above them was like a great crystal bowl of azure uplifted to a dizzy height. In after years Aristodemos never saw such a sky without the repeated heart leap of this happy hour.

"See this temple—two storied," said Leonidas. "Those who come to Sparta exclaim upon it. To us it is familiar. "

"I have never seen one temple built upon another,"

said the boy. "What is the story?"

"Suppose it hath none," smiled Leonidas.

"But it hath, it hath! There is no temple without a story!" begged the boy.

They mounted to the upper temple and bowed before the Aphrodite Morphio. It was a strange image of cedar wood, its head veiled and its feet bound with fetters. The boy asked why the goddess was bound.

"There is a reason," said Leonidas reluctantly, "but I do not think it is a pious one." For while some in Sparta thought the fetters kept the inconstant goddess from running away, others frankly admitted that they were for punishment.

In another temple they marvelled at the large "Egg of Leda" where it hung by ribbons from the beams. The boy began to dream.

"Is it not strange we do not see the gods, Leonidas?" he asked in childish puzzlement. "They are very near and so strong and bright."

Leonidas looked down at him, half awed.

"I should think it strange to see them, rather," he answered.

As they neared the next little holy house they were aware of a soft humming within like the sound of many bees.

"It is the Robe House," explained Leonidas, "where the women weave the sacred robe for Amyklaian Apollo—a new robe every year."

It was the season for the sacred weaving and there within the large, shadowy room were maids and matrons, pacing softly to and fro in front of several upright looms, looms bright with many coloured threads. It was really the happiest place in Sparta with its merry jest and exchange of news, its constant activity and its steady growth of a beautiful art work.

One maiden weaver especially caught the glowing attention of the boy. In mid-floor before her loom she paced, flushed in the warm morning, drawing to her bosom the level wooden rod from which the leashes like lyre strings stretched forward to the warp. Now she reached forward holding the rod with her left hand while she flung the shuttle with its trailing thread through the soft purple warp, caught it with skill and flung it back again. She was a lovely active figure, bending, rising again, with white arms flashing out to catch the flying spool.

Another maiden sitting in the full light of the open door had a finished fabric on a frame before her. She smiled up at Leonidas as he came in, then turned again, absorbed, to her embroidery. Under her quick fingers grew the shape of Apollo himself throwing the disk, and his dear Hyacinthus—the boy he loved. There was wonderful action in the divine figure. The bend, the backward sweep of the arm holding the disk, were one with that type that later flowered out at Myron's hand. She laid on her colours as with a brush. There was no suggestion of threads, except that the silk shone as no pigment can. The maiden craftsman was all unconscious of her gift save the joy of it which beamed in her eyes as she worked—a level content that comes only to those whose hours are businessfull and whose dream is coming true.

Aristodemos had a rare glimpse of her happiness. "She looks as if she were singing," was his comment. And he never forgot her.

"Nay, Gorgo doth not sing," said Leonidas simply, "but she maketh beautiful robes for the god."

They came out into the dazzling sunlight leaving the women at their sacred work and went back to barracks.

But it was soon apparent that Sparta looked but sourly upon this new friendship of Leonidas for a half-Spartan boy. "A king's son," they said, "should comrade with pure Spartan blood." Aristodemos was conscious of many a scowl and whispered comment. Leonidas as if unaware of their displeasure devoted all his leisure to Aristodemos and taught him many things.

Then one evening two old Ephors came into the

barrack and summoned the young ilarch. "We will talk to thee of this matter of Gylippos's boy," Aristodemos heard them say; and Leondias, white with anger, followed them off.

Two days passed, but Leonidas did not return. Even Aristodemos had not known how desolate the place would be without him. And as for the boys—"Ay, it was you, you half-breed," snarled Eurytos, giving Aristodemos a covert kick.

"We had the best ilarch in Sparta," said Philammon. "He shall not go to another company."

"We'll kill you!" And Demonax made a rush at Aristodemos. The harsh-faced captain in Leonidas's place had a tough job keeping the ugly pack in order. But Aristodemos was too bitterly anxious to heed the harrying of the boys. His friend! His captain! What were those brute Spartans at? Prison—chains—beatings? Yes, of course the Spartans would beat even a king's son to force him from this friendship. Thus the boy tormented himself with guesses, watching the while every turn for a glimpse of the beloved face. There was no sight or hint of his friend. Leonidas seemed completely swallowed up.

But the fourth morning, as Aristodemos awoke, Leonidas walked quietly into the barrack. The boys with a great shout sprang to greet him. They caught his hands, shoulders, feet. Demonax threw his arms about him.

"They shall not take thee from us!" they yelled tumultuously.

"No," said Leonidas quietly, "I have come back to stay. In order now!" he commanded sharply. "Look to those tumbled rushes—Quick! It's time!"

The boys scattered to their duties. Leonidas began to issue the orders for the day.

Aristodemos stood in his corner speechless, white, the picture of misery. Doubtless the Ephors had regulated Leonidas. To them he, Aristodemos was naught. Now Leonidas must choose some other boy, perhaps this Demonax—or even Eurytos. Desperate anger seized him.

Leonidas was sending out a band for fresh rushes. He seemed unaware of the white quivering figure in the shadow. But as the boys left the doorway he turned quickly and walked over to Aristodemos.

He laid both hands on the thin trembling shoulders and looked long and lovingly into the upturned face.

"To-day," he said quietly, "we will work at thy spear-throw. We have lost three days."

But Leonidas never told what befell in those three days.

THE SPARTAN

CHAPTER NINE

For the Honour of Artemis

Months lengthened into years. For Aristodemos and his captain these years were full of the strenuous activities of Spartan comradeship—spearmastery, which Leonidas gravely taught him all one sultry summer, skill of bow, swordsmanship, niceties of drill which the boy would miss in the general discipline. Through all this training ran the impulse of their mutual soldierhood and the glorious battle peril to which they both looked forward. All day they were together, and at night, upon rush heaps, side by side, the boy's hand would reach out and lie in the strong soldier palm through the still hours of sleep. It was the saving of the boy, for Sparta herself afforded him no life.

These days the stranger singers who came to the Karneian festival noticed among the stolid Spartan faces one intent face with eyes dilated, a boy tall and gaunt with growth, who did not applaud with the rest but gazed and moved his lips. But even the singers who remarked him could not guess how Aristodemos drank in their songs as one who must go thirsty for a year again. And having listened, Aristodemos would wonderfully remember, through silent repetitions and singing aloud in the hills. Sparta had naught for a growing mind. He must snatch everything from chance comers. He dared not miss a single song for his meagre treasury.

All this troubled Leonidas.

"It is better to listen to songs and to judge the rhythms," he said, "than to sing too much thyself. That is for poets and such like." And one day he found Aristodemos by the river side trying with great distaste to clean out an ill-smelling tortoise shell.

"What is this?" he asked.

"Oh, I am no Spartan, nor soldier; nothing, nothing—not even a poor singer now. To-day in the chorus my voice broke. It is gone—gone! I shall forget everything!" The boy flung himself face downward on the grass.

"Was it a lyre thou wouldst make?" asked Leonidas picking up a ram's horn that lay beside the shell.

"Yes, a lyre—and thou wilt call it a folly!"

Leonidas stroked the bowed head.

"When the child is half and the man is half," he said musingly, "strange toys are needed. Though never saw I so evil smelling a toy."

"But it will be clean when I scoop out the creature and wash it."

"Nay, boy. I will get thee a well made lyre."

"Get me a lyre?" asked Aristodemos, incredulous.

"Yes. Put the horns into the tree hollow and come. Demonax wants thee in the Dromos. But," added Leonidas anxiously, "I would not have the Polemarch know of thy restless doings. He might seek his own remedy. And it is too soon for that."

It was but a few days after this that the Polemarch himself came into barrack and beckoned Aristodemos with his finger. The youth scrambled up from his place at the mess and presented himself. The old man searched his face and said in a low voice:

"Artemis Orthia requires thee. Thou makest thine offering next full moon."

Aristodemos looked at the man for a moment stunned. He could make no answer. He well knew what the notification meant. Aristodemos had often seen on the low marsh lands south of the city where the mists stole in at evening and the sun beat hot all day the Sanctuary of Artemis. The image it enshrined was that very one which Iphigenia had tended in the Tauric land. And among the Taurians, so the Spartans said, the xoanon had acquired a taste for blood. Therefore every year they scourged certain boys before the altar so that blood might flow upon it and the image be appeased. Some accused the Spartans of scourging the boys purely for the discipline. At any rate the Spartans bestowed a prize upon the boy who best endured.

This, then, was the meaning of the Polemarch. Aristodemos was to be scourged before the altar the following month.

The Polemarch's eyes followed the boy as he returned to mess. It was time to look after this adopted son of Gylippos.

But Aristodemos finished his breakfast and save for a slight paleness in his browned cheeks gave no hint of disturbance. Even in the choral dance he leaped lightly, and if his gestures seemed a little loose and ill directed he was not different in this from other boys of fifteen.

At the first moment of freedom he walked away westward toward the hills. Once in the seclusion of the woods he flung himself down upon the mould with clenched fists.

"I will not! I will not!" he said aloud.

He had seen the rite. He had seen Tisamenos, a tall thin boy, fall gasping under the lash, and die at the altar foot.

Was he afraid of death? No; he would gladly have died for the State with such men as the devoted Boulis and Sperthias. Aristodemos well remembered the day when the preposterous trousered Persian heralds had appeared in Sparta with their demands for submissive earth and water, and how the Spartans had flung them screeching into a well to get earth and water for themselves. And he remembered how the portents and the Sacred Laws had demanded two Spartan lives to expiate the herald lives destroyed. He could even now see the two devotees leaving the altar hand in hand for the journey to far Persia, while the awestruck city gazed in silence after them. Gladly would he have died with

Sperthias and Boulis. Death could be a joy, death with a purpose. But this wanton suffering leading no whither!

His keen mind, the inheritance from his Attic fathers, awoke and lifted itself with the problem, dividing the justice from injustice, the foolish from the purposeful.

Ah, the shameful mutilation of the scourge! He had seen in Sparta men with scarred backs and welted faces. And he knew that these marks were no fair-earned battle scars. They were mere deformities. And now he was to be thus wantonly marred!

For the first time since he had loved Leonidas he again thought of escape.

It was long after the evening meal that Leonidas, searching in great anxiety, found him pacing back and forth like a young lion in the wood. He had worn a path where he had walked.

"I will not do it!" he said in a voice that was all edge.

Leonidas had not yet spoken.

"I did not expect thee to turn afraid," he said bitterly.

"I am not afraid!" said Aristodemos in the same loud, expressionless voice.

"Then why refuse the pain?"

"I do not—But such vile pain! Fit for barbarians!"

"And what of thy talking? Thou wouldst so gladly die with Sperthias and Boulis. And this is not even death."

"Sperthias and Boulis! Do not speak their holy names!"

He stopped before his friend.

"Ye gods in Olympos! Dost thou not see the difference?"

"Yes," said Leonidas, "I do see a difference. But can we prevent the image crying out for blood? We do our best. Oh, but thou grievest me!"

"Do not say that! Do not say that!" cried Aristodemos, struggling with his heavy breaths. "Thou art my friend, always my friend. But this scourging is not for me."

"No, no," repeated Leonidas slowly, "not for thee."

Then he fell silent once more.

But the boy uneasily broke in again.

"What will they do in Sparta when they find that I am gone?"

"Dost thou not know what they will do?"

"No," wonderingly.

"When a youth fails his man friend who hath taught him is punished for him. He is accountable."

"But they will not punish thee, Leonidas!"

"Will they not?" returned Leonidas, with a gleam of a smile. Then he added solemnly, "Child, it is not for that I care."

At this, quite unexpectedly, the choked stream of the boy's affection leaped free.

"Leondrion—Leondrion!" he cried, using the name that no one else dared use with him. "Oh, I have denied thee, I have denied thee!" He wept in passionate repentance.

Leonidas was always a little confused by such extravagance of emotion.

"Nay, thou hast broken no oath. Do not speak such words in thy haste. The gods' ears are sharp."

Leonidas sat beside him speaking no word until Aristodemos grew quiet. Then he said:

"Thou shalt not suffer unready. There are still many days in which to train and harden thee. That shall be my work."

So in the days that followed Aristodemos received over and above the Spartan discipline, a special toughening at the hands of his friend. Every morning runnings and liftings, every afternoon rubbings and beatings, until the muscles grew hard and malleable and the skin was as tough as a panther's. From its very activity it was a joyous companionship in spite of its sombre purpose. Aristodemos's affection warmed and expanded anew. Never again was he to mistake the quiet aloofness of his friend. To be sure, Leonidas would often sit without a word the while the boy poured forth some rapturous new enthusiasm. But Aristodemos could always be certain that later, perhaps in a breathing space between wrestling or as a spear left his hand, Leonidas would make answer. He never spoke without sight and insight.

As the day of the trial neared, Leonidas watched his charge with increasing solicitude. It was the boy's gaiety that now troubled him.

"But," said Leonidas severely, "to-morrow is the day of Artemis."

"Then be not in league with the Goddess to make it to-day," retorted the boy with a nod.

The morning came, and Leonidas scanned the boy at breakfast with grave misgiving. He was pale as ivory. The muscles which Leonidas had hardened with such care seemed powerful and quick, but not brawny like those of Demonax and Alpheos, who were also in the trial. How thin he looked! His delicate chin had a tremour about it.

"Eat!" he commanded in a whisper. "Leave nothing!"

Late in the morning, when the sun was hottest, the six boys who were to endure the scourging set out at the head of the procession from the Market Place. They were decked as for sacrifice, quite naked and crowned with willow garlands. They passed Aphrodite's double temple, the Leda Shrine and the Robe House, silent this festival morning, and so out of the town.

Before them, quivering in the hot air of the river meadow was the temple of the Moon Goddess. In front of it stood a broad marble altar decked with willows and bearing the Xoanon itself. This image, stiff, erect and crude, had already that cold look of face which later became distinctive of the Virgin Huntress.

Every altar has an aspect of quiet waiting. But this altar was cruel in its quietude. The broad sun shone dazling on its white surface. At its side waited also a tall Virgin Priestess, whose long, bright yellow robe hung folding about her feet. Directly in front of the altar, on a low platform, stood the officer with his ready scourge.

THE SPARTAN

In utter silence the procession drew near, in silence the six boys moved to their place before the altar, their heads bowed, their young backs shining with the sweat of the long walk. Leonidas saw with concern that Aristodemos stood last of the six.

The priestess made long prayer, then suddenly she turned, took the ancient image from its place and lifted it with both hands high above her head. It was the signal. The first boy mounted the platform.

Then the officer lifted his great arm, and swept down the sounding lash.

The young Spartan did not wince. He only shifted his position a little that the officer might strike more straight. Then he stood motionless while the terrible scourge cut the air, blow after blow. Aristodemos forgot his own impending trial in pity for the boy. Bloody welts appeared across the slender boyish back, at sight of which a deep breathing went through the crowd, and the Priestess's eyes shone, cruel and bright, with a premonition of ecstasy.

At last the strong flogger rested. The boy walked unsteadily away into the embrace of his company.

"He did not fall! He did not fall!" the awed crowd whispered. And, "The prize! The prize!"

Demonax next advanced. Demonax had developed into a beautiful youth, bronze-dark, lithe and full of strength. His beauty unconsciously touched the officer and the blows fell not quite so quick nor hard.

"Oh!" moaned the Priestess, the image lowering in her hands. "So heavy! So—heavy! Beware of the wrath—!" For the heaviness of the image measured the weakness of the blow.

And Demonax stamped his foot.

"Spare not, fool!" he angrily cried.

And so the pitiful rite went on with its sad misapprehension of its God, that old ignorance which in some new form so easily resettles in men's minds whenever loving Deity has lifted it away. It was that old instinct of self torture, of bribing the god, of paying for a grudged blessing. Even in the face of the gentle Christ men utilize His sufferings to barter for their souls in a sort of heavenly market place.

Suddenly Aristodemos awoke to the realization that his own turn was come. Alpheos had fallen and was being carried off, seemingly dead. As in a dream he mounted the three steps and stood on the low marble platform close to the stained altar. He shuddered as he saw the blood dripping from the faded willow garlands.

Then like fire the first blow fell.

He swayed like a reed, cried out sharply, then clenched his fists and stood erect.

The scourge twisted like a snake about his shoulders. It stung as if its poison were red hot. Each stroke at first came in agony distinct. Then the pangs merged and the great anguish pervaded his whole body.

Then, stroke! stroke! stroke! again. That interminable rhythm! He thought that he could bear the pain of it, if it were not for that vile singing of the thong above his head. Blood poured over his shining skin.

> *"As when some woman of Maionia*
> *Staineth ivory with purple,*
> *So thy thighs were stained*
> *And thine ankles beneath."*

The crowd grew breathless, for Aristodemos still kept his place, standing with fixed eyes and expressionless face.

Suddenly he fell.

Again that strange, relieved sigh passed through the blood-fascinated crowd. Leonidas sprang forward. But before he could reach the altar, Aristodemos had struggled to his knees, then up to his feet. Looking straight into his friend's eyes he smiled to him, a curious, bright, intimate smile, and gave his back once more to the scourge.

Some minutes more the lash rose and fell. At last the boy sank silently down and did not move again.

Leonidas was instantly over him with shaking hands, weeping for the first time in his life. And Makaria, running with unwonted access of love, gathered him up in her arms and carried him, so strong was she, to a litter, while she cried loudly:

"He is dead! Oh, my son! My son!"

But Leonidas pushed her away and felt about the boy's heart.

"No," he said. "He liveth. But the Gods alone know how long he will live!"

"And the Crown!" interposed the smiling, satisfied Priestess. She stepped down to the litter and laid the "Willow Crown of Artemis" upon the unconscious face.

Then Leonidas himself with his Helot carried the silent litter to Gylippos's house.

CHAPTER TEN

At a Place Called Marathon

Twelve long days and nights Leonidas bent over the unconscious boy.

"It is for me he dieth," he said, while that smile at the altar smote heavily upon his heart.

Men and women came to ask after the "Bomonikes," the Altar Victor. "Never before," they told Makaria, "did one fall under the scourge and afterward rise again."

A fever set in on the second day, and Aristodemos lay with cheeks bright red and body paling from unacquaintance with the sun. He looked small and childish there on his narrow bed, more like the little boy who had come from Athens than the growing youth of Sparta:

Makaria was favoured with the unexpected sight of a king's more kingly brother bending over her boy and dressing his wounds with careful fingers, while the tears ran unheeded down his cheeks and beard.

Sometimes for hours Aristodemos would call the name of his friend, a slow, unending call. Sometimes he would beg him to forget that he had forsaken the altar and fled the scourge.

"The scourge was hard," he would plead childishly. "Thou canst not know how hard it was, Leonidas!"

"But thou tookest the scourge, and nobly. Dost thou not remember, little one?" Leonidas would urge with breaking heart.

But long before the sick one could be convinced, his fevered mind would be up and away. His whole delirium was a search for his friend save one day when his fever went low. Then Aristodemos wandered all day long with his father, prattling child-talk in Attic Greek.

It was while Aristodemos was still in the dim inaccessible places that the city of Sparta was suddenly startled to its very centre with news. An Athenian herald, Pheidippides, who had run all the way from Athens in two days, stumbled pale and forspent into the Agora. The Spartans carried him in their arms to the rulers.

"Men of Lacedæmon," he gasped between labouring breaths, "the Athenians implore you! Hurry, hurry to their help! Do not let our most ancient State be enslaved by barbarians! Eretria, look—Eretria is already taken and ruined: And Greece is weakened by the loss of no mean city!"

The so long dreaded Persians had come at last!

Now it happened that this was the ninth day of the month. It lacked yet two days until the full moon. Of course no godfearing Spartan could set out upon an expedition until after his full moon. Therefore they said, as they sat in slow, solemn council:

"After two days; after two days."

"But do ye think the barbarians will observe to wait for your cursed full-moon?" cried the Athenian in passionate entreaty. "They are upon us! The Medes! Do ye not hear? Stronger many times are they than all the states of Greece. By sea they come! By land they come also. Think how close they are! The burning of Eretria lighteth up the very sky of Athens. Two days! Why, the barbarians will have razed Athens in your damnable two days."

A few of the Spartans, Leonidas among them, urged an immediate start. But the mass prevailed, and the precious two days were lost.

On the third evening, at the first peep of the clear full moon, the army marched. They hurried night and day to reach Athens. But, while they were yet marching, the Athenians and their allies had met the Persians at a place on the eastern shore called Marathon. And Marathon had been won.

The day after the battle the Spartans arrived at a

city which was delirious with joy.

"We have sent the Mede back!" cried the Athenians. "With our single arm we have sent him back! Ye were not needed in this matter, O ye Spartans. But go and look!"

So the envying Spartans passed through the city and marched on to the Marathon plain, so covered with the dead, with strange, outlandish dead, that the Spartans could only gaze in silence. Miltiades, the Greek general, had vowed to Artemis a he-goat for every slain enemy. But there were not enough he-goats in Attica to make good that vow! It was a wilderness of death.

In the midst were gathered glittering heaps of spoils—gold rimmed shields, garments of precious purple, swords, with ruby-crusted hilts. At the head of the guard which kept these riches stood the noble figure of the honestest man of Athens, Aristides, whom they loved to call "The Just."

As for the Athenians, they looked into one another's awed faces, saying:

"Not so strong are we! The invisible Gods fought upon our side!"

It was indeed a power invisible that had won them their victory, the power of the Greek mind, a sort of diviner Herakles vanquishing the vast Python of the oriental army. Æschylus was in that fight, and Aristides, and probably Antenor, leaving his sculptor work. And Phrynichos, who had been writing fiery dramas of the Persian peril, had laid down his war-compelling pen to take up war itself.

Is it wonderful that such men as these came home awestruck at their own achievements, humble yet proud as gods, their hearts vision-sown as a spring garden, potent for a blossoming which has been the world's unending joy?

Such were the things the Spartans saw at Marathon and at Athens.

Thus it came to pass that Aristodemos, awaking one day from his long illness, was aware of his beloved warrior coming in heated from the march, his crest sweeping the low ceiling of the room, who told in excited words how Athens had met the arch-enemies of Hellas at Marathon, and driven them back over seas; and how, after the manner of a miracle that city was become the saviour of Greece.

CHAPTER ELEVEN

The Spring-Time of Hellas

"Grant them with feet so light
To pass through life."

Pindar.

After the passing of the fever, Aristodemos recovered quickly. His well-trained body soon mended and righted all its wrongs. But no slighted Aristodemos was he who took up the Spartan life again. Now he was Aristodemos the Altar Victor, Crowned of Artemis. He was never laughed at now. He was in a manner consecrate. As he walked along the narrow streets, his arms modestly hidden in his cloak, "carrying virgins in his eyes" (the Greek phrase for the pure look of youth) the Spartan boys, who so passionately loved honours, would whisper, "Our Bomonikes."

But better than honours was his own sense of victory. He could endure! Oh, the uplift of it! He had now no dread of Spartan life. Its very hardness was become a delight, for he had mastered it. He had beaten the Spartans at their own game. His hard-got strength was his own. Pindar has voiced this divine effrontery of youth:

"He that hath lately won glory
In the time of his sweet youth,
Is lifted on the wings of his strong hope.
And soaring valour.
His thoughts are above riches."

But indeed, all Hellas was youthful then. It was the

potent brooding springtime of a nation. Her great works were not yet, but all the stuff of them was in Greek hearts. Never was an awakening more splendid or fuller of creative joy than this awakening after Marathon. Everywhere new thoughts were budding and fresh desires. Poets fared from city to city, their hearts aflame with half formed melody. Statues hitherto straitened in eastern or Egyptian bands were opening eyes, freeing hands and arms as if they were alive. The first "Philosophies," then wonderfully new, came whispering across the sea from Ionia, hazarding their bold guesses at the central principle for the whole universe, and widening men's hearts with a glad surprise like the surprise of a child who for the first time looks up aware of the fathomless blue sky. There was a springtime exuberance in everything men did and thought.

Boy though he was, Aristodemos was subtly stirred by this mighty impulse. Not all the barriers of Sparta could keep it from him. In a note of song, a festival enthusiasm, an expression of some powerful stranger face, it spoke to him; and the heart of the stripling leaped up responsive.

Happy is he whose youthtime is coincident with such youthtime in the world.

Aristodemos's first act upon attaining complete soundness was to sacrifice and give thanks to the Eurotas. Rivers, with their ceaseless flow, were ever associated with the flowing life of youth. He proceeded willow-crowned to the stream. In the still morning there followed him his stately mother, his friend Leonidas, his Helot slave newly assigned to serve him, Gylippos, still walking like a man of arms, his old eyes twinkling with pride, and behind them all Antiphon, bent double with years and burdens, scarce able to move his aged legs along the way. It was a devoted, intimate procession, each of them blessed in the youth's blessed victory.

As he stretched forth his hands, dropping his gifts into the stream, his mother noted a new grace, a strengthful sureness of gesture which she had never seen in him before, which was to be the peculiar charm of his manhood.

That evening Makaria brought forth from a deep chest the precious violet himation of his father and gave it to the boy. Even in Lykos's day this festal robe had been carefully laid away in wild thyme, the scent of which now, like the very presence of his father almost overcame him. He took it with trembling hands and dared not put it on, though Makaria urged him, so bright and close in that moment came Lykos, that gladsome figure.

Old Gylippos watched with keen, peering eyes.

"Hast no love of Athenian finery?" he said chuckling. "A Spartan shift is good enough for thee, eh lad?"

"Yes, Father, I think so indeed," answered Aristodemos modestly. He was thinking, though, how little worthy he was to wear his father's mantle.

Gylippos, well satisfied, stalked away to the Dromos.

This river ceremony to which the old man had walked so proudly proved to be his last forth-faring. That same morning while watching the boys at their disk throwing he began to totter and fall, and they bore him home again to Makaria. There he lay through the winter months, filling the hut at first with his irritable demands. Then he grew gentler, as if death had already touched him and given something of its calm.

His constant desire now was Aristodemos. Many times a day he must look at the boy, turn him around and approve of him. It was Aristodemos who must rehearse to him all the news of the Dromos, of disks, race, leaping. Nor would he take his slender sick-man fare save from the boy's hand. Aristodemos had never thought to love him until now.

He died in the first springtide of the year, as the old are wont to die—sleeping. Aristodemos wept at his going. Henceforth he himself was the head of the house. Though like all active Spartans he continued to live in barracks.

Makaria these days moved very proudly through

the Spartan streets, and followed her son's doings with an almost servile admiration.

"Thy mother loveth and honoureth thee," remarked Leonidas. They were throwing the disk in the Dromos, where Aristodemos's skill was gradually creeping up to the record of his friend. Aristodemos paused, thoughtful, with bowed head, disk in hand.

"She loved me not when I was poor and unheeded. I think it is my victory she loveth more than me."

Leonidas gave him a quick look.

"I would not have thought that," he said.

The boy seemed to have an inherited keenness that forced him to see, whether he would or not.

At eighteen Aristodemos passed out of the ranks of the boys. He became a "Youth," an "Ephebos," as they called it. The very word was charmed. For to the Greeks the stripling at the wonder-verge of manhood was the most beautiful thing in the world, the most appealing. They spoke of him with a sort of awed tenderness such as we use toward young maidens. It was the sacred season—this brief period of early bloom, of unbounded expectancy. Was it not a breath upon mortals from the gods, making them godlike for a little time, a mysterious sweet light making the youth himself, while it rested upon him, a holy thing?

Therefore the youth must enter upon it with certain symbolizing acts and sacrifices. Spartan youths then for the first time allowed their hair to grow like Spartan men.

Aristodemos's golden locks had long ago been clipped in the mourning ritual for his father, and their continued shortness had always seemed to the boy a kind of love-sign which his invisible father might perhaps see and be glad of. He now let them grow with a certain ruth. Soon they were a golden abundance framing his spare calm face. When he exercised he must needs draw them close in a woolen fillet, as was the habit of Spartan youths.

And with his lengthening locks there came an indescribable change upon the boy, a loveliness of shoulder, a firmness and glow of flesh so living as to seem scarce fleshly at all. It was that fateful approach of manly perfection, the evanescent grace mysteriously blooming out of the awkwardness of the Greek boy, his very awkwardness being transmuted into a beautiful shyness, an almost reverence, in all he said and did.

In this newness of life Aristodemos had an easy erectness, as if upborne by his own living breath. Every ripple of his body was vital. When he ran, his feet had a Hermes lightness; when he hurled the lance, it was with a buoyant directed strength into which passed all the training of the years. Even when he stood upon the throwing line mentally measuring off the course for his gleaming diskos, the very fingers of his upraised left hand showed themselves light, separated, defined, ready to obey the finest motions of his wit.

And the joy of him all centred in his face, in the calm forehead where life had set no pain, in the clear eyes with their trick of looking beyond, in the full rich mouth with its habit of thoughtful smiling as if from an inner gay repose. His was not the face we usually think of as Greek—the Hellenistic face with the thin lips and attenuated nose. It was the fuller, manlier face of the early time, a face of purpose and control.

Aristodemos began now to visit the altars of the gods with wistful new prayers. The Deathless Ones had grown strangely real to him, no longer the mere bright forms of his childhood, but clear-known persons who loved and sorrowed, knew and cared, a vast and ever-present company.

Of them all it was Apollo who stood forth to his growing mind as his own god, the inevitable ideal of the young Greek. Pindar long ago at Lykos's burial had spoken of Apollo in words which as a little boy he could not understand. But now the youth understood. Through his waxing needs and knowledge he knew his god! When a melody would sing itself through his brain he would say, "Apollo hath touched me," with the instinct to look over his shoulder.

For before the eyes of his mind Apollo stood clear, a fair young man with trim, close-filleted head, vitally young like the worshipper himself, but taller and more glorious than any mortal youth could be, erect, with full breathing chest and neck like a fair column, and with that face of imperturbable, calm brightness.

To the adoring youth Apollo was not the god of music's ecstasy alone but of music's law—indeed; the god of all well-ordered thoughts and actions. Aristodemos knew that look of the god's eyes—knew it as if he had met him—that look of noble rebuke too calm for wrath, full of a power that was almost sad, almost but not quite loving. It was Apollo who stood and stretched out his great quiet hand over contending men and restless passions, and always upon his face was that look of dignity and calm restraint.

But whole periods would come when Aristodemos would not think of the greater gods at all, but rather of the thousand little ones who suffered with the change of seasons, and whose loves and sorrows were all uncured. Often in the late afternoon Aristodemos would start out full-breathed for a run, for his energy was inexhaustible. Leaving the lowlands behind he would swiftly climb the Taÿgetos by a wild gorge he knew. Here every shadowed glade had its peeping faun, its possible satyr. Merely to go into the forest was to set free in his mind a hundred stories which he implicitly believed, stories which awakened his keen young sympathies, his admiration, wonder, questioning. He had a power of imaging which kept him all aglow.

Through this gorge poured down a wealth of noisy waters taking fearful leaps into black pools whence they sent up their deep-voiced thunder. Then they poured out again over the boulders with laughter at their own invincible purity. The nymph of such a stream—what a wild, sweet creature must she be! Sometimes the youth loved her, sometimes feared her, as he sat by the joyous tumult.

THE SPRING-TIME OF HELLAS

From these cool shadows he could look down over the level Spartan plain with its silvery olive stretches, "the holy bloom" which wherever found was Athena's, and which always brought to Aristodemos the very breath of his childhood. Sometimes glancing through the near, slant forest spaces he almost fancied that he saw the mighty Virgin herself with stately feet moving in the godlike folds of her dress, coming tranquilly down the glen to him. Then his very breath would stop. For gods had been known to seek out their faithful worshippers and even claim them utterly.

It was in this mountain wilderness that Aristodemos began to practise his art of singing and song-making. His necessity for expression urged him to a patience of effort that would have amazed his simple hearted Spartan comrades. Song after song did he make, though never one that spoke his heart. His voice, too, he tried, low and high, but it never rang true to the imagined sound within. And all the while a new self-consciousness held him silent below in the Spartan chorus.

So he strove alone, struggling to set free his thoughts in song, yet coming no nearer to expression, and seeming at last to lose even the clues of his inspiration.

But one bright, windful morning the youth-chorus was chanting away at an old Herakles song, beating out the rhythm with their feet. Suddenly above the united tide of song rose a clear, manful voice, not loud but absorbing all the others into its own certainty and sweetness, swinging them out of their heavy rhythm to its own compelling emphasis. Speech it was rather than song, the outgoing of a soul from its depths into the light, a full, unhindered utterance. They needs must be swayed whether they would or not.

With wondering faces the youths sang through to the end. Then they turned upon him.

"What, Aristodemos! Bomonikes! Who dreamed that thou couldst sing—and like that!"

"Oh, yes, yes! Listen!" cried Aristodemos passionately with strangely shining eyes. And breaking into song again he leaped into the centre of their orchestra circle and began to improvise upon the story as he had never improvised before. He was wildly unconscious of what he did or even that he was singing alone. As Plato says:

> *"The poet is a light and winged and a holy thing,*
> *And no invention is in him 'till he hath been inspired,*
> *Is beyond his senses, and in him no longer is his*
> *mind."*

How Aristodemos sang! How he acted his song with his quick leapings and his vivid changing face! He sang of Herakles, the great kindly hero, faring from town to town, helping and healing sorrows. And, as Aristodemos sang, he too fought the nine-headed Hydra, wrestled with Death and saved Queen Alkestis alive, journeyed to the far edge of the world and fetched the golden fruit of Hesperides and flung, as he ended, the almost visible apples into the Spartan throng.

The youths crowded up to him with wild delight.

"Again! Again!" they demanded. "We will sing with thee! Thou shalt be our Choragos!"

He stood a moment shaking his loose locks at them, flushed, laughing, bewildered. Then the dreamful, preoccupied look crossed his face again, and again his voice rang out.

It was a song of his own, one of the many that he had almost created in the forest, a song of that impetuous nymph of his own mountain gorge. At the strophe he paused in the growing story. He nodded his bright head to them with a gesture of command. And the chorus in mighty volume flung back his melody, still warm from its creation.

So they sang in swift antiphony until the whole city gathered in happy excitement around the orchestra. Henceforth Aristodemos bore a new name in Sparta. He was called Aoidos—"the singer." And it was a love name. For Aristodemos had given to the starved minds of these Spartan youths something which they had lacked. He was become necessary to them. In work, in the games they sought his companionship. Nothing was complete without him. And yet they gave him a certain wondering respect. Genius was holy, even in Sparta.

"I love to see thee companioned," said the large-souled Leonidas. "I am proud when they seek thee!"

"Proud? Thou?" laughed Aristodemos. "But I am loved by the bravest soldier in Sparta! Not that much canst thou boast!"

But something in the brightness of the face, the joyous nod of the golden head, struck Leonidas with that shrewd ancient fear of the Greeks.

"Be not so openly glad, Aristodemos," he said. "Remember the signet ring of Polycrates the fortunate one, which the gods returned to him from the sea before they came to destroy him. Some things the gods will not brook, and for the too-happy man there is no escape, turn he this way or that!"

CHAPTER TWELVE

The King is Dead

Kleomenes, the King, had just returned from a disgraceful exile in Arkadia. He had dispossessed his co-king Demaratos in favour of the weak Leotychides, had tried to bribe the Delphic priestess, and, most infamous of all, had committed sacrilege by burning the sacred grove in which some enemies of his had sought sanctuary. Finally, he had fled from the anger which his evil deeds had aroused in Sparta.

Recently, however, the Spartans had called him back to his kingdom to keep him from plotting with the Arkadians against his own country. There was but little rejoicing at his return. Now he walked the streets of his city, wild-eyed and restless, his robe disordered, his sceptre swinging in his hand. The people shrank away from him or meeting him cast down their eyes, afraid to look upon a sacrilegious man. The unwary ones he maliciously struck in the face with his sceptre. Upon which his brothers, Leonidas and Kleombrotos confined him. For by this time he was stark mad.

"Do not call him 'brother'," urged Aristodemos to Leonidas as they talked together. "He is but thy half brother. I am thankful he is no full kin to thee. Thy brother Dorieus was right. This man was never true born king."

"Hush!" said Leonidas. "He is sacred, for he wears the crown."

"But," persisted Aristodemos, "how can he be sacred? He hath committed sacrilege. And Kleomenes was not truly born as Dorieus and thou."

THE KING IS DEAD

He was referring to the story of King Anaxandrides, who was the father of King Kleomenes and of the brothers Dorieus, Leonidas and Kleombrotos. Anaxandrides had married in his youth a wife dear to his heart. No children had come of the wedlock, but when the Ephors demanded that he put her away he had answered:

"It is no good advice that you give me to put away my wife. She hath done no wrong, and I will not."

Upon which, after much wagging of their wise heads together, the Ephors pronounced, "Keep her, then. But take thee another wife besides. Lest," they added significantly, "the Spartans make some unwonted decree concerning thee. For if thou care not, we at least may not let the Eurysthenid line die out amongst us!"

The second wife promptly bore him Kleomenes. Now, however, unhoped for joy, the true wife also bore him a son, the high-spirited Dorieus. Again she bore him Leonidas and again Kleombrotos. But the unloved wife bore no more children.

Dorieus from the first showed the noblest possible temper, excelling all the youths in skill and strength, and gathering devotion to himself by his very nature. But Kleomenes grew up gloomy and solitary. He fed naturally upon the crueller customs of the land. All the unlove of his parents seemed to live in him. His chosen friends were of vulgar spirit like himself.

But when Anaxandrides died the Spartans kept the letter of their law and decided that Kleomenes, as the eldest son, was the rightful king. And Dorieus, who had himself confidently hoped to succeed his father, thereupon found Sparta unbearable. He therefore asked the Ephors to let him found a colony in Sicily. And he had sailed away with a band of young men who were glad to join themselves to him.

Leonidas gave no sign. If the rule of Kleomenes chafed him, no one ever heard him say so. He laboured on in his absorbed fashion at his daily round. He was not quick to greet and he lacked altogether the knightly fascination of his elder brother. But he had loved that brother with a complete devotion, and grew more and more silent after his departure. Lately the elders and even the Ephors had begun to find themselves turning to Leonidas for his opinion; and no one of them ever thought of questioning his rarely uttered judgment in Dromos or in the Place-of-Meeting.

About this time the first sinister mutterings of the Persian storm began to reach Sparta from across the Ægean. Xerxes, the new childish ruler of the Medes, was hot to be revenged for Marathon.

Aristodemos came one day in great excitement to Leonidas.

"The Persians are coming again!"

"Will the whipped cur fight again?" said Leonidas contemptuously.

"But if the cur have a great pack of curs with him, Leonidas?"

"Nay. Believe not all thou hearest from travellers."

So Aristodemos went away ashamed of his excitement.

A little later, however, at a festival, the place was gusty with news.

"And this time," insisted Aristodemos, "it is the old wine merchant who cometh every year from Kyme. He saith there is no nation in Asia that will not furnish fighting men. One sendeth ships, another boats for bridges. Old Syloson saith they are already at work upon a bridge across the Hellespont, an immense bridge of ships such as man hath never seen. Syloson himself carried rope for the bridge from Egypt. Oh, Leonidas, I surely think a great war is befalling!"

Leonidas listened in silence, his black brows gathering down over his eyes.

"Dost thou not believe it!" pursued Aristodemos.

"The Ephors do not believe it! They tell us the Medes do but come against Athens and that Sparta, being beyond the Isthmos, is safe."

"And thou? What sayest thou?"

"That none but dolts would say such a thing!" broke out Leonidas wrathfully. "But I find no Spartan that sees!"

"Then thou hast all the while believed the Persians are coming!" cried Aristodemos, throwing arms about his friend. "We'll fight them together!"

"Yes, we shall fight together, if Sparta doth not hang back behind her hills until the Medes trample her very vineyards. Come, I will talk with thee." And the two strode out Colona way to the foothills, and sat them by a stream as turbulent with its rush down Taÿgetos as their hearts were turbulent with thoughts. There they held deep converse together, the first of many on this ever widening theme.

"Oh, I would that my father Lykos had lived to see this day," said Aristodemos finally. "Or that he had even lived to die at Marathon."

"Doubtless he hath left the strife to thee," said Leonidas. "It is a noble legacy."

As the friends walked homeward, they scarce knew whether their hearts were fuller of fear for their city or of fearful joy at the deeds they might be set to do. But the summer passed without event. The great Orient seemed to forget its stirrings and lie down again.

One frosty autumn evening Aristodemos was vigorously swinging along toward his quarters. The stars above were pricking through the twilight and the slender moon hung thin-edged and keen against the sky.

"Hello, Aoidos!" called out Alpheos from the dark within. "Hast seen Eurytos and Demonax!"

"No."

"Well, thou'st missed it!" cried Alpheos, eager to tell. "We've had a great hunt and got a monstrous boar. But Eurytos had a near call from old Thanatos. Crazy fellow! He stumbled on the boar alone and tried to fetch him without help with some famous stroke or other. Tusker turned on him and Eurytos slipped. Gods, he was as good as dead! But before we could get to him Demonax had jumped out of the bush and hewed the boar's head nigh off. Here they come! Here they come!"

The clamorous rout came shouting up the road, waving their stubby swords. The ponderous boar they carried swinging from a pole, his bristly snout trailing blood along the path. And in the twilight they carried upon their shoulders the merry Demonax brandishing the huge tusks and clashing them together.

"Sing it! Sing the hunt!" he demanded as Aristodemos ran out to them. And Aristodemos, joining the marching crowd, broke into a wild song to which Demonax clashed time with the tusks.

"Into the forest went I forth,
I met a boar with raging jaws,
Fierce was he, but fiercer I!
Fiercer I! Fiercer I!
I smote him with my sword!
He fell down in his blood!"

So they sang it on, far into the darkness. Then they feasted together after the glorious hunt. The years had knit Aristodemos very close to these fierce fellows, his table-mates. There were only fifteen of them. Together they had toiled and striven through summer heats and winter snows. Together they had slept, together wakened with the dawn. Together they had suffered the scourging of Artemis. They had had their boyish fights even from that first morning when he and Demonax had tussled in the river. But time and close conditions had developed a mighty devotion in the little band. And the great Spartan oath of fealty which they had recently sworn to each other was all unneeded after the ceaseless knitting of the years.

At last after the feasting the torch had to be stamped out and they lay down to sleep. Aristodemos fell asleep instantly and was quite undisturbed when, an hour later, two men tiptoed in among the sleepers, shook Leonidas awake and took him out with them. He was therefore all dazed when Leonidas returned alone just before daybreak and whispered sharply in his ear:

"Aristodemos, come! Come quickly. I have great

need of thee!"

It showed how instinctive his Spartan discipline had become that Aristodemos, as he stumbled out all shivering with sleep, asked no questions, but marched along silent at Leonidas's side as if under orders. The dark streets were deserted. They met only one young man stealing back like a shadow from visiting his wife. For Sparta forbade open marriages to the young, but really encouraged them in secret.

The two came to the river at the very place where the boys had frolicked together that first early morning. The stream flowed darkly in the white dawn as they threw themselves down in the familiar spot.

Only then did Leonidas turn to his friend and speak in a low, tense voice:

"The king is dead!"

"The king?"

"Kleomenes. His feet were in the stocks. To-night he demanded a knife. And when he threatened, his keeper was afraid, being only a Helot, and brought him one. With it he killed himself, cutting and horribly hacking his body. Thou wouldst never know him. Oh, it is horrible, horrible!

"And," he added quickly, "I did not tell thee last night, Aristodemos, not even thee. Word has privately come to me and to the Ephors that Dorieus also is dead, fighting nobly in Sicily."

"What—splendid Dorieus? Thy brother Dorieus!" And with his quick instinct of love Aristodemos threw both his arms about his friend.

But Leonidas shook him off and seized his shoulders roughly.

"Thou art not well awake! Thou dost not see what this means!"

Aristodemos looked up a bewildered instant and found Leonidas gazing deeply, strangely, into his eyes.

"Boy, boy!" he whispered. "I am king!"

And even as he spoke a great change fell upon Leonidas. Was it some divine sense of his lineage from

Zeus breaking in upon him, some sudden consciousness of priestly mediation for the State? Aristodemos
saw his face alter, soften, then grow mighty with power
and isolation, the power to stand out like a rock upon
the coast and take the force of things himself. It was
the birth of his kinghood in him.

Instinctively Aristodemos bowed low before him. But
Leonidas lifted him with a swift passion that in him was
rare.

"No, no!" he cried. "Do not leave me alone! All
Lacedæmon is put into my hand. And—and—it is lonely
to be king!" It was a cry of great personal need. Yet in
it was a dignity not to be broken through. He was speaking now again, thoughtfully, but with that same sorrowful intensity.

"Yes, I am king. But they are children, our Spartans. Mine, mine is all the care."

"But Leotychides," said Aristodemos. "He, too, is
king."

But Leonidas shook his head.

"Leotychides doth not see. The day is full of Fate.
Oh, Aristodemos, all Asia is upon us! Yet he doth not
see. Our Spartans do not see. The Ephors do not see.
I must fight this fight alone, first with mine own people,
then with people of the Barbarian. Thus desperate is
my stand. But thou," he added, "thou seest, my 'Listener.' Thou wilt always see."

He kissed him solemnly, took his hand, and together
they walked back to the town.

Already, though the sun was scarcely risen, the
streets were full of folk. The harsh clash of cymbals
resounded in mourning for the dead. Women crouched
before their doors lifting their wail and beating their
breasts. Men were casting lots to determine which of
the family should put on the mourning garment. Mounted
messengers were clattering off in every direction with
notifications of the king's death.

Leonidas still holding his friend's hand strode
through the commotion to the king's house. The citi-

zens stepped out of his way and bowed their heads as he passed. And as they watched him out of sight they realized that they were glad of him, that they trusted him as they had not trusted a king for generations.

When the month of mourning had passed Leonidas was crowned. He made his first high-priestly sacrifice for the people. After the crowning and the sacrifice the old Ephors came to him. They had something important to say. The young king, in short, must take himself a wife, and that forthwith.

Leonidas looked at them with a proud, quiet smile.

"And if I be already wed?" he said. "And if before many moons, I can give you an heir to the Eurysthenid line?"

The Ephors looked their amazement.

"Gorgo is my wife," he told them. And his proud face shone.

At this the Ephors were glad, for Gorgo was the cleverest and best loved maiden of royal lineage in all Sparta.

CHAPTER THIRTEEN

The Violet Robe Changes Hands

It is incredible how far away and unreal the "Eastern Danger," with all its menace of huge war preparings, seemed to the Greeks. Athens indeed had some guesses at the menace. But Sparta, in her protected valley, had none. So the little states of Greece prepared no defences, no armies. Instead they but celebrated their festivals a little more faithfully. It were well in any event to honour the gods. Even the young king, Leonidas, biding his time, knew that he could not yet urge the Spartans. Perhaps he also felt that in the path of such a fate it was good first of all to win the favour of the gods.

So this spring he, with the other Spartans, entered with especial ardour into the Hyacinthine feast. With them he re-lived that tender ancient story of the youth so beautiful that Apollo himself had been wont to lay aside his celestial aspect to be near the lovely boy. In the meadow of Amyklai, only two short miles from Sparta, the two, one day, were flinging the disk. Doubtless the God was instructing the lad, just as Leonidas had many a day taught his boy friend Aristodemos. But the god struck Hyacinth with the flying disk and killed him. Then grief most terrible seized the god, who himself could not die. But ere the soul of Hyacinth could flit forth wailing down the steep way of death Apollo caught it in his hand.

"For swift the act and short the way

THE VIOLET ROBE CHANGES HANDS

Of gods who are eager to an end."

And Apollo breathed into the soul a new life and set it upon the warm meadow, where it sprang up in likeness of a flower. And on the purple petals the weeping god wrote his cry of woe, "Al." And now everywhere the soul of Hyacinth springs abroad in the busy fields of men and in far mountains alone, bearing always the grief word of the god.

The first day the Spartans celebrated the death of Hyacinth with fasting and lament, turning with that curious Greek compassion to their own beloved dead and for them making sacrifice. For in the Greek heart, under all its brightness and easy joy, lay ever this thought of death, a profound and secret melancholy for which they knew no cure. It was never quite fear. Rather, it was a manly compassionate love toward the dead themselves, those languid ones who could think only pale thoughts and feel only half desires.

Even when the Greeks sang gladdest in the sunlight, this sore pity was tugging at their hearts. Of annihilation they never thought. They were too close to nature for that, and felt too intensely the imperishing quality of life. But to be away from the bright sun seemed to them a mysterious, eternal illness. As Achilles says,

"I would rather be the lowest slave among the Living
Than rule, a king, among the Dead!"

So on the first day of the festival of Hyacinth the Spartans gave themselves frankly to that thought which they were accustomed to keep fearfully in the background.

There was one beloved "Dead" to whom Aristodemos gave a devotion which he could not share with the other worshippers. For his father Lykos were all his gifts, and thoughts. His old love had imperceptibly grown through these years into actual worship, as seemed natural and right.

He hastened away to a lonely meadow-altar which he knew. Faint with fasting he laid the cakes and rich grape clusters upon the altar. Then he lifted the wine cup in both hands and pronouncing "The Offering to the Dead" turned it and let the rich stream pour to the ground. The wine bubbled a moment on the earth, then sank below—into what darkness, what mysteries! Where did the spirit invisible take it up and make it his own?

He remained a long time standing by the altar musing thus, never doubting that the spirit did take it and did know.

But on the festival's second day Hyacinth lived again—the wide pervasive life from Apollo. In the newness of his life all newness of life was celebrate—the sprouting of the fallen seed, spring's whole dear mysterious return. From every hill and vale the people gathered hyacinth and crowned all altars with its purple. Sparta was a riot of the glorious colour and the odour. Everywhere was music of flute and cythara. The Spartans, usually so chary of hospitality, this day kept open house. All hearts sang of life—life—life! In its faint prefiguring fashion it was the Spartan Easter Day.

On this day they brought forth the new Apollo-robe from the Robe House and bore it down to the god at Amyklai. Leonidas the priestly king headed the stately procession wherein, in her little wicker chariot among her purple-crowned virgins, rode Gorgo, carrying on her bosom Leonidas's year-old son. Aristodemos wore for the first time his father's violet robe. He was Choragos, and his heart, so wistful yesterday, was to-day brimming with the festival gladness.

Those ancient processions, flock leading, flower laden! Shall we ever catch their spirit of frank communion with the physical outer joy, their sweet commotion and laughter—here a snatch of song, there an eloquent dance, and everywhere the gods with their approval and their almost visible beauty!

They came to Amyklai amid its bower of trees. Here

the priests clothed the archaic image with its rich votive robe. Then the youths and maidens danced the famous "Hormos" or chain dance. The youths charged across the meadow as in battle rush, simulating the fling of spears and the quick crouch under uplifted shields. The virgins, gay decked and lovely, moved barefoot over the soft bloom of the grass, uplifting their arms, bowing and springing with the gentleness befitting them. Then for a moment youths and maidens mingled in confusion. And out of the confusion swept a chain of youthful forms, each maiden's outstretched hand lying lightly as a bird over the hand of a youth. Forward in flinging joy swung the bright and living line. And when it broke amid merry laughter the virgins scattered like flowers over the meadow. But the youths closed ranks and joined the men in close soldierly formation.

Then Aristodemos, the Choragos, lifted his laurel branch. And instantly there rose upon the air the full voice of the Spartan State.

Oh, the glorious tide of the voices of men, moving in elemental strength, in sheer and mighty unison, rising and falling broad from note to note within the freer bounds of the old Greek scale! We have forgotten in our modem polyphony the strength of archaic unison, the mighty advance of a single sufficient tune. Like an army it moved, that massive melody, sweeping every man's heart out beyond himself into the greater heart of tribal manhood.

So the festival of Hyacinth ended.

The people, weary with rejoicing, hastened back to Sparta. But Aristodemos could not at once go back. The music which he had led and controlled had left him exalted and strangely restless.

He crossed the meadow toward the little town of Amyklai. He still wore his festive violet robe, the soft folds reaching to his feet. The white border of it was embroidered with flowers and many nymphs dancing in wild fleet joy, so that as he walked the little nymphs seemed peeping here and there among the moving folds.

Crowned with iris, moving thoughtfully along the way his lyre of ancient tortoise pattern swung upon his shoulder, men meeting him might almost have thought that Phœbus himself was come down again to search among the hyacinths for the dead boy.

By the wayside he passed an altar, lately visited, but standing now deserted in the quiet afternoon sunshine, the myrrh, fragrant and delicate, yet scattered upon it, the faint smoke yet rising. A puff of wind bent the thread of smoke aside and blew its sweet odour across his face. What thousand memories of childtime sacrifice it stirred in him! Something, half fear, half joy, gripped him at the heart. Were the Deathless Ones still hovering about the late-left shrine? He seemed to feel their presence in the sunshine.

It was with something of a shock that he passed from this quietude into the village market place. It was an untidy spot. Venders were breaking up their booths, and scattered branches and food leavings lay littered all about.

The festival crowds had attracted many merchants to Amyklai. Among them Aristodemos noticed a slave trader, a swarthy, hooknosed Phœnician. He seemed to have the leftovers of his stock on his hands, having sold out at Corinth or at Argos on his way south to the Laconian Gulf. On his slave bench sat only a decrepid old man, asleep, an evil looking, lame Scyth, and a child. Aristodemos looked at them with half-conscious pity turning in his mind that old philosopher's question, "Is the whole man enslaved or his body only?" It was his habit to question thus.

As he stood there the child, a boy of about three years, scrambled down from his place and made toward him with outstretched hands. A chain trailed from his bare waist to keep him from wandering.

"Take me!" he cried, stretching up his arms to Aristodemos, impatiently folding and refolding his tiny fingers.

THE VIOLET ROBE CHANGES HANDS

"Get back!" shrilled the Phœnician. "Son of a dog! Thou misbegotten!" He outstretched his, terrible hand, with black finger tips drawn together at touch—a menace known to all the East. "Wait!" said the gesture, and the face with half-bared teeth completed it. "Wait till I kill thee!" So vivid was the menace that the child cried out, threw arms about Aristodemos's knees, and hid within his robe. Aristodemos bent quickly, and lifted him in his arms.

"Thou Tyrian demon!" he cried in deep anger. "What a power is this to let forth upon a baby? He hath done no harm."

But the child was not frightened. He looked out at his terrible owner with triumph in his baby eyes and snuggled closer in Aristodemos's arms.

The Phœnician now began to see further than his beak. Here was a possible customer. There was instant change in him. He was cringing, smiling with that exaggerated vividness of face which only Orientals know.

"'Tis a good boy, Master," he said. "Not long will it be till he can fetch and carry with the best. He's older than he looks, Master. Fifty drachmas and he is thine. Ei! by Eshmun!" he whined. "A beggarly fifty drachmas! Fifty drachmas!" clapping his hands together in a sort of despair, "and I could have had a hundred if I had sold him at Argos with the mother."

"Then thou hast sold the mother without him?" queried Aristodemos with disgust.

No, curses on her soul! She died at Argos. Devils were in her that she should die on my hands. Ahai! the good food I put into that mouth! The times I let her rest along the way! The very slaves waited on her. But she died! She was that breed, Master. She must have the world or nothing!"

Aristodemos could picture that matron delicately bred, breaking her heart for home.

"Whence came she!?" he asked.

"Mercy of Hades! Should I know? We got her at Chios, but Chian traders—thou knowest—rummage everywhere. But this I know; her home was to the west. Yes, and when she came to die she made the other slaves turn her that way. Ay, she could make them do what she would, that woman!"

Aristodemos looked with new interest at the child's lovely body and brave little face. Pure Greek he surely was, and Aristodemos's blood boiled hot to see a Greek enslaved.

But he shook himself free. He could not buy the boy. He put him abruptly down and turned away. He heard the child behind him break into a surprised wail, then stop bravely and begin to call after him.

"Take! Take! Take!"

Aristodemos hurried away to get beyond the sound. But up the quiet street the pitiful voice still followed him, "Take! Ta-a-a-ke!" Oh, the pleading of that faint word.

Suddenly the call ended in a piercing shriek of terror! Aristodemos rushed back. The man was beating the child with the butt of his whip. The child was holding his arms over his head to ward off the blows. Seeing Aristodemos again, the Phœnician snatched up the child by one tiny arm and held him painfully dangling.

"Thou again!" he sneered with an extravagance of surprise. "Will the jackal smell at what is not his own."

"But I will buy him!" gasped Aristodemos. "Let go the child—let go, I say!" For the child's screaming was dreadful to hear.

But at the magic word "buy" the Phœnician began again to act his traditional part. This was the great Oriental game.

"Let go? Let see thy money first. The fifty silver drachmas for this splendid boy, Thou Spartan! Thou'st not a drachma to thy name!"

Aristodemos winced. "I can get Spartan money," he said uncomfortably. "But no fifty drachmas for a baby slave. I'll give thee five."

"Spartan money!" The Phœnician laughed his scorn. "Yea, iron money! And Master, who'll give me the mule to lug the price away? Now what have ye else?" The trader had come to his point. He moved closer, dragging the child by the tense arm, his black eyes fixed with a glitter of greed upon the violet robe.

"Thy old cloak, Master," he said, plucking at it. Aristodemos drew back, feeling that the fellow had profaned a sacred thing. The man grunted with a gesture of finality.

"Heh! I saw at the first thou wert no buyer," he sneered. "Now clear out, while I finish the beating!" He turned and dragged away the child, beating him as he went.

"Yes, take the robe—take it!" cried Aristodemos, running after him, unfastening the brooches at his shoulders. "But drop the boy!"

The man literally did drop him, so in haste was he to clutch the costly garment. It was indeed many times the price of a slave child. Aristodemos saw for an instant the dear beautiful thing in the vile hands. Then he lifted the wailing baby and, clad only in his short chiton, hurried from the darkening market place.

How the little one clung to him, still wailing as if the terror would not depart! Once clear of the town, Aristodemos sat down by the wayside, distressed and puzzled. "For the gods' sake, little son, do not cry so!" he pleaded. He tore apart the foolish waist chain and flung it fiercely into the brush. The violence of the movement caught the baby mind. The child stopped crying a moment, then with a sudden laugh mimicked the fling and gesture.

"Bad chain!" he chuckled.

But Aristodemos, seeing the bruised little body and laughing face started up to hide his tears. "Come, thou little soldier!" he said. "Let's get home to Sparta!"

Then he began to think. "Home to Sparta." What would Demonax say, with his sharp, ready tongue? This story would be rich spoil for him. And Leonidas, too! What a soft-headed fool he was, buying babies along the road to save them from whippings! He could hear his fellows jeering and feel that quiet tolerance with which

THE SPARTAN

Leonidas sometimes regarded him. This would be the worst of all.

He began, too, to regret the loss of the violet robe. Now it was in those scoundrelly hands, and strangers would finger it and haggle over its price!

The child felt his change of mood. He began to look up anxiously into Aristodemos's face, and to whimper as if the bruises hurt again.

"There—there; be still," said Aristodemos looking about him, glad that the road was deserted.

He noticed a coin hanging about the baby's neck.

"What is this?" he asked, lifting it and trying to amuse the child.

"Men-di," said he, slowly and distinctly.

"Mendi? Is that thy name?"

But the child shook his head so emphatically that the curls whirled across his face. "Men-di," he said again, and lifted the coin in his chubby hands and kissed it. It seemed an act learned by rote.

"Nay, if the coin be 'Mendi' as thou sayest, what art thou?" said Aristodemos, touching the strong little chest with his finger.

The child thought a moment, then answered with a wise nod,

"Men-di."

Aristodemos could make nothing of it.

Then the child buried his face in Aristodemos's shoulder with the shy laughter and feigning that babies use with those they love.

"I truly believe thou art playing with me," said Aristodemos a bit sheepishly.

He walked on in silence. But the child continually interrupted his thoughts, tossing his hands about, or gravely touching Aristodemos's nose, eyes, lips, as though counting. Then, reaching for the chaplet on the crowned head, he slipped it quite over his own curly pate. When a hare darted across the road he almost leaped with delight from Aristodemos's arms. Now and then he suddenly was afraid of the Phœnician, peering over Aristodemos's shoulder, and then creeping closer into his arms. Finally he fell asleep.

Aristodemos walked slowly on with the little silent creature in his arms. What a graceful body it was. He even began to think him more beautiful than Leonidas's son—yes, and cleverer. He forgot that the child was older.

When he came into Sparta it was quite dark. He hastened to his own house.

"Mother!" he called at the doorway.

She came out, still in her festival dress, her strong face smiling. Had she not good reason to smile, at this son who was a leader of the festival and best friend of a king? But when she saw him she hardly recognized him in his short chiton and bearing a child in his arms.

"What?" she said, as her smile died and her eyes grew sharp. "What is that?"

He hesitated, and looked down at the child with real timidity. The little one awoke, and feeling Makaria's cold stare, nestled closer to Aristodemos.

"The child is mine," he stammered.

"Thine?" she demanded in a tone of wrath.

"Oh, no, no, Mother—not that." And the red swept quickly over his young face. "I bought him at Amyklai from a slaver who was killing him. Oh, Mother, I think he is the son of some great man. He did not know the rites of supplication. But all childishly he supplicated. The gods love not him who refuseth a supplication. Thou wilt take him into the house."

"Into the house—a strange child to rear! Aristodemos, wilt thou never learn manful ways? What new softness is this? And what, in Hermes's name, dost thou want with a slave's babe?"

"I did not want him," said Aristodemos, wearily feeling that he could never make her understand. "The child was being crippled. I had to save him. He will not trouble thee. Give him but a corner to sleep in."

"Yes!—and a chance to steal!" answered Makaria angrily.

"Steal! He is too young. Besides he is nobly born. Look, Mother, how beautiful he is." And Aristodemos impulsively held the naked form out to her lying full across his strong young arms. But no suggestion of tenderness came into Makaria's face; blows were in her look.

With a quick exclamation Aristodemos gathered the little one back to himself, gazing down upon the child, while the utter first tenderness of the father-thought welled up and overran his heart. Then he turned upon her and sternly said:

"Woman, take the child! Take him and wholly care for him! In this thou shalt obey me!"

Then Makaria smiled, and she understood him, too. She kissed her son, and took the baby from his arms with that deftness which mothers do not forget.

"Ah, foolish Aristodemos," she said. "The time is at hand when thou shalt raise up sons of thine own to this my house. The slave child doth but teach thee. The gods bless thee soon, my son!"

"Yes—yes, Mother," assented Aristodemos, scarce knowing what he said. After which the manful young soldier strode out through the starlight to barracks with flushed cheeks and steady, lighted eyes.

CHAPTER FOURTEEN

The Gathering Storm

Next spring, the spring of four hundred and eighty before Christ, the fitful activities of the Orient against Greece suddenly coalesced and gathered to a focus. It was as though the winds of the four heavens had swept together and the whirling tempest had begun to move steadily upon the devoted little land. Now the shipmen brought no scattered rumours, no tales of half events. "The army," they said, "is fully gathered. The Great King's whole incredible host, fifty nations of armies, with camels, elephants, chariots, Nisian horses, Indian dogs, eunuchs, concubines and female cooks, hath set out from Sardis. It is already moving north-ward up the coast of Ionia."

Then Greece awoke.

It awoke in terror. The frightened states sent hurried embassies to the Oracles, which the Oracles sent hastily home again with confused responses of wailings and warnings. They sent off spies to Asia, who came back alive every one. The Great King had caught them and courteously shown them his camp. Then he had carefully sent them back home again to tell the Greeks how great the king was. "All the marshallings of the world taken together," they reported stammering and with heads awhirl, "would not make the sum of this which cometh against us!"

Even the Spartans, who had been rejoicing secretly over a possible downfall of Athens, began to wear grave faces. Now at last the young king of Sparta knew that it was time for him to act. He took his young "Listener" and went up to the Council of the Greeks at Isthmos. The Ephors were already there. He must keep hand upon the doings of Sparta.

To the ardent Aristodemos, so long confined in narrow Lacedæmon, this was a wonderful mission. To be at the very centre of all Greek activity at the moment when upon that activity depended the very existence of Hellas! No Persian Dread could quench the hope that was in him. His head swam with visions of great deeds.

Reaching Isthmos they hurried out to the "Precinct," where the Council sat. The solemn "Pines of Poseidon" looked down upon strange comings and goings. The victor statues stood stark among the restless throngs. The place was a ferment of conflicting rumours. Yesterday a sea-captain had told the Council that the Great King's wonderful floating bridge was builded and that across it the nations of the East were already pouring into Europe. "Seven days and seven nights have they poured across!" gasped the merchantman. He himself had beheld the gold-bespattered "Immortals," the festooned gaudy guards, the Sacred Chariot, Xerxes himself and his delicate silken litter, and half a hundred nations of wild fighters, hideous hordes of jungle folk, shuffling, lash-driven multitudes, children of darkness, moving to overwhelm with sheer ponderousness of numbers the quick free children of light.

The Council looked into one another's startled faces. How little had they to depend on! And now returned the disheartened envoys whom the Council had sent to summon the Greek States. Argos was distrustful of selfish Sparta, and would not come. The Cretans were prevented by an oracle. The Corcyreans sent a fine mouthful of promises. As for the tyrant of Syracuse, he must be made commander-in-chief, or not a step would he budge! Canny states, all! They must first see which way fate was like to leap before taking their stand. Helpless and small indeed showed the little League at the Isthmos in the face of the impending storm.

But it was the mighty stimulus of the danger rather than its gravity that laid hold upon the young Aristodemos. The clash of mind against mind, plan against plan, set him all aglow. What men! He had not known that there were such men, so wise, so quick-seeing! And the sharp, clipping speech of Athens sounded wondrous sweet, after the years.

It was an Athenian, too, who was the moving spirit of the Council, that was plain to see. Aristodemos faintly remembered this Themistokles as a half grown boy at Athens, at the Kynosarges gymnasium. Even then Aristodemos had felt his restless charm. Now he saw him a bearded man, keen, fearless, sufficient. He was always springing to his feet in the Council, persuading, denouncing. With what passionate eloquence did he set forth his plans! How bitterly he frowned when affairs went wrong, how grandly sighed when good policies prevailed! Aristodemos came quickly to rejoice in the ascendency of this swift, urgent man.

One day there came into the Council a new soldierly fellow from Athens. Even Leonidas remarked him and said:

"Of such men will come our deliverance, if the gods grant us deliverance. That man is a fighter!"

"Who is he?" asked Aristodemos.

"That man? Dost not know him?" spoke up an Athenian sitting near. "That is Æschylus of Eleusis who fought so brave at Marathon and lost a brother there. He hath won dramatic prizes at Athens."

Another day came the aged poet Simonides, a hale, cheery old fellow. Aristodemos listened eagerly to his short, clear speaking. As the Council broke up for the day the old poet noted the adoring look of Aristodemos, who was waiting to see him pass.

"Young man," he said, turning to him abruptly, "art thou wont to be called beautiful?"

Aristodemos was too confused to answer.

"Thou art o'er-young for councils," added Simonides, watching him shrewdly.

"But even the young must think for Hellas now," returned Aristodemos with face alight.

"I think they must, young man. And who brought thee here to the Council?"

"King Leonidas."

"And whose word of all the wise ones likes thee best?"

"Themistokles. Oh, he it is who sees!"

The old man leaned forward, reading the young face. "Sow that in Sparta!" he whispered intensely, and went his way.

Next day Aristodemos made a new friend at the Isthmos, young Kimon, the son of Miltiades. Kimon walking in the Way of Pines met Aristodemos and stopped short. A moment later he contrived to meet him again.

"Now, whence art thou, child of Hermes?" he demanded. "Let's see—art breathing or a breathless vision?"

"Didst speak to me?" said the startled Aristodemos, who did not understand such talk.

Kimon laughed merrily.

"Beautiful innocence! Surely thou'rt from Sparta!"

"Yes, from Sparta," responded Aristodemos. "But I was fathered in Athens."

"In Athens fathered and in Sparta bred! Why, man, that's perfect! How cam'st upon so happy a fate?"

Aristodemos told him.

"Ah!" cried the elegant Kimon, "that Spartan discipline! It is beyond praise!"

"Hast ever tried it?" queried Aristodemos.

"Well, no."

"Better taste it first and praise it afterward."

"Well said, Hermides!" laughed Kimon. "Well said!" He took Aristodemos's arm. "Come, I would hear more of thy foolish wisdom."

In an hour they seemed old friends. Aristodemos never dreamed that Kimon had been through all manner of debaucheries at Athens. The young man was slender and quick, with the light blue northern eyes of his Thracian mother, and for the rest all Athenian with a polished grace that completely won the simple bred Aristodemos.

This Kimon, who afterward planted the shade trees of Athens and made the Akademia a green and watered place, had varied interests utterly new to Aristodemos. He had, too, a dawning genius for generalship which spoke now and then with a sure, deep insight of the present bewilderment. Leonidas was a little puzzled at the attraction of the light-seeming Athenian for Aristodemos. But all thought concerning the matter was forgotten in a sudden excitement.

Envoys from Thessaly appeared in the Council with an imperative and hard demand.

"Ye Greeks must defend the Pass in the Vale of Tempe. Then we can shut the far door of Greece against the invaders. Come ye up to Thessaly with a strong force, and all we of Thessaly will join you, a no mean army. But if ye come not up then know that we will surely join the Persians. For we stand at the outpost of Greece, and it is not right we should perish alone in your defence."

Themistokles sprang to his feet, crying:

"They tell us the truth, these wise Thessalians. Tempe is the place! We can bar the Persians at Tempe!" And he broke into a mighty harangue, urging the Greeks to go.

But the Ephors of Sparta looked black.

"Umph! Thessaly! What has Sparta to do with Thessaly? Sparta defends her own? The law saith—"

Here Leonidas, who had moved over to where the Thessalians stood, intently listening to them, strode back to his Ephors. It was the commencement of that bitter difference which was to increase to the king's dying day.

In the end he had his way. But the grudging old men would only send an army of Perioikoi under Euainetos, one of the under-generals. "No king nor Spartans yet," they said stubbornly.

Leonidas returned wearily to his friend.

"Yes," he said. "In some sort I have prevailed. But I would liever fight five battles with the Persians than one such mean battle of words!"

All the way back to Sparta the two were busy with conjectures and hopes of Tempe, sometimes stopping midway in the road in their absorption. They knew now that the war was on. To Leonidas this free and understanding intercourse with his friend was wonderfully refreshing after the dull strife with the Ephors.

"What is it in thee," he said, "that so lighteth darkened things? Thou hast made me forget the Ephors."

"Do forget them!" answered Aristodemos with glowing confidence. "Thou art so glorious right in this matter. Even they must see it. Sparta will surely play her part with All-Hellas."

"All-Hellas!" He sounded the new phrase with a ring that made Leonidas look up. Not for naught had this young man listened to those great-minded men and heard that compelling word so constantly sounded. "Hellas, Hellas" and "Our Hellas"; and again, "We must save Hellas." We can not think how new was that word "Hellas" then. Its broad conception had lifted Aristodemos at once out of his green enthusiasm to a deep, controlling passion. Not for Sparta, not for Thessaly, nor for Athens was the impending fight, but for something infinitely more precious—for that fair essential fatherland of no evident borders. For the cities of Greece; ay—but also for the gods of Greece, for the clear thoughts, the daily life, the sacred flowers, for the still more sacred manhood—for the whole possibility of being a Hellene.

Henceforward life for Aristodemos could set but one way and have but one activity—to fight for the freedom of Greece against the dark barbaric world. None but a Greek could give to a conception so idealistic a devotion so passionate.

CHAPTER FIFTEEN

The King and The Ephors

Leonidas and Aristodemos found the Market Place crowded with the Spartan citizens all anxious for news of the doings at the Isthmos.

Leonidas told them of the stand to be made at Tempe. Among the crowded, serious faces there were many, especially of the younger soldiers, that seemed to respond with comprehending looks.

Then Aristodemos went quickly home. He had scarce turned into his own street when he heard a joyous cry and a quick patter of small feet, and was brought to a halt by the little slave-child's arms flung about his knee.

"Master! Master!" cried the gleeful little voice.

Aristodemos swung him to his shoulder.

"Who bade thee call me 'Master'?" he demanded.

The word did not sound good on free-born lips.

"Antiphon, he say, 'Master, Master, Master,'" sang the child.

Here old Antiphon himself came hobbling out, quite beyond speech with happiness at the "Little Master's" return. Who shall say that children outdo the aged in joy?

"Oh, Antiphon," cried Aristodemos, embracing him, "this hath been a famous journey for me! Men have I seen; real men, Antiphon! All Athens was at the Isthmos."

"Men from Athens?" quavered the eager old man.

"Yes. Themistokles was there, Simonides, Kimon the son of Miltiades—"

"And didst thou see thine own love comrade again,

after so many years?"

"My love comrade?"

"Yes—Pindar—" The old man stopped, confused. "Nay, he was Lykos's friend; I remember it now. And thou—thou—art not Lykos, but—Little Master, Little Master," he repeated dreamily.

Aristodemos took his old paidagogos's arm, to help him toward the house, and thus, with childhood in one hand and old age in the other he went on with his eager telling.

"Antiphon, thy Little Master will be going into battle, and that soon."

"Into battle? Into battle?" cried the slave, all his joy instantly scattered. "Oh—oh!"

"Nay, do no lament, Antiphon. Give the gods thanks, rather!"

Here Makaria's voice called out from the house.

"Well said, my son!" and she ran out lightly to greet him and took him to herself. "Tell me," she cried, "tell me something of this war."

"Why, Mother, thou'rt a very soldier thyself," said the young man admiringly. Mother and son went together into the house, leaving the two to wait outside, if perchance they might get some further glimpse of the beloved home-comer.

The weeks that followed were busy with the incessant preparation for war. Leonidas was the mind and force of everything, redoubling the discipline, marshalling the auxiliary army of Perioikoi, giving forth everywhere his own serious courage and putting the power of Sparta in full readiness.

Then, suddenly, one afternoon, to the consternation of all, appeared Euainetos with his whole Tempe army, rather sheepish and full of excuse.

Leonidas fronted them in the square.

"The meaning of this?" he demanded.

"The allied Greeks have abandoned Tempe," they told him. "We got us up there, and then those Thessalian fools showed us that after all there was another pass by which the Persians could come through."

"Ye were the fools!" cried the king bitterly. "Ye! Never name the Thessalians!"

"But, O king, could we hold the one gate with another wide open?"

"Ye? No, I suppose ye could not! Ye were not Spartans! But Zeus Almighty! What a feeble fling!"

The king turned to Aristodemos a dark, set face.

"I must quick to the Isthmos," he said. "The Hellenes will be meeting again. Stay thou here. If aught looks wrong, send me Kriton, secretly." And he was away.

Next day the consequences of the Tempe folly began to trickle down to Sparta.

Now it was, "Thessaly hath kept her threat! She hath embraced the Persians!" Now, "The Dorians have 'Med-ized'!" Now, "Every northern state hath gone, Lokria, Malia, Phthiotid-Achaia—even the City of Thebes! All, everyone, has 'Med-ized'!" "Med-ized." They put it in that one famous, hated word.

Then, close upon the heels of all this, stumbled other breathless frightened runners into Sparta, gasping out that the terrible host was already around the northern Ægean and swarming straight south upon Greece, drinking the rivers dry and devouring harvests at a meal!

Through the uproar of these days Aristodemos kept steadily at his work with his company, of which he was now the captain. And he watched the mood of Sparta like a cat. What he saw disquieted him. No sooner was Leonidas out of Sparta than the All-Hellas policy began to fade. The Ephor-spirit was abroad.

"The Ephors—" "The Ephors say—" And then, "Isthmos—" "The Isthmos—" Aristodemos heard it at every street corner.

Soon, too, the Tempe fiasco began to seem tolerable.

"What could ye expect? Away up there by the north wind—! In our own Lacedæmon, now, we could—"

Oh, the madding, witless talk!

Dissatisfaction was everywhere. It showed in the

very motion of the drill. The fact was, Sparta did not much care what happened outside of the Peloponnese. To her thinking all these efforts for a defence of northern Greece were but so many Athenian plans for a defence of Athens, and were not at all essential to a defence of Sparta. The Great King was aiming only at Athens. Let the flood sweep. It would probably ebb short of the Isthmos. But if by any chance it should touch the Isthmos, why, the Isthmos was the place to make the effectual, great defence. Sparta would make it there.

That was all that concerned Sparta.

Would Leonidas never come? It was now mid-August. The season of the Apollo Karneios was at hand. But the men were silent as they pitched the festival tents, and there were no festival faces. At last one day, Aristodemos, watching up the northern road, espied the dusty, hurrying company with the familiar soldierly figure striding far in front. He ran out to his friend.

"What is it? Where do we make stand?"

"At the Hot Springs Gates. At Thermopylæ."

"And the fleets at Artemisium?" For the two had often pondered over this plan.

"Yes. The Athenian ships under Themistokles and the whole fleet of the states under a Spartan general."

Leonidas walked on, too absorbed to talk.

"Let the Ephors be summoned," he bade the herald and moved through the excited, gathering crowds toward the Skias. In the Skias, one by one the deliberate Ephors assembled, rigid, solemn-faced old men, about as open to convincement as a city wall. Last of all King Leotychides wandered in, greeted his brother king, and took his regal chair. The Ephors sat down, wordless. Leonidas stood in his place before them, intent and very serious, far more the advocate than the king.

O King Leotychides and ye, Ephors of Sparta," he said, "The Hellenes at Isthmos now propose to defend the Pass of Thermopylæ. They believe that this is the true Gate of Greece. There is no other way by which the Barbarian can come in. This Gate of the Hot Springs is a single pass—a mere narrow wagon track between Mount Oite and the sea. At that place even the water-way is defensible, for the great island of Eubœa thrice narroweth the sea into throats. No Persian ship can even reach Athens save by battle in those straits. The ship of Athens and the allies will defend the seas. A Spartan may command them. The Hellenes desire the men of Lacedæmon to defend the Pass on land. Thus, O king and Ephors, can we keep the Persian altogether out of Greece."

There was a long silence. It was as gall and worm-wood to these old Ephors that Spartan arms should by any chance help another state, even in defending Sparta. They shook their touzled white heads. "Too far away," they grumbled. "Tempe over again. Is Sparta to be forever marching north on fool's errands? Let Athens fight her own war. At Isthmos we will build us a wall. And at Isthmos we—"

Here Leonidas leaped up.

"Are you Ephors blind?" he thundered, breaking bounds. "These Persians have eyes to see and noses to smell salt water. While you are at your cursed Isthmos puddering with your wall, what's to hinder the Persian from sailing clean around Peloponnese and swallowing Sparta at a gulp? Your bones would rot in Isthmos, where the Persian land army would get you. Better for Sparta were they rotting there now!"

The Ephors buzzed with indignation. Yet the com-mon sense of the speech had penetrated even their skulls.

"Let Athens send her soldiers too. Why doth she send ships only?" they persisted sullenly.

This was really the vulnerable point of the scheme. But Leonidas met it quietly.

"Athens is sending all her ships, a mighty fleet, and filled with fighting men. She dares not offend the gods by neglecting the Olympiac. When she hath made her sacrifice she will send her army also to Thermopylæ."

"Hum—h-m-m. The mighty gods. Yes. Well, we have our festival too. It is meet we celebrate our Karneia before we think of going to war."

"Yes; but, oh, ye Ephors of Sparta, that's the very point. If Sparta hang back now, our allies of the Peloponnese, whom we have brought as by the hair of the head up to the mark, will straight distrust us and Med-ize one and all! That way lies our peril!"

This last shaft went home. The Ephors thought awhile. Then they laid their heads together.

"Well," they said at last, "do thou then, O King, go thyself. And take thine own guard that is appointed thee by law. The king's going will hold the allies faithful. They will join thee on the march. When we have kept our Karneia, we will send thee the full Spartan army to Thermopylæ. The Medes are not yet so very near. Sparta will be there in good time."

For a moment the king stood motionless, with eyes half closed. He seemed to be looking out the open door. For aught they knew he might be counting the pillars of the temple across the way. Then he opened his eyes wide and searched the Ephor faces.

"This a deed of deeds that ye are putting into my hands," he said. "If ye surely come as ye say before the Persians come, well. If not, I can hold that Pass—for a little time. But if ye shuffle, if ye delay and postpone, I call you before the gods to remember that ye betray your king and your choicest Spartans to the Barbarian!" He went out of the Skias, leaving the Ephors with their own uneasy thoughts.

Meanwhile, the fighting men had marshalled on their field, and now stood in ranks awaiting the king, the King's Guard to the fore. Aristodemos watched them standing there, immovable as men of bronze. He almost felt himself rebuked for his own restlessness that drove him to such constant looking toward the Skias. An hour went by. Still the ranks stood impassive, looking straight before. Aristodemos through the silence began to realize the all unspoken love of these men for their general.

At last up the Skias Way there was a separating of the crowd. And along the parted path, newly dressed and in full war panoply, King Leonidas came quickly and stood before his soldiers. A long breath and a grating of armour ran through the ranks. Then fell the silence again. And upon the silence came the supreme voice of the king.

"Men of Lacedæmon, the armies of Greece will face the Persians by sea and land at Thermopylæ. But first, the Athenians must celebrate the Olympiac and we our Karneia. Therefore your king and the King's Three Hundred will go at once with our allies to hold the place. We march in the morning."

Then he turned with brightening face to his own Three Hundred.

"Ye are fortunate, O men of Sparta, for to you it is given to be the saviours of Hellas. Ye go out to fight the innumerable Barbarians. It is not for Spartans to fear them. There be many humans, but of men not many. If ye esteem numbers, all Greece is not able to match even a small part of the Persians. But if ye esteem courage, our number is sufficient.

"Not every man of the King's Three Hundred is permitted to go. Especially not those who have no sons to keep their lines in Sparta. Let the roll of the chosen be called. Then fill we up our full number again."

The herald with the roll of the King's Guard stepped forward.

"Dienekes!" he called.

Dienekes, proud as a god, stood forth.

"Chilon!"

"Epikydes!"

"Alpheos, son of Orsiphantos!"

"Maron, son of Orsiphantos!"

To this fateful rollcall the men responded with a kind of exultation, while the envious army looked on. In such fashion had the coming of the real captain wrought upon them.

THE SPARTAN

Aristodemos had to make two preparations for the departure. He must free old Antiphon. And he must procure a son to keep his line in Sparta. He could make the slave-child his son. He had never questioned the high birth of the boy. He could trust his line to him.

He hurried to his own house, brought out the two wondering ones by the hand, and led them into the king's house to Leonidas. Only a king might perform an adoption. Adoption was very real to the Greek mind. It created actual kin.

"Ah," said Leonidas, smiling at their coming. "I was wondering how thou wouldst manage thy going and thy son. And now thy son will be older than mine!" He led them to the altar and kindled it. The four stood close about.

"What is the boy's name?" inquired Leonidas, keenly studying the child.

Aristodemos also turned to the little fellow. "What shall it be?" he wondered. "Oh, thou little stranger, if thou couldst but tell us!"

The child looked from one to the other. Then, feeling that something was expected of him, he timidly but with his little exact gesture, lifted his coin and pronounced again his word, "Men-di."

"It is a sign!" exclaimed Aristodemos much awed by the occurrence. "Mendi shall be his name."

So Leonidas pronounced the adoptive words before the gods and placed "Mendi, son of Aristodemos" into his new father's arms. The young man held the child for a moment with a great sense of possession and joy. Then he turned to Antiphon.

"But oh, no, no!" cried the old slave, suddenly guessing his intention. "No, Little Master! Thou wilt not cast me away!"

"Not I, thou foolish Antiphon! Up from thy knees. I am only making thee free. I will care for thee as ever."

But the old man was completely bewildered and frightened.

"Free? Free? Oh, Little Master, why should I be

free of thee?"

"Because I go to battle, Antiphon. If I should not return, thou knowest they might deal hard with thee. Come, we have no time to lose."

But the old man, still upon his knees, lifted up his pitiful withered hands.

"I am thy paidagogos!" he pleaded. "Thy paidagogos! Dost thou not remember? Thy paidagogos!"

Aristodemos tried to lift him. But the king looked on with wise, pitying eyes.

"Urge him not," he said. "The time is past."

"Well, then, dear Antiphon," said Aristodemos, "I'll have to grant thee slavery. Keep thou my son. Thou shalt be his paidagogos so long as thou livest."

"But I am thy paidagogos," repeated the old man stubbornly, as he scrambled to his feet at last. And still scared and trembling, he led the child away.

Aristodemos returned to the barracks. He awoke next morning long before "the first white thought of dawn," springing up full awake as if the inborn sense of great events had summoned his sleeping mind. The familiar little street, glimpsed through the barrack doorway, seemed as strange in the starlight as some place which he had never seen before. The day-of-deeds, so long dreamed of, seemed, now that it was about to dawn, itself a dream.

Aristodemos hurried with his company to the river. There they bathed and anointed their bodies with perfumed oils. Then they returned and armed and adorned themselves as never before in their lives. This was the Spartan preparation for war.

As they came out from the barracks, Aristodemos caught sight of his own little household of slaves, with his new son, his mother, and Antiphon, waiting for him with almost worshipping eyes. He hastened over to them, his armour bright in the gray increasing dawn, and Makaria, beholding him, thought that never mortal had been so splendid as this her son, full armed.

THE SPARTAN

He wore his Lacedæmonian bronze cap, from which his golden locks escaped and lifted in the wind. From the shoulders of his cuirass, newly burnished, swung back his crimson cloak of war. His legs were greaved in bronze. The short sword of Sparta played at his thigh and his right hand held his long, tough spear. The great, gleaming Spartan shield which he bore reached from neck to knees. This panoply weighed near eighty pounds; but the young man moved easily about as if its weight were naught.

Makaria kissed him with swelling heart and laying her hand on his shield rim repeated exultingly the old Spartan mother-phrase:

"With it or upon it, Son!"

"Yes, Mother, I know!" responded the young voice solemnly. Then Aristodemos bent to kiss his wondering little son. Finally he turned to Antiphon and laid his hand on the old bowed shoulder. The aged man was sobbing to himself with downcast eyes.

"There, there, Antiphon? Dost thou love war so ill?" he asked tenderly. He leaned to kiss him. But even as he did so the bent form suddenly folded together and Antiphon fell in a heap. Aristodemos dropped shield and spear and was instantly down trying to lift him. But something in the set waxen face startled him.

"Mother!" he cried.

Makaria looked, then answered her son's gaze.

"Yes, he is dead."

"Oh, Antiphon, Antiphon!" said Aristodemos. "Art thou so fain to be thy little master's paidagogos, even into Hades?"

He drew up the coarse cloak and covered Antiphon's face.

"Mother, thou wilt bury him fittingly?"

"As thou thyself, my son," answered Makaria.

And Aristodemos, silently weeping, walked toward his place.

In the broad dim field the three hundred Hoplites of the King's Guard were already in line, full armed and ready for their marching to Thermopylæ. The attendant Helots were standing close at hand with the ready baggage-train. Around them were drawn up the ten thousand spears of the armies of Sparta. And beyond, the gray-beards with the women and children crowded the confines of the field. The king was about to make the sacrifice, for it was needful to catch the early attention of the gods, before they should be otherwise occupied.

Then suddenly the great war song rent the still morning air.

"Paian, O Paian!" thundered the whole army, clashing spear against shield as they sang. And even while they sang, the great orb of the sun spilled his fire over Parnon's crest and pouring down the changed, reddening slopes fell upon Eurotas, which suddenly ran blood red between his reedy banks.

"It is war—war!" whispered the awestruck people.

The herald lighted his torch at the king's fire, with which to kindle the parting sacrifice at the border of Lacedæmon. Preceded by this sacred flame the little column began its march. It wound through the narrow streets sounding the battle pipes, out into the country, across Eurotas bridge and northward on the well-known road.

The Spartan people followed them for a mile beyond the town, then stood and watched them winding down into a little valley and up again over the farther hills, a long bright file with the torch flaming at the head and the dull body of Helots bringing up the rear. The sound of the pipes thinned to a thread in the air. Then they were altogether lost in the distance.

CHAPTER SIXTEEN

The King's Guard Marches

All through the summer day these strong men toiled along through valleys hot under the burning sun, over breezy hilltops, by the ripening harvest fields which they were going out to defend through little villages whose people ran out to gaze with awestruck eyes at them— the "Invincible Spartans."

Invincible Spartans? They were only a little band of clean-cut untried men marching straightforwardly north to defend their land; while far away the whole rich Orient was moving southward to meet them. They were very proud of their simplicity, proud of their contempt for wealth, proud to be satisfied after years of toil with a single branch of laurel; proud of their law, and of their ability to be obedient to their law. Their virtue had in it something of a stubborn Puritan quality.

This going forth of theirs was not reasonable. It was neither strength nor hope that made these men resist. It was rather their almost childish inability to be anything other than "free."

When once the little army had left Sparta well behind they gave their armour to their Helots to carry. They travelled two abreast, often breaking from the ranks to wander at will. Discipline was not strict in a friendly land. A campaign was always something of a holiday, and after their first awe of the setting-out was over they began to talk and crack their rough Spartan jokes. They had been comrades from earliest boyhood, and all that boyhood had been a training for just such an hour as this.

THE KING'S GUARD MARCHES

Leonidas walked in the lead, now glancing back at Aristodemos who marched at the head of his "lochos," now pausing to pass a quiet word down through the column. For the most part he walked entirely alone, deep in thought, holding in his heart his plan. But the old tired look that had haunted his eyes was gone. In its place abided the strength with which yesterday he had spoken to his army. The very lift of his head was confident. At last he was moving along the open way of deeds. No more word-bandying now! The soldiers had only to see him marching thus silently at their head to feel a sense of adequate leadership which was worth a hundred words of cheer.

At eleven they halted for breakfast—their first meal that day, and an hour before sundown stopped for the night in a pleasant little valley near Tegea. Then began the brisk, orderly confusion of encampment. The soldiers with a clamour of bronze stacked their armour in the midst. The Helots brought up the carts, unyoked the horses and swiftly pitched the tents of skins, then gathered fuel from the hills. And from the cheery camp-fires savoury smells of roasting soon rose upon the evening air.

The little tented town was pitched wheelshape around the king's tent and the stack of arms. About the first circle of tents ran a street, then there was another ring of tents, beyond which were the Helots with the carts and tethered horses. Outside of all paced the watchful sentinels.

After a happy meal—not the frugal supper of the barracks, but the feasting of war—the soldiers dispersed through the tidy avenues to their tents. The camp was soon asleep. Only Leonidas, intent upon his problems, could not sleep at once but walked alone beyond the camp nodding to the men on guard, who silently returned his salute and wondered that the king should so walk about, when he had such an excellent opportunity for slumber.

At Tegea next morning five hundred men of that

city joined the superb little Spartan Three Hundred. Quickly thereafter came five hundred from Mantinea, and one hundred and twenty from the tiny hill town of Orchomenos. And as they marched a thousand more Arkadians swelled their ranks at various places along the road. To Leonidas's great relief, the Peloponnese was responding faithfully to Sparta's prompt decision. Little Phlious added her two hundred and Mycenæ eighty men. And as they passed through Corinth that city gave four hundred, as a pledge of her good faith. So they marched on hopefully.

They had pitched their tents for the night on the much-discussed Isthmos. Aristodemos in the starlight was making the last round of the Helot camp—a duty assigned to the younger captains—when his ears were greeted by a great howling from one of the tents. He ran over and thrust his head into its noisy blackness.

"Hello!" he shouted. "What's all this row? Sure a toothache is no such matter!"

"Oh! Oh! Oh!" came the voice. "It's Eurytos."

"Eurytos! Why, I thought it was ten bulls. What art thou doing off here among the Helots?"

"But, oh, my eyes, my eyes!" wailed Eurytos. Your Greek was never one to suppress his feelings.

"Well, then, we'll have the surgeon."

"Oh, no, never mind the eyes! I care not for my eyes!"

"Then why sayest eyes?" Aristodemos, groping about the floor, came upon a feverish hand.

"Come, old fellow, what's the trouble?" he said cheerily.

"Yes, yes, I'll tell thee." Eurytos caught Aristodemos with both hands. "It was my stumbling. I could not see well for my burning eyes. And they said the surgeon, and my Helot must care for me. But my rascal Helot hopes to lag me clean out of the ranks and save himself from going to war. Oh, Aristodemos! Think, to be left like a sick hound—and my first chance—and the great fighting!" He broke into wailing again.

"But Eurytos, this is damnable business! Where is Demonax?"

"Demonax seemeth to have a kind of dread of me."

"A kind of pig selfishness!" exclaimed Aristodemos, so wrathfully that Eurytos felt himself bound to stand up for his friend.

"But he had me cared for and helped along in the ranks."

"Well, I'll be a better friend to thee than that. Where is that Helot of thine?"

"But wilt thou help me, Aristodemos—thou?" For ever since the boyish mutton stealing the two had not been particularly good friends.

Here the Helot stole in with guilty haste. Aristodemos flung him wrathfully out and began to beat him with a tent stake. But the poor cowering back in the starlight gave him a sudden revulsion.

"No," he said. "Let thine own master deal with thee. Call me those fellows from under that cart yonder."

Five Helots ran stumbling out to him. An angry captain was something to dread. Aristodemos chose a stocky country Helot.

"Here, thou! Do thou care well for Eurytos and see that the surgeon bathes his eyes. And see thou bring him to me at sunrise. Lag and thou'lt have a beating that thou'lt tell thy children and thy children's children after thee. Now fetch him water."

"Thou'lt not let them cheat me of my chance!" Eurytos cried as Aristodemos reentered the tent.

"Ask this fellow here!" laughed Aristodemos. And lifting Eurytos's head he gave him a long, cool draught. Then he was off and upon his rounds again.

Next day Eurytos marched beside Aristodemos. He scarcely needed the Helot's help. The assurance of the going sang in his blood. "See, I am well!" he cried gratefully though there was still a flush of fever in his cheeks and his eyes were swollen. "Thou art a very Paian for healing!"

From the Isthmos two days of rapid marching

brought them to Thebes, where the seven hundred ardent Thespians joined them. There, too, Leonidas forced the wavering Thebans to give him four hundred men. Thebes had been reported as having already Medized. Now they marched with possible traitors in their midst. Leonidas knew this and thereafter had Aristodemos share his tent. It seemed in these days that he needed, constantly and close, the man he supremely trusted.

Northward still through the Bœotian land Leonidas led his growing little army. In the west they saw, as they marched, the soaring, sacred mountain of Parnassos, pure white against the intense blue sky. Not one of all those beauty loving men thought consciously, "It is beautiful." Yet not one of them but was greatened for his task, by tile image of his sacred mountain in his heart.

They came now into the rough hill country of the north, mounting the narrow steep roads and crushing the yellow gorse with their heavy feet in the mountain glades. Here the hardy mountaineers of Lokris joined them. Leonidas had summoned them to come in full force. And now they were climbing the high mountains of the Kallidromos range. The men grew silent as they toiled upward, among the fragrant pines and across the shining rock faces.

They reached the farthest ridge where the islanded blue sea suddenly opened far below. Then they made their way down the steeps and came to the little village of Alpenoi. And going downward still they came to the water's edge. There they turned westward along the shore, and were at last at the Pass of Thermopylæ.

CHAPTER SEVENTEEN

The Hills Fought for Hellas

It was probably Leonidas himself who gave us the saying that "Greek mountains fought at Thermopylæ as well as Greek men." He made now no pause. He left the camp a-making and summoning Aristodemos went on in haste to view them standing there so grandly at their post—his Titan soldiery. He was greatly concerned to examine this place on which he had hazarded so much but which he knew only through uncertain report. The Greek captain had no maps. He was entirely dependent in his strategy upon hearsay and hasty observation.

He saw at once that the shore did not run from south to north, but from east to west where the Malian Gull sweeps around westward into the Malian land. Leonidas and Aristodemos were therefore entering the Eastern Gate, a mere wheel-track, so narrow that they two could have clasped hands and reached from the cliff to the reedy sea.

They did not stop here but looking keenly about them came into the broader mid-pass. Here the Hot Springs from which the pass was named gushed forth covering the ground with brilliant red and yellow deposits. Their footsteps sounded strange and hollow. A few steps beyond the springs brought them to a second narrow pass where there was a half ruined old wall which had been builded across the road in some forgotten Phokian border war.

"We must rebuild this wall," he said. It was the only

word he spoke.

Again the mountain receded a little from the shore. Finally three miles from the Eastern Gate they came to the third or Western Gate of the Pass. The mountains here swept grandly forward to the sea's edge again leaving but the single wheel-track between; and even this track ran slanting along on the debris of the cliff. Thermopylæ as a whole was much more defensible than they had dared to hope.

Leonidas stood a long while looking out across the narrow Malian fields toward the tumultous mountain country in the north. Then he returned to the Phokian wall.

"Here will we make our stand," he said. "May the gods favour us!"

A sense of great uplift filled the younger man. In the grandeur of this silent place of mountain and sea, the nobleness of what they were to do overflowed his heart. He looked into Leonidas's face and saw it all alight with the same thought. The great event was prophesying itself in their hearts.

A scramble of hurrying feet broke the silence. A Theban soldier came running up, his face ugly with selfish fear.

"Come—come!" he shrilled breathlessly. "News—terrible news! We—we—must retreat, before—"

The king seized him with his heavy hand. "What is this thing? Tell!"

"The Phokians have come. They say—they say—"

"What is it they say, lout?" demanded the king.

"Another way round—a little path over the mountains! Oh, Thermopylæ is even as bad as Tempe! We must get away!"

The king turned without a word and fiercely started on a run hack through the Pass, Aristodemos and the Theban at his heels.

He reached the camp none too soon. The allies were already in an uproar. Leonidas glanced toward the camp of his Three Hundred. But nothing save the quiet scorn with which they went about their business indicated that they were even conscious of the hubbub. Then the king's voice rang out like a trumpet.

"Men of Hellas! You are not cowards but men! What fear is there of a little mountain path? We can easily defend it, even as we can defend Thermopylæ! Now let marshal the army!" he commanded.

Then while the officers were hastily shouting their orders he sent a word to his Spartans, and immediately a great hymn of Tyrtæus rose like embodied strength upon the air.

"That will be their wine," said the king quietly. "Now where are those Phokian news-bringers?"

The Phokian captain and his men were close at hand.

"It is a little matter," said the hardy mountaineer.

"A little hidden path up yonder in the mountain. Wherefore should it raise such outcry?"

By the time Leonidas had got his information clear the troops were standing silent before him in close array.

"Now," cried the king, "who will guard me this path?"

At once the whole thousand Phokians lifted up their spears and shouted, "Give it to us, O king! These mountains are our own!"

The army waited motionless.

Again Leonidas took the brown rough Phokian captain and plied him with searching questions. Did he realize the menace of such a path? Was it defensible? How? Were his Phokians trustworthy? Could he depend upon their alertness?

"We can defend Thermopylæ," the king went on. "But if ye fail above, our struggle here is naught. Day and night ye must keep faithful watch. We have the gate; but ye hold the key."

"Be we not mountain men?" returned the captain soberly. "We know mountain fighting."

So at sunset the thousand Phokians marched out

of the camp. They seemed light-hearted at their going. Was it their native love of hill doings? One old fellow in the Lokrian ranks seemed to think otherwise. He gesticulated derisively after them.

"Aha! Yes!" he growled. "And glad enough ye are to get away from Thermopylæ and hide ye soft in your silly path. Ye know the Medes'll never come that way!"

The king heard him and knit his brows but said no word.

That night Aristodemos sleeping in the king's tent heard him rise and softly reach for his cloak. The young man raised himself upon his elbow.

"Leonidas!" he whispered.

"Yes."

"Wilt thou not sleep, at all? Thou hast sore need."

"I can rest better outside. My bed is become the fighting place of thoughts."

The tone was more needy than Leonidas knew. Aristodemos was up at once and fastening on his sandals. The cool air met their faces as they passed outside the tent. Night was abroad. The full summer moon was sailing the deep sky and the ground was wet with dew.

"It is the Karneian moon," said Leonidas. "To-night they are keeping the festival. In three days it will be finished. And then—Oh, Aristodemos, I wish I were sure of the Ephor mind! Will they then send the army, or will some new mummery of delay lose us everything to Persia?"

"But will the Ephors dare, Leonidas? They can not give over thee, their king, and all thy chosen Spartans!"

"No—no. I think not. Therefore am I here. But Aristodemos, we stand perilous between. From north the Persian cometh, from south the Greek. If Greek come first—But if the Persian first—Ah, may some god make slow the Persian feet!"

They moved on past the glittering stack of arms and down a radial street of the camp. The tents were unclosed. But most of the hardy fellows preferring the open air lay sprawled asleep in front. The long spears which each had planted in the ground beside him glistened in the moonlight everywhere, standing like an upright ready army beside the sleeping ones. The king looked intently upon them, face after face. He had known them every one from childhood.

"How trustfully they sleep!" he said, half awed. "They have given me their care. They are my children. But soon I shall use them as never mother used her child."

They passed Demonax, a very picture of warm breathing life.

"How many of these," whispered the king, "shall see again the little hills of Sparta town?"

They walked on in silence. Aristodemos could scarce recognize his friend in this tender expressive mood. By day the king was full of discipline, inexorable.

Again the king broke silence.

"Aristodemos, dost thou remember that oracle which Delphi gave Sparta three years ago when first we knew that the Persian would come again?"

"Which oracle, my king?"

"It ran thus:

"Ye men of wide spaced Sparta,
Either your city must fall
By the hand of the children of Persia,
Or if not then know
That a reigning king of your city
Shall die in your city's stead.'

"'One or the other' said the oracle, 'one or the other.' Aristodemos, ever since Tempe that oracle hath increased in my ears."

"Oh, no, no!" cried the young man catching his thought. "In what way couldst thou die alone and save Sparta?"

"Nay, I speak not certainly. But the Fates may be requiring a payment for something. Who knoweth?"

Neither of these men was in any doubt as to the

truth of the oracle. Interpretations might fail; but oracles never.

"At first I did not think it was I," went on Leonidas sadly. "Then Tempe failed, and it was left to Sparta. Then Sparta drew back and it was left to me. Now the Phokians are gone. Perhaps all will go at last."

"But that hath no meaning!" broke in Aristodemos almost savagely. Thy Spartans can never leave thee. And I—How could that be, Leonidas? Now if the oracle had said, 'A king and a king's friend'—" Aristodemos was pleading as if Leonidas were indeed a veritable seer.

The king straightened shoulders as if shaking off a weight.

"Well," he said, "we are here to make stand for Hellas, not to question destiny. Why should I doubt the Ephors of Sparta? Sparta will come to her king, and come quickly. I saw it in the soldier faces ere I left." His mood was completely changed. He was joyous and conscious of his strength, Then on a sudden his head dropped to his breast. "Ye gods," he laughed, "how suddenly sleepy I am! Let us back to bed ere the gentle Hypnos leave me!"

In the tent Aristodemos unclasped the king's cloak, and loosened his sandals. Service was privilege now. And scarce had Leonidas stretched himself when he was sound asleep. But the young man lay beside him full awake until the dawn, thinking ardent thoughts.

The days passed. Now the season of the Karneia was by. Doubtless Sparta was already dispatching her army.

Then one day the Greek fleet appeared. A runner from the lookout post down the Straits came leaping along the eastern road into camp wildly gesticulating and shouting: "The fleet! The fleet!"

The men scrambled hilariously up the heights to get sight of the ships. This coming of the fleet was the first genuine movement for the defence of Thermopylæ. Presently they saw the distant Eubœan Strait blossom white with sails. Steadily, royally, they came! There were two hundred and seventy-one ships of them—the Athenian ships in the lead. They filled the broad waterway with sudden life. Like glorious birds they rounded the sharp point of Eubœa. The soldiers on the crags could see the sails shift and flutter at the turn and could catch the measured flash of the falling banks of oars. Then the whole fleet swept out eastward toward Artemision, the sails thin edged against the sun, the galley's beating tiny oars upon the blue.

Every hour of the Persian delay now was of priceless value. At any moment the whole Spartan force might arrive to make the defence complete. Scouts were ready on the high southern hills to signal by fire the first joyous glimpse of the Grecian approach. Yet for the little army at the Pass every hour of such delay was perilous too. Every morning began with the anxious questioning, "Have the Spartans come?" And, "How near are the Persians?"

The dead weight of these days fell upon the captain of the host. It was Leonidas who held the spirits of these men in his steady hands. He made them rebuild the Phokian wall, needful for defence and equally needful to busy the fretting men. He kept up a daily gymnastic. He kept full the supplies at Alpenoi. At times he was stern and hard. Again he cheated them with precarious hope. And always he made them feel that the gods were on their side.

The watchers on the southern hills came and went all openly. But there were other scouts whose northern goings and comings were more secret.

"What now?" asked Leonidas intently, as one of these scouts reported at the king's tent.

"It is strange," said the man. "Last week I was sure that the Medes were still at Therma. I had tidings of them there. But now I find rumours that they are as near as Krannon."

"From whom hast thou this?"

"From a shepherd who hath it of a corn trader."

The king's face darkened bitterly.

"Thou must take horse and ride hard to Sparta. Unless the Spartans have already started, the Medes will be here first!"

Next day the king went out repeatedly past the nearly restored Phokian wall and out beyond the farther gate of the Pass, looking long and quietly across the Malian plain. "A three days' journey," the scout had said.

The third morning broke with lowering sky and a gale of wind. Then rain began.

"It groweth fierce out there by Artemision," the sea-wise told the king. "This wind is the Hellespontias. The fleet can not hold in this!" And sure enough by mid-morning the ships could be made out staggering back again down the Strait, chased by the blinding storm. Again the soldiers climbed the heights and saw them careering in the gray of rain and sea. Where were they going? What was this to mean? Was the little army to be left entirely unsupported? Were they going to abandon Thermopylæ altogether?

A thirty-oared galley broke away from the fleet and came reeling up the Malian Bay toward Thermopylæ. The soldiers crowded down from the hills to the booming shore.

"What is it? What is it?" they shouted through their hands, while the men on the wet decks shouted back to them, and all their shoutings were drowned in the voices of the storm. At last the ship made land. But no defeated faces were these aboard her.

"Did ye see the signal?" cried the soaked sailor men as they piled out. "What? The ships? Oh, they've only run under the lee of the land till these winds blow themselves out. But didn't ye understand? The whole Persian fleet came down late last night. It's anchored, many ships deep out there on the windward strand beyond Cape Sepias! This storm is smashing them up by the hundred! Old Boreas is doing the fighting for us! Ei! Ei! Didn't the oracle say, 'Pray to the winds'?" And the exultant sailors capered about wildly on the shore.

THE HILLS FOUGHT FOR HELLAS

"Ei! Ei! Boreas!" shouted the amazed soldiers. They seized the dripping Athenian mariners and carried them in noisy procession through the camps. And all the while a very Deukalian flood was beating down upon them from the heavy skies.

"Our ship is to bide here," reported the captain, Abronichos, to the king. "We're detailed to notify the fleet if things go wrong by land. And Polyas of Antikyra will be sent to us if the fleet be disabled."

Toward noon Leonidas went out again quite beyond the Pass and as far as the Asopos River in the Malian plain. The rain had lightened a little. He gazed long and anxiously toward the northern mountains. The Persians would certainly strive to meet their fleet at Thermopylæ. He was sure of that. But the day dragged on and finally with a relieved sigh he turned back.

"We have at least one day more," he said aloud. But scarce had he got back into camp when a curious shadow appeared over the shoulder of Mount Othrys, moving down the thin white streak of road. It was followed after an interval by another shadow, and yet another, and at last by a steady dark stream. Now the stream worked out on a lower reach of the road, a quivering thing, shimmering throughout its length even in the rain, as with myriads of pointed spears. Now it took on a single broad colour, now red, now yellow, now purple, as the different nations rounded the turn dividing, spreading down the slope. So it began, softly amiably; but never ceasing, terrible even in its silent beginnings. For it was the unmeasured unmeasurable power of the East, pouring in like the power of waters to overwhelm and destroy.

Leonidas resting in his tent suddenly heard the cries of terror. Scouts were running in followed by workers from the wall spreading alarm and panic as they came. Aristodemos never forgot Leonidas's look of mingled pain and patience as he started up. But neither the king's pain nor his patience lasted long. He rushed out and quelled the panic spreaders with an authoritative shout. He hurried through the allied camps. The men so jubilant this morning were now clamorous with terror. "The Spartans are not come! The fleet hath fled! We are abandoned!"

Leonidas scourged them with his wrath, whipped their very faces with scornful words. He called a council at once. Most of the leaders were for instant retreat. "To the Isthmos and hold the Peloponnese! To the Isthmos!" The old selfish cry again. How like a curse it sounded in his ears!

"Ay! And will ye let them into Greece?" he cried to them with impassioned pleading. "Will ye let them pick your country as a dog a bone? They will do it! They will do it! And what will ye say when ye meet the Spartan army on the road? Not far off are they now! And what word will ye have me send to the waiting fleet? 'Go back, O Fleets, for your armies are fled to save their skins!' Oh, what desertion shall be like your desertion? What traitor hath ever betrayed all Greece at once? O, Hellenes, we can hold Thermopylæ! We can hold it, I say, till Sparta comes!"

Finally, as by some divine contagion, so much more potent than any contagion of evil, Leonidas's enthusiasm swept into them.

"Ye will stay? Ye will stay?" he cried.

"Ay, we will stay!" they shouted sternly back.

As for the Three Hundred, they had gone at the very first to their station outside the Phokian wall. There they watched the first Persian horsemen come dashing across the Malian plain, watched them curiously as they marked out the monstrous camp. They could plainly see the baggage wagons lumber up and the trains of strange sumpter beasts and the tribes and tribes of men. Then in the early twilight another Persian host came into sight, pouring along by the coast road of the Malian Gulf. From both sides the Malian plain was filling with humanity like a vast pool, at the foot of Othrys Mountain.

"Ohe! The Persian arrows will darken the very sun!"

chattered a Theban whose curiosity had brought him out further than his courage.

"What of it?" said Dienekes with a grin. "It's all the better to fight in the shade!"

"And look at the tents already!" cried Hyllos. "Those pretty fellows mean to get in out of the rain before night!"

"And they'll get another soaking," laughed Demonax, "when they come out to fight in the morning!"

But the Persians did not fight on the morrow. Through that whole day, too, the vast army continued to arrive and fill the plain. A third day passed. On the fourth morning the clouds broke away leaving a clear-washed sky. A signal of smoke from the lookouts down the Strait announced the Greek fleet's return to Artemision. Still the Persians sat unmoved in their multitude of tents.

Precious days! Sparta's precious opportunity!

Over in his silken tent in Malia the boyish Great King was waiting for his Persian fleet to break through the Strait and come to him with needed supplies. The storm had not shattered that fleet quite so completely as its enemies had hoped. Let it once show sail in the Malian Gulf and those foolish fellows in the Pass yonder would disappear like rabbits. Had not all the Greeks thus far promptly fled or Med-ized at sight of him?

Among the Greeks in the Persian camp was that unhappy Spartan king whom Kleomenes had ousted, and who had become the reluctant and incongruous subject of the Persian. The young king now pleasured himself by sending for the rugged old Spartan.

"What, Demaratos," said Xerxes, "thou dost never mean to tell me that those Spartans of thine will try to make a stand against us."

"O king," said the Spartan, scratching his head—that head which an unlucky response might so easily lose him. "Dost thou want a true answer or a pleasant one?"

Of course the king wanted a pleasant answer, and

of course he said he wanted a true one.

"Well, then," said Demaratos bluntly. "They will fight."

"Fight?" The king shook with laughter. "Oh, Demaratos, what kind of nonsense art thou talking? Why, they are not a mouthful."

Demaratos did not like to be laughed at. But finally he said:

"They will fight. Do not regard their fewness, O king. If a thousand are there, they will fight thee, or if less, they will fight thee."

The king grew indulgent to the old man. He held up his slender fingers.

"Account me this reckoning," he drawled patiently. "One of my guards can fight three Persian soldiers. Now suppose a Spartan could fight twenty. Doubtless thou, having been, as thou sayest, a king of them, couldst fight twenty. But, O Demaratos, I have a thousand Persians for every Greek."

The old Spartan shifted his feet.

"O king, live forever!" he broke out. "I was sure at the first that thou wouldst not like the true answer."

The king looked at him curiously, fingering the jade clasp of his belt.

"Under what marvellous lash, then, are they driven Demaratos?"

"Under no lash!" replied Demaratos, dangerously near to losing his temper. "The Spartans are free. Yet not in all things free. Law is their master whom they fear—more than ever subject of thine feared thee. And Law hath commanded that they flee not out of battle from any multitude of men, but stand and win the victory. Such a sort, I say, are my Spartans!"

Xerxes laid back his royal head and laughed. But he did not comprehend. More than words were needful to bridge that abyss of difference between the mind of Persia and the mind of Greece.

The next day Xerxes sent a rider to the Pass to spy out what these absurd Spartan men really might be doing. The Greeks let him ride close up within the Pass and look his fill. He saw in front of the Phokian wall the lusty, laughing Spartans busy at their gymnastics, leaping, wrestling, flinging. A little apart from these Demonax, Chilon and some others were combing their long black hair and binding it up with fillets and flowers. The scout returned and described all this to the king.

"Demaratos, Demaratos!" laughed the king in triumph. "What sayest thou now? These thy invincible warriors are playing childish games. They are dressing up their hair like women."

"O king," said Demaratos, his old eyes alight with memory, "all that too is our Spartan custom. We needs must crown our hair and make it beautiful when we are about to face death!"

A look of pity crossed the young king's face.

"Ah, Demaratos, age hath surely crept upon thee. Thou talkest solemn nonsense to thy king."

Next morning Leonidas received a writing from the Great King. He smiled broadly as he read it aloud in the midst of a group of his Spartans. The letter said:

"Foolish mortal, what use to fight against the gods? Serve me and thou shalt rule all Greece."

Leonidas turned quickly to the waiting messenger. "Say this to thy king," he said. "'If thou understoodst happiness thou wouldst not covet the happiness of other men. As for me, I would rather die for Greece than enslave her.'"

That evening as Leonidas was walking with Aristodemos in front of the Spartan camp another messenger crept out of the bushes with another tablet for the king. Leonidas read its imperious words in the light of a flaring torch.

"There is no more time for your folly. Send me your arms."

THE SPARTAN

In his slow, difficult hand Leonidas scratched upon the same tablet:

"Come and take them,"

and handed it back to the messenger. Then he turned quietly to his friend.

"They will attack us to-morrow," he said.

At dawn the Spartans saw a great stir among the Persians. Soon the heavy masses of fighting men began to move solidly up to the western entrance of the Pass. Among the Greeks there was no fear, no demurring. They ate their breakfast silently, in silence armed and began to form their line of defence. Oh, the intense quiet of these men in their memorable preparations! Leonidas, passing among the allies, looked in vain for signs of that panic which had so often baffled him. It was gone like a mist before the clearing heat of action. Looking into their grim expectant faces he felt their united strength enter and strengthen him.

Leonidas drew his battle front across within the Pass but in front of the Phokian wall. The main part of his army he kept behind the wall, ready to sally forth by companies or nations to the fight. His masterly Three Hundred would, of course, take the first onslaught. There they stood, about thirty men front, in the narrow place, shield lapping shield, spears level in the sun, their familiar faces showing set and fierce under the low drawn helmets. Down the line he noticed the Athenian jaw of Aristodemos take on an expression he had not before seen.

"Here they come!" called Leonidas.

Then whizzed and cracked the whips above the massed Median heads.

"Steady now! They're upon us!" sounded his clear, confident voice. Then the howling, trampling multitude, the wallowing waves of humanity, broke into the Pass between the cliff and sea.

The Three Hundred—wall of brass—stood motionless until the others had come within spear length. Then, "At them now!" rang the quick, vibrant command. And like a single brazen engine the shields and spears lunged forward.

The Median front went down like wheat. The multitude heaved backward, crushing into the cliffs and throwing hundreds sidewise into the sea.

"On—now on! Drive them! Drive them out of Hellas!" rang out Leonidas's voice like a trumpet. And up over the heaped bodies of the slain the Greeks advanced fighting with the sure unceasing activity of the trained, while more and more the masses of the Medes behind kept pushing and crushing their helpless comrades forward into the Pass.

Aristodemos felt the soft flesh crush beneath his feet, the warm blood fill his sandals. Then he forgot, and knew only that he was pushing, pushing, using his sword at close range, and putting forth the greatest effort of his life.

"On, on! Out of Hellas drive them! Well done, Dienekes! Careful there, Hyllos! No, to the left! A-ah, good!"

So the Three Hundred fought forward inch by inch into the Pass. Aristodemos seemed strangely strong, strangely aware. Once he suddenly swept his shield upward, he knew not why, and against it crashed a well directed blow. Had he seen it coming? Or was it some god had lifted his shield?

"Good luck, Aristodemos!" cried the instant voice. Did his king see everything?

Now the work grew steadier. He was thrusting into massed dark faces, crashing down wicker shields and glimpsing behind them the starting eyes. Then—the sudden outgush of life. Ah, the wet, red work of war!

Then, somehow, in an instant the whole struggling mass of the Medes seemed to dissolve and flow away. A vile contagion of panic fear had melted their hearts and turned their strength to water. The Spartans could see them fighting their way back with shameful frenzy through their own broken ranks in their agony of desire to get away. What had done this? Was it the whole-sale killing, the rock-like resistance of the Greeks? No. It was rather the Greek essential strength impinging upon the barbarian essential unstrength.

So they had them out of the Pass. Day cleared before Aristodemos's eyes. He found himself free and breathing deep.

"Now to the wall! Back to the wall!" ordered Leonidas.

The Spartans came back again to their place within the Pass. The Helots tenderly bore the two slain warriors to the rear through the reverent opened ranks. Then the fighters flung themselves flat upon the ground for a little rest.

The respite was not long. Soon they saw marching into the further Pass a column of tremendous warriors, superbly armed and splendid with crimson and gold. They came with the swing and steadiness of tried veterans, setting lion faces to the task they had to do. An exclamation of wonder ran through the Spartan ranks as they scrambled to their feet.

"Aha!" said Leonidas. "The Immortals! By Pollux, the Great King hath a mind to end it! Stand close, now, close! Spartans, this grapple shall try ye!"

Then, "Hail Paian! Alala! Alala!" shouted and sang the Greeks, and charged solidly down the little slope to the broader way between the passes. But this was stubborn work! Not an inch did the splendid fellows give, plying with skill and gigantic strength their swords and short spears. Had the Spartans met their match?

Suddenly, at a sharp cry from Leonidas, the Greeks faced about, giving their cuirassed backs to the "Immortals," and fled like deer, though in unbroken formation, up toward their wall. The Persians, with a yell of triumph broke after them in full pursuit.

Then again that sharp command. Again the Spartans faced about. "Alala! Alala!" And down again the gleaming spear line swept, killing and crushing endlessly.

THE HILLS FOUGHT FOR HELLAS

Far skilfuller fighters than even the "Immortals" were the Spartans, and they wielded much longer spears. This trick, too, was one of a hundred such—of their daily familiar drill.

Fresh battalions of the "Immortals" rapidly pressed forward into the places of their shattered comrades, whom fresh companies of Spartans seemed to slay almost at will as they crowded up the narrow, slippery way with hope of winning some foothold within.

Then the Thespians and other allies killed and crushed and crushed and killed succeeding "Immortal" companies, until the heaped and dripping rock afforded no more foot-hold even for men to fall and die, and the sea itself heaved red with "Immortals" slain. The sun climbed to noon, but the fighters stopped not for the heat. It began to decline, but they paused not for weariness. It went down behind far purple mountains. The long summer day was at an end when even these infuriate men must obey the behest of night. The little roadway at the foot of the quiet cliffs lay blocked and hideous with the terrible work.

Noisily wailing their dead, the Persians got themselves back to camp. But the Greeks took their five precious slain, and laid them forth upon the beach— heroes these upon whom they looked half sorrowfully, half enviously.

And now the blessed rest after the terrible toil! How hungrily did the tired Greeks eat their meal, how instantly drop off to slumber!

Aristodemos hurried with Leonidas to the tent. He wanted to shout aloud, to sing. He was bursting with the sense of accomplishment and issue. Who can conceive how the first victory overwhelms the heart of the young soldier?

"We have proved it, Leondrion!" he cried passionately, almost on the verge of tears. "We have proved the Pass. We can hold it till our Spartans come. Oh, what was Marathon to this!" Body and mind had been too stretched to quiet down at once. Aristodemos was also a little feverish and had strange pains back of his two bright eyes. Leonidas did not share his elation. He sat with absorbed eyes, looking off upon the sea, tapping restlessly upon the doffed helmet at his side.

"My king!" Aristodemos loved to call him so these days. "What art thou thinking underneath that frown?"

"Thoughts that would mislike thee," answered Leonidas.

"Then out with them! They'll eat thy heart like a fox, else."

"I am thinking of the Phokians, Aristodemos," said the king very soberly.

"Yonder on Kallidromos?"

"Aristodemos, if they fail us on the mountain we are lost."

"Leonidas, thou art tired. Why should they fail? Their place is easier of defence than ours. Besides, the secret path is—"

"Secret? Secret?" The king repeated the words with a sudden energy, almost of anger. "Fall not into that trap, Aristodemos."

He turned to the young man as if to talk the matter out.

"Know, if thou wouldst be a soldier, that no place is secret—no place. This our Phokians will not believe. I have warned them, reasoned, urged. I have been sending men to observe them. The report is always the same. The Phokians feel secure in their mountain place. They do not watch—not even now, Aristodemos, when the Persians are in the plain scarce ten miles away from them!" He sprang up and began to walk about.

"A path? Why, there would be no path except there were those who tread it. Yet the path is fully defensible, as thou sayest. If they but watch! If they but watch!"

"But they must watch, Leonidas."

"Aristodemos, that Phokian position is every whit as important as this that we have defended here this day!"

The young man's face flashed responsively.

"But surely, thou canst compel them to watch."

Leonidas did not answer. He closed his eyes as if to shut away some thought. Then he spoke in a low voice.

"No. They are proud hill folk. They are already angering at our Spartan prodding. No, nothing but the stern fact will make the Phokians watch. Aristodemos, wilt thou go to-night into the Persian camp, and find what the Persians know of this path! It is impossible, but that they learn of it soon. But be thou before them and warn the Phokians. And fight thou with the Phokians in their inevitable fight."

Aristodemos lifted a dazed face. But Leonidas did not speak again.

"Art thou bidding me go forth from this thy battle place, Leonidas? Oh, and art thou still thinking to die alone? When hast thou heard," Aristodemos faltered on, "that two sworn friends fought separatewise?"

"When, indeed!" answered Leonidas, and again fell silent.

Then Aristodemos spoke with quiet conclusiveness.

"Send one less near to thee, Leonidas. I must abide with thee here. Thou and I have sworn the oath to-gether. The real fighting place is here. Any Spartan will go yonder for thee and fully obey thy command."

"My command, yes. But in this matter I can give no command. I can only say 'Go' and he that goeth, must himself conceive and fulfill all the plan. It is a bare chance. Yet we must seize every chance. And none but thou will find a way out of each emergency. It is thy deed. Hellas asks it of thee, not I. Dear friend, I would send another if I could."

Something in this finality made Aristodemos look up. He saw tears coursing down the king's cheek and beard, and knew of a sudden how sorely he was besetting him.

"When shall I start, my king!" he said steadily.

"Oh, boy, dear boy!" said Leonidas, feeling suddenly

that this adequate warrior was after all but his own eager "Learner." "This is no little duty that I lay upon thee. Hellas hangs upon strange hazards now. And thy glory in the Mountain and ours here in the Pass are one. Hellas will be in thy hand even as it is in mine. Equally as it is in mine."

The young man's face began to shine as the deed grew large within him. He put his arms about the king with a tenderness that was almost more than Leonidas could bear.

"My king," he said presently, "thou wilt tell some others of this my enterprise, so that if I die and be found among the enemy, men may not say that Aristodemos was—a Med-ized—"

"Have I any treasure so dear as thy honour?" interrupted Leonidas sternly. "But, first thou shalt rest. Then go to Alpenoi village and buy clothes from off some peasant back. After that come to me again before thou goest away."

He made Aristodemos lie down and sat beside him silent for an hour while he slept. Then he roused him in the darkness. Aristodemos hastened up to the village, bought and put on the rough unaccustomed dress, hiding his short sword in the folds. Then he hurried to put his armour safe in one of the little houses.

"Who's that?" called a rough voice as he entered—a voice he knew.

"What, Eurytos? Thou here? I thought thou wast with us below to-day."

"Oh; no, no, no!" cried the poor fellow. "I can not see at all. And ye have fought it—ye have fought the battle! I am a useless log!"

"Nay, thy sickness will be passing soon," consoled Aristodemos absently.

"But now Demonax saith openly it is a plague. And I must not come back among the men. He saith it will run from me to them."

"Nonsense, nonsense! Eurytos, listen. I am leaving my armour here. I go on business for Leonidas.

Wilt thou keep it by thee till I come again?"

"Yes. I will be thy Helot since I am no longer soldier," answered Eurytos fretfully. And he reached out groping hands for the cuirass and helmet.

"Whither goest thou?"

But Aristodemos was already gone, hurrying down to the camp. He came quickly into the king's tent. The king started. It was a shock to see by the flaming torchlight his friend in that degrading peasant dress and without the beloved Spartan arms. It was as if distance had already yawned between them. The doubtful enterprise was oppressive to these men of open deeds.

Leonidas took the young soldier hands with fierce pressure, while he gazed into the frank devoted face— gazed as if he could never cease. His lips trembled as if forming words. Then he turned swiftly away, bowing his head.

"Go!" he said. "Oh, go quickly!"

And Aristodemos, though he saw the great heart breaking, could not but obey.

CHAPTER EIGHTEEN

Anopæa, the Chimneyhole Path

Aristodemos plunged along in the dark, blind with sorrow. At the edge of the camp a hand was laid upon his arm. It trembled like Antiphon's hand, and Aristodemos started with a quick terror of the supernatural. Then he saw that it was Megistias the old priest, he who read the omens for the Spartans.

"I know thy going forth," he said. "The king hath told me. And I want thy help. Thou knowest—" he hesitated, "the gods are hard to learn. At times they hear not; at times they are away. And to make sure, do thou give me a sign. If the Phokians be overcome and the Medes master that path, light me a fire on the height, even a big fire, that I may see it and warn the Greeks to their escape." He thrust into his hands the flint and tinder, the priestly apparatus for altar lighting.

"And this," adding a little sack of food. "And this—it may serve thee well," giving him a small sharp dagger. "Hidden weapon needs be small."

Aristodemos nodded silent thanks and promised. Then he quickly resumed his way.

Leaving Alpenoi he took the Phokian high-road direct away from the sea. The storm had lessened through the day, and in his intensity Aristodemos had quite forgotten it. But now the solid masses of cloud were rolling up the sky again. The darkness was complete. Suddenly a ripping light flashed the distant mountains on his sight—the forest, the white winding road. Then heavy thunder shocked the hills, reverberating endlessly. Then followed a torrent of rain, the mighty wind driving it in from the sea. Aristodemos thought with a shudder of

ANOPÆA, THE CHIMNEYHOLE PATH

Themistokles and his ships tossing upon the dark waters off Artemision.

Could he but have known what this historic storm was really achieving he would have taken wondrous comfort. For centuries afterward the Greeks gave thanks to Boreas for the Persian ships that went down that night. The Greek ships, lying sheltered in their own waters, suffered not at all. Surely the gods were doing battle for their own.

But of all this Aristodemos did not know. He strode along with the wind at his back, the primeval forest rocking over his head. He passed a little fountain by the road-side where the quivering lightning showed it. Here one of Leonidas's scouts barred the way with his spear. Aristodemos gave him the password and hurried on, leaving him to wonder. Just beyond the fountain he turned off the road and began to climb the steep path up the mountain. As the night deepened the storm increased in fury. Aristodemos was buffeted by low branches, driven again and again out of the path, recovering it only by the lightning flashes.

Throughout the mountain forests the great wind kept up its roaring. If the Persians were already informed of the path surely they would even now be pushing through. To Aristodemos's lively imagination such a possibility easily became a certainty. He began to hasten still more in spite of the darkness and the rough way, impatiently pushing aside the tossing branches, hurrying when the lightning gave him a view of the path. An older scout would have taken matters more coolly; but to Aristodemos it seemed as though the Persians must be already upon the mountain.

About midnight he gained the top and neared the Phokian camp. Ay, Leonidas was right. Aristodemos had to kick the sentinel awake to give him the countersign. That individual had snuggled under a rock to keep out of the wet and lay there snoring and steaming in his cloak. Aristodemos hurried on into the camp, breathing quick with excitement. But the camp lay peaceful in its mountain fastness. There was no opening in the forest. The tents were pitched here and there in the rough places among the trees. Secure indeed the Phokians seemed to feel. But the little path went straight on through the camp. It could easily lead an enemy up to it from the farther side.

He groped among the tents and came upon the captain of the guard squatting asleep beside his sorry fire. Aristodemos sat down by the fire and watched him. Presently the man started up and recognized him.

"Why, hello, Spartan," he yawned, stretching himself to his feet. "What art thou doing up here?"

"Better ask what thyself art doing. Dost not see that ten thousand Persians could come upon thee unaware in this din of storm?"

"Ten thousand owls! Who told thee that the Persians know the path? I tell thee it is untrodden."

"If they do not know it now, they surely will know it."

"Well, and if they do come," said the captain testily, "we can easily hold them yonder at the gully head."

"Pray the gods ye can!" said Aristodemos solemnly, rising. "We below are holding the sea pass, and if ye but hold this place secure a few days until the allies come ye will save Greece indeed."

The officer impressed by his seriousness looked long after him, then thoughtfully resumed his place by the fire.

Aristodemos passed on to the outmost picket, a mere boy who stood there at his post leaning upon his spear, the rain running in streams from his helmet upon his shoulders. He gave him the word.

"Merciful Gods!" he added, "thou'rt the first I find awake."

"Yes, captain, yes," said the Phokian dazedly.

"I am not thy captain, but the king's scout. See here, I'll take thy watch awhile. Growing boys need sleep."

"But I have a beard already," objected the youth, stiffening behind his upright spear.

"Beard or no beard, thou wert far toward dreamland. Here, give me thy spear."

The youth looked sharply into the friendly face. "Yes, I am tired," he admitted. "Wake me in an hour." He rolled himself in his cloak and in a moment was asleep.

When Aristodemos waked him, sure now of his wakefulness, he himself lay down to sleep. He had been in active battle all day and had need of his faculties for the morrow. About four in the morning he awoke, a strange taste in his mouth and a dull aching in his head. "Could a little honest fighting do this?" he wondered.

The boy was standing stiff in his place.

"Goodbye, sentinel," said Aristodemos cheerily. "Thy watch is almost out."

"A good hour yet," returned the boy. "But if more captains were like you there'd be better watching done."

"Watch for thine own life's sake," said Aristodemos. "Sooner or later the Persians are sure to come."

"That's the king's, word, isn't it?" asked the boy.

"Ay, and a true one."

Aristodemos wrapped his wet cloak tight about him, groped his way to the path and started down. The rain was now pouring steadily, the wind sighing and moaning with a thousand voices. Last night he had been easily moved to excitement, but now his mind was steadily clear. Already he was working ahead in his thoughts while following down the difficult way. Plainly his enterprise was threefold. First, he must find out to a certainty if the path were already known to the Persians, and if it were not known, he must get into a place where he could detect its first betrayal. Then, last and most desperate of all, he must if possible seek some chance to prevent or thwart such a betrayal.

Three more days of Persian ignorance might mean everything to the Greeks. The days of the festivals, both Karneian and Olympian, were over. Now was the time when the Spartans had promised to come in full force to Thermopylæ. The allies might be expected any day.

Meanwhile, the fate of Hellas and of his dearest friend might lie in the success of his audacious venture. His face was set and rigid at the thought.

The morning broke gray and struggling with clouds. In the first light he discovered a Malian shepherd picking his way along the path some distance below. Aristodemos hurried toward him with a Malian greeting. But the man turned with a startled and malignant look and, without reply, struck into the woods and disappeared. Aristodemos plunged in after him, but he had vanished hopelessly in the wilderness of crags and trees. The encounter disturbed him greatly. The man was probably some poor outlaw or escaped slave. Yet Aristodemos could not put from his mind that startled glance.

He began now to examine the path for any signs of passers through, whether of flocks or mountain folk or Persian scouts. He noted the soft mould underfoot, and lower down where the path entered the gorge of a stream, the bushes and rocks in the way. As the path left the gully and neared the level country Aristodemos rejoiced to find it more and more choked with undergrowth. It was difficult at times to find the path at all. Patches of delicate fern often completely filled the way, and not one frond was broken. The path was wholly unused and might well be forgotten.

He looked out over the plain where he could see the tiny houses of Trachis in the distance, and to the north where the great multitudes of tents showed the Persian camp. But there was no guard nor sign of attention to the spot where the precious path reached the plain.

He paused for a while to think. If the Persians knew this path, surely some interest, would be centring here. Should he stay and watch the place? But then, the Malian recurred to him. Possibly there was no harm in the man. But the menace of his presence grew upon Aristodemos. What was a shepherd doing there so early in the day, so far from human habitation and without his flock? Why had he so fled and with such an evil look?

ANOPÆA, THE CHIMNEYHOLE PATH

Aristodemos had seen a trapped fox look so once long ago. If the man had any wicked design he would surely go with it to the Great King. And if Aristodemos himself could but get close to that same Great King—Yes, the Great King's tent would be the place of all news bringers. Could Aristodemos penetrate to it?

He had only the day. By nightfall he must return to watch the entrance of the path. It was a perilous scheme, possible only because the Persians were not over watchful for spies. What indeed could a spy discover save the stupendous incredible power of the Persians? And they felt that only madmen could look upon them and still dream of resistance. Yet if he should be caught it would involve not only his own death but the loss of his watchfulness, upon which Leonidas was depending.

He decided sharply, and did not hesitate again. He crept cautiously along the lower cliffs which curved seaward ever nearer the Persians. Presently he espied through the thick copse a Median sentinel pacing to and fro before the intrenchment that edged the camp. He had no notion of falling into such hands and noiselessly drew back moving further seaward, circling the camp until he found a tribe of the North Greeks who had joined the Persian horde. With them he could deal. For a time he watched them from his hiding place. Then with quick determination; cutting a shepherd's crooked stick, he half ran half stumbled down into their midst.

"Hey, hey, what's this?" called a soldier in the Thracian dialect.

"What's this?" was the shepherd's indignant response, "I've lost my best ewe, and that's what!"

"Lost a ewe, have ye? Well, and I wouldn't wonder if some other rascals hereabouts may have lost a sheep or so. We dined yesterday. Let's see, was it twenty or thirty thousand sheep we ate?"

"Twenty thousand sheep!" echoed the shepherd. "Why, only Persians eat after that fashion. An' ye be'nt Persians."

"No, we be'nt Persians," laughed the man, imitating the shepherd's uncouth talk; "but we be Persian allies. And thou, young sheep-shanks, be'st in the Persian camp."

"Ai! Ai! Ai!' squealed the countryman dropping upon his knees with such an awkward fall that the rough soldiers laughed again.

"Oh, don't tell the king! Don't tell the king!" he pleaded.

"Tell him? Dost think the Great King takes note of such as thee? Why, he wouldn't take the trouble to eat thee!"

"Pray the blessed gods he won't!" The shepherd was white about the mouth and tears of pure terror stood in his eyes. He began to supplicate the man, clasping his knees.

"Help me! Save me! Let me serve thee! I will fetch wood, water—"

"Dost know these parts?" queried the Thessalian, interested.

"Know these parts? Why, Master, I was born in that little field up yonder whilst my mother tended sheep. And she e'en tended them the rest of the day I was born, and then brought me home at night, up in the mountain. "I was born with the sheep and I was always a-tending the sheep all through these hills."

"Dost know where good water is?"

"Good water? Why not? Such water as never thou tasted."

"Good, then," said the man. "Up from thy knees, fool, and get to work."

He watched the young shepherd fetch from the tent the large earthen jar, adjust it to his shoulder and lumber off with it. Aristodemos had the true Athenian genius for acting. The bend of the shoulders as from burdens borne too young, the stupid way of looking straight before him, the very twist of his cloak and of his tongue were all perfect. No one would have suspected the dull peasant thing, shambling along with his water jar, of a particle of intelligence or grace. Yet all the while the sharp eyes were seeing and the quick ears hearing.

Soon he was lost in the confusion of the monstrous camp. From tent to tent, from nation to nation he went. All was excitement and confusion. The hour of battle was at hand. They were renewing the attempt to push through Thermopylæ. Everywhere was rite and sacrifice, a thousand religions; everywhere the discussion of orders and news, a thousand tongues. Oh, how clear before the mind of Aristodemos stood now that devoted line of Greeks waiting at the Pass! He found himself half turning to speed back again and take his stand among them. Then he remembered with a pang that he must serve here.

But the barbarian jargons baffled him. Was he never to hear a word he could understand? On and on he went through endless avenues of tents, keeping his direction by their facing eastward for the facilitation of prayer. Had all the world come out against his little fatherland? Yes, and seemingly all the ages of the world. Here were savage Ethiopians, their bodies smeared with warpaint their primitive arrows tipped with stone. Here were slim Medes in soft silken elegance, the weariness of civilization in their faces. Wisdom so long had been their portion that it had passed over into weakness. He came upon quiet-faced Indians in garments of tree wool, and wild northern Scyths wearing pointed caps half as tall as themselves.

"An their heads were indeed so long," muttered Aristodemos contemptuously, "would they not move heaven and earth to make them round again?"

"What's that?" said a voice near him; and he found himself face to face with a Phthian Greek. Alas, there were all too many Greeks in that multitude.

Aristodemos melted imperceptibly again into his slouching attitude.

"I did but wonder," he said, "who be those black men yonder smelling worse than many goats?" He pointed to a strange half naked band of ebon savages who wore upon their heads the skins of horses' heads, with the ears set upright, the mane serving for a crest. They seemed creatures of some unwholesome dream.

"Those," said the Greek, "be Libyans. Men say that where they live is sand only, stretched out like the sea. But shouldest see their hair! 'Tis a black sheep's wool, and no hair at all."

Aristodemos moved on, but the man kept garrulously with him.

"What be these?" he asked again, as they came to a new camp.

"Dost not know Persians?" said his companion contemptuously. "Where hast thou been? Yet these be strange outlandish Persians who have not learned to live in houses but flit as birds, seeking food. They ride horses like madmen. And what, think ye, is their weapon?"

"I see none," said Aristodemos, peering at them. Then he suddenly closed his eyes with a momentary blinding pain.

"Well, it's a queer weapon," the man talked on, not noticing. "Those long ropes they make into a cunning loop. Then, as they gallop they fling them out over an enemy's head, and suddenly turn and draw it tight; and having entangled, they kill."

"A strange weapon, truly. Which way are the Thracians?" asked Aristodemos.

The man told him.

"And where is water? I'm hunting water for my master. "

"Well, art setting thy nose straight away from water. Here, this path!"

"Past the king's tent there?" asked the shepherd, blinking stupidly.

"What—that? That isn't the king's tent, fool. The king's tent is over yonder in the middle of the camps. Thou askest many questions for a slave!" And the man eyed him sharply.

"I am shepherd, not slave," muttered the countryman. "And these be strange sights!"

ANOPÆA, THE CHIMNEYHOLE PATH

Aristodemos followed the Phthian's direction and presently came to the river, a small stream running swift from its late leap down the hills. He knelt, bathed his hot face and drank very thirstily; then sat down by the brink with his jar.

What now to do? Was he getting nearer to the Great King? He sat there in the rain, watching for some servant who might look like the king's to whom he could join himself. But none came. Slaves came and went, fetching water, a monotonous procession. Horses and camels were brought to drink. Aristodemos was not a patient soul. He was discouraged, sick in eyes and head and very wrathful of heart. And oh, his Spartans were fighting even now at Thermopylæ!

After a while a great hubbub and clatter drew near, and a gang of slaves crowded down to the river, surrounding him in noisy confusion, and began to dip their jars into the stream. The officer who drove them was gorgeously apparelled. Now, many a Persian general had such a retinue. But to the simple Spartan these could belong only to the king. This was his chance. His heart bounded again with the joy of his enterprise. He dipped his jar with the rest. At the sharp crack of the officer's whip the slaves huddled together again, Aristodemos in the midst. His cheeks burned shamefully as they moved off together and he felt through his cloak the bitter sting of the lash. He could have killed the man for that humiliation.

They wound through the camp until they came within sight of such a tent as overtopped all dreams of the Great King's glory. It stood on a low hill, spacious and billowing, rising in purple pinnacles, many chambered and luxurious, much frequented of pale slender men in silks and gold who moved softly as though in nearness to a god. Aristodemos had been lucky in his ignorant guess. This was indeed the Great King's tent and he was among his stable slaves.

They marched past this tent and on to the next. Aristodemos caught a glimpse through the lifted flap of

a gilded stall and a brazen manger glinting in the shadows and of the king's world-famed white Nisian horses.
Here also rested the king's chariot and the king's litter
with its heavy gold embroidered curtains. They passed
around to the rear where all was a confusion of slaves,
camels, asses, bales and cookery, and the air was loud
with profane talk and Asiatic altercation.

Aristodemos set down his jar with the rest of them,
and then adroitly dropped down himself behind the jars
at the very edge of the stable tent. In an instant he had
rolled under the great tent fold and lay breathless. He
was not observed. The slaves, too, had sat down by
their jars. He began to creep on with infinite slowness
under the circumference of the trailing curtain. He had
looked sharply as he was passing the stable, and knew
where he wanted to lie. At length he reached the front
where, lying close, he could watch the approach to the
king's pavilion. He was here, here at last, at the Great
King's very door! It had happened so quickly that he
could scarcely credit his senses.

In front of the stable stood a line of guards, motionless, with bared swords. They were so near that he
could smell the perfume on their beards. Within the
tent behind him the servants were grooming the horses
and polishing the harness and chariots. The place was
crowded with soft-stepping slaves each at his narrow
unthinking task.

For hours Aristodemos lay there watching. The
ground was wet beneath him, the tent fold suffocating.
But he was all oblivious of such external matters; while
one overwhelming impression laid hold upon his mind -
the vastness of this multitude come to destroy Hellas.
He had heard of Persian greatness. For ten years he
had heard of it and he had thought he comprehended.
But it was one thing to listen to travellers' tales or even
to stand with dear Hellas at his back, defending her with
definite deeds. It was quite another to float in the midst
of the enemy, like a straw on a boundless sea. The
remembrance of his passage through the camp over-

whelmed him. What chance had little Hellas against all the world? Nay, had the gods foredoomed her disaster? What use to fight against the manifest will of the gods?

He buried his face intensely in his folded arms. Could Hellas die? His whole spirit rose and revolted. "No—No!" he almost cried aloud. Then he recalled yesterday's struggle—the intelligence, economized orderliness and quick, disciplined effort of his Greeks. And then—the preposterous contrast of this incoherent dead bulk of humanity, scourged on to slaughter. The contrast—the contrast! Like a flash of light he saw it. Yes, yes! Cleverness, wit, faith and farsight! These alone could save the Greeks. These were their true weapons. Mind, mind alone, was precious.

He began to count the real thinking men of Greece, frankly putting himself in the number. They were all too few. He began to see that even to die for Greece might not be so noble as to live for her. At least it was not so needful. His body grew tense as he lay there. He felt uplifted and made strong.

He looked out at the constant stream of officers and messengers going to and from the king. There was no joy in their faces, no look of enterprise or plan. The battle must be going ill for the Persians to-day as yesterday. These men plainly knew of no way as yet to come at the Greeks or to get through Thermopylæ.

Aristodemos began to long for dusk, when he could creep back and guard the secret path. Then, even if the Persians should discover it, he could leap on ahead up the mountain and rouse the Phokians. This quiet began to irk him. His whole body twitched and ached in its unchanged position. He was wet and hot and very weary. Struggle as he would his thoughts merged and grew confused.

Had he slept? For suddenly he thought a guard had struck him on the forehead, and he awoke with that same blinding pain in his eyes. Only this time it did not cease, but kept its maddening pressure until the air grew black before him and his body quivered with the groans he dared not utter. Water began to pour from his swollen lids, scalding his cheeks. Even in his agonized confusion he knew what had happened to him. It was Eurytos's sickness. Here in the camp it was come upon him, a worse foe than any Persian. And he alone with his enterprise! What was he to do?

The pain slowly receded. He could see again. But a flare of fever rushed through his limbs and made the closeness of his hiding place almost insupportable.

Suddenly he forgot both pain and suffocation. He lifted his head a very little to listen more intently. Two men had paused not very far from where he lay. They were talking in low tones and were evidently waiting to go in to the Great King. One was a Persian-clad, courtier-like Greek. The other—

Great guiding Pallas! It was his Malian shepherd. And no shepherd, but a soldier! Aristodemos could not mistake that face. He was talking Malian Greek.

"I will not tell it to thee. No; only to the Great King himself will I tell it."

"But thou canst not come to the Great King's presence, Ephialtes; whereas I serve his person. And besides, this is his hour for sleeping."

"They say the king can not sleep for grief since so many thousands of his men, even his Immortals, have perished and still the Great King's way is barred."

"Oho!" exulted Aristodemos in his hiding. "And hath the battle gone so well this day?"

"And by my life," the Malian went on, "the Great King would be proper glad to have his nap broken by my information."

"Thy information! The king will not be trifled with. For a less annoyance men's heads have flown off ere now."

"Oh, I'll not trifle! I tell thee I know a way to catch these Spartans in a trap. Eh?" he sneered, "thou'd be glad enough to tell it thyself and get the king's reward. But I know, and thou knowest not."

So they haggled over precious Hellas!

Meanwhile the true heart in its covert prepared for sacrifice. Aristodemos's first impulse was to edge back and get away with the warning to the Phokians. But as he raised himself he was overswept with a dizziness that seemed to whirl him in space. The torturing paroxysm in his eyes almost deprived him of his reason.

"Oh, Eurytos," he groaned. "How hast thou crippled a helper of Greece!"

He lay for a moment, helpless. Plainly he could not count on many periods of usefulness. How could he ever make his way back through the tangled camp? No. He must act now. To spring out upon this man and kill him with his plot untold would mean his own death, too. But it was his only chance.

Unfastening his cloak that it might fall away from him, and slipping sword from scabbard, Aristodemos silently moved to his feet. Then he leaped at the Malian.

But a Persian sentinel whom Aristodemos's failing eyes had not seen standing in the opposing shadow of the king's tent perceived him as he stood up from his hiding place, and with the quick instinct of a fighting man sprang to meet him.

Aristodemos, though surprised, caught him under the arm with a deep thrust, flung him backward: with the weight of his rush, and made on at his Malian. But the interference had given the Malian a chance to turn and dodge under, so that the stroke which Aristodemos sent at his throat but ripped his shoulder open. The Malain yelled with pain as he leaped out of reach, and the Grecian courtier blocked Aristodemos's way. An instant only there was a close, swaying encounter. Then he, too, fell with a death cry.

But now Aristodemos found himself facing a full score of the Immortals who at the noise had sped from the king's tent. To their bewilderment he flashed straight into their midst, cutting right and left. He would die dearly. His long hair shook out terrible and bright over his shoulders, and the Spartan war cry, "Alala!" rose instinctively from his heart.

Three more men fell before the Medes could close with him. Then above the din rang out the voice of Hydarnes, the leader of the Immortals, giving a sharp command. Aristodemos's sword was stricken out of his hand. He began to fight with his teeth in true Spartan fashion. But his arms were pinioned from behind, his legs were tripped and he went down under a great weight of men. His breath was crushed out. He could not even struggle.

After a little the weight gradually lifted. "Now to the gods!" he thought. But to his surprise no blow let forth his life. Instead they securely tied him hand and foot. As he lay there helpless on the ground a splendid tall man stood looking down upon him. Aristodemos could not understand what he was saying, but there seemed more of wonder than anger in his look. Then four men lifted Aristodemos and bore him away as if he had been a corpse, while others carried away the veritable corpses that lay where he had fought.

Oh, cruellest of all, why did they not kill him? The Malian had escaped! The Malian had escaped! The path would be known. He had failed. In vain as they bore him away he tried to catch some glimpse of the Malian. But what use now to see him? He groaned aloud. His bearers gazed at him in pity, thinking he had received some terrible injury. But his leathern jerkin had served him well. He was quite unwounded.

They laid him at last in a white tent, where he groaned and wept in anguish of spirit. Later a timid, soft voiced physician in turban and long robe came in and looked upon him, feeling his body, which was now in high fever. He shook his head dubiously.

"Internal wounds—bleeding," he said in Chaldean to the attendant, and left a healing drink. What did such kind treatment portend? Aristodemos could not fathom it.

Presently a gruff voice questioned without the tent. Then a short old man stalked in.

"How fares it with thee, son?" he said in clear Doric. Aristodemos almost rose from the bed. He strained his eyes in amazement.

"I know thy voice—thy face," he cried. "But who art thou?"

The old man scrutinized Aristodemos. "I hoped I might know thee," he said. "Thou'rt Spartan, for I heard thy war cry; and only a Spartan could fight as thou." The old eyes exulted. "Aha! I told the Great King a Spartan was good for three Persians. But thou wast good for five!"

"I know thee now!" said Aristodemos, his voice trembling with eagerness. "Thou'rt our King Demaratos."

The old man was intensely pleased. "Hast remembered me all these years?" he said. "And thou?"

"I am Gylippos's adopted son, Aristodemos."

"Yes, yes, I remember thy coming. Makaria's son. Yes. I did not think thou wouldst grow so brave a fighter. But now thou hast come to thine end."

"King Demaratos," said Aristodemos, looking toward the tent door. "Can they understand us?"

"Thy guards? No. What wilt thou?"

"Help me!" Then, as the old man began to shake his head, "Not for my sake, but for Sparta's."

"I love not Sparta. And no mortal can save thee. They are to sacrifice thee to-night before they set out. Thy valour and beauty are noised abroad through the camp as a good omen."

"'Set out?' Demaratos! Whither?" asked Aristodemos in dismay.

"I know not."

"Hath the Malian gone in to the king?"

"Yes; and hath told him somewhat. It is with the Malian they set forth."

"Oh!" groaned Aristodemos. "Oh, thou must save me, Demaratos. Thou must!"

"Art afraid?" asked the old man sharply.

"No, by the blessed gods!" said Aristodemos so fervently that Demaratos's old heart leaped at the sound.

"But I have work to do. I must not die till it be done!"

"There spoke a Spartan!" said the old man. Then added again, "But I love not Sparta!"

"Thou lovest not Kleomenes," said Aristodemos. "No more do I. I openly said so even before the gods punished him."

"Punished?" exclaimed the old king. "How was it? Tell me. I did not hear in Persia."

Aristodemos related all the horrible story and how the Spartans rejoiced that he had been so justly punished for his crime in deposing Demaratos. The old man listened, breathing hard and fast.

"Ah, the gods have avenged me! They have avenged me!" he exulted.

"Demaratos," pleaded Aristodemos, "wilt thou let Sparta die for lack of me?"

Without answer Demaratos called to one of the guards. The man quickly brought a cup of water.

"Thou'rt thirsty, son," said Demaratos, lifting him tenderly. As Aristodemos drank, he felt, the thongs on his arms and wrists loosen though they still hung in place. Demaratos made no sign. But as he put him down again he whispered:

"They'll loose thy feet to walk to sacrifice."

"Where do they make sacrifice?" asked Aristodemos in a monotonous voice.

Southward of the camp by the river Asopos. They have there a sacred place. The gods receive thee, my son. It was good for my old eyes to look upon thee here."

He was gone. Aristodemos lay on his couch, softer than any he had known since he was a little child in Athens.

A chance yet to save the Phokians. A miserably slender chance. But even so it put new life into him. He lay intently thinking. How slow the moments crawled. Twice, thrice, the agony in his eyes returned; but each time passed, again leaving his eyes red and streaming. The attendants, noting his pain, secretly wondered if he would live to the evening sacrifice.

CHAPTER NINETEEN

A Sacrifice to Ormuzd

At dusk came the priests and their attendants. Two guards lifted him and loosed his feet. Aristodemos held his arms rigid and dragged his feet as if in utter weakness. The guards were surprised to see him walk at all.

The rain had ceased. Solemnly in the soft fragrant twilight the procession wound its way through the camp, headed by the white-haired priest. Their torches twinkled in the dusk. Men looked after them with reverence and forgot to exult as they watched the young captive with the bowed head and the strangely intelligent face. He was in the flower of life, and so soon would be no more!

The aged priest, a Magian wise in the learning of his ancient sacred race, was unaccustomed to human sacrifice and very unwilling. His face was pale and awe-stricken under his white tiara, and he looked up with troubled eyes to his well-known stars inquiring of them even as he went.

When they reached the river it was dark, with the moon not yet risen. There was no altar. The Persians sacrificed simply at an "unpolluted place." They paused on the very brink of the river; for it was to the river they were about to offer their victim. The attendant priests surrounded the place. The high priest stood in the midst near a little rick of fresh-cut clover upon which the slain victim was to be laid. Aristodemos, half lifted by the guards, advanced feebly to his place.

He began to sway from side to side. They looked at him in wonder. Then almost inaudibly he began to chant, twitching his whole body in a rhythmic nervous way. At this the soldiers reverently drew back, recognizing the sacred insanity. Every Greek was familiar with religious ecstasy. And Aristodemos had rightly conjectured that the "divine state" would be held sacred by the barbarians as by his own race.

He began to sway faster. He gasped for breath. His eyes wildly rolled. The hot fever of his skin and the redness of his eyelids added to the reality of his feigning. Indeed at times the feigning almost became reality to himself and he felt the strange lightness, the sense of swinging out into space that precedes ecstatic utterance.

His rich voice thrilled the crowd calling out into the night: "Apollon! Apollon!"

The sensitive Orientals about him began to fall under the ecstatic spell, uttering low moans, swaying, clapping time with uplifted hands.

Now the stately old Magian stood ready in the midst, holding his bundle of tamarisk twigs. By him a young priest bore the sacrificial knife.

And then Aristodemos freed his arms.

The two priestly heads, old and young, cracked together like two hollow nuts. They themselves were flung against a tree trunk and fell in a huddle. Then Aristodemos in one strengthful moment broke through the line of guards and plunged into the stream.

There was wild confusion. The Persians were half dazed with religious ecstasy. The reluctant soldiers, full of supernatural terror, caught breath and began the chase. The scattering crowd were yelling wildly:

"Ahriman! Ahriman! It is a satan of Ahriman!" The wails of the priests over their leader added to the din.

Aristodemos had time to swim a little up the stream and clamber out on the other side before the clouds of arrows and javelins rattled after him. He leaped into the wood, pitching through the underbrush. How he made his way among the rocks and trees he never knew. He heard pursuers crashing after him and calling to each other in the dark. If he held his course they could surround and catch him. He therefore faced about and at the risk of running into them slipped back toward the stream.

The stream was his only guide. He knew that farther up the mountain the bed of the torrent itself was for some distance the only path. He crouched down. A soldier was within ten feet of him, going slowly, beating the bushes. He lay flat on the wet moss. The man drew nearer, paused, beat his way past him, and went by. Aristodemos began once more to creep on slowly upon his hands and knees. He found a small hollow filled with high, rank ferns. He felt a little ledge jutting out over its higher side. Under this he curled himself like a fox and waited. A man might walk fairly into the hollow and not perceive him.

It was so dark that he could not see the wet leaves that brushed his face. The moon should rise soon. Yet he feared that even when it should be light he would not be able to see. For the pain in his eyes redoubled the moment he was inactive. And there in his little hollow he began to pray. He prayed like a saint in confidence of his holy cause. Was not defence of his Hellas defence of the holy gods, of all that was holy in the world. And his prayer went high, for his gods answered him. The pain lifted like a cloud.

Now he could see, as it were, a gray mist moving upon the ground, now boles of oak trees standing out, now a glitter of wet leaves close at hand and tiny flowers and ferns upon a boulder. At last the brilliant slant of a moonbeam struck through the forest, revealing all. Meanwhile the calling through the forest had ceased. The awe stricken soldiers had quickly given up the chase. He was free to seek the Phokian camp.

He came out of his hiding and looked about. At some distance was a fuller light where the little stream parted the forest. Toward this he hurried. Following the stream he finally began the ascent and in a few moments came to the place where the footpath from the plain struck into the gully.

THE SPARTAN

Aristodemos felt sure that the Persian troops had started out, according to custom, directly after their sacrifice. But they could not have reached this place as soon as he, for his way through the woods was more direct and shorter. He listened for some noise of their approach. He went a little down the path. But in the broken moonlight his dim eyes could see no sign that they had passed. A moment he stood intently listening, but heard no sound save the little stream singing in the silence. Then with hot eagerness he strove upward.

They were behind him; but how far behind? He could climb faster than such a body of men; but how much faster? Everything depended upon his speed, the gaining of precious moments for the Phokians. The way up the stream was steep and rough, with riffles halfway to the knees, with little cascades white in the darkness, boiling among boulders, with dark pools and slippery ledges in the shallows.

He felt sure that the Phokians, if roused, could hold the path. He could hardly credit the hope that rioted within him. And he so short a time ago had looked death in the face! Half way up the mountain the path left the torrent and he could push on faster.

Just before dawn he became aware of a rustling noise ahead.

Could the wind play so in the dead leaves?

He gained upon it. It grew louder and more insistent. Then measured and regular.

Oh, cruel gods! It was the tramp of many feet.

He could not know how the unwilling old Magian had hesitated long before consenting to offer a human victim. The Persians had been obliged to set out after their ordinary sacrifice and let the human sacrifice take place after they had gone. They had been hours ahead of him on the way.

Aristodemos darted out of the path and with incredible activity and swiftness began to climb around the Persians, striving desperately to outstrip them. Save at the path the crags seemed inaccessible. It was sheer climbing upon hands and knees. He vaulted chasms that in sober mind he could not have half leaped, swung into depths by hanging vines, and clambering out upon the far side paused at the top for a single deep breath and dashed on, conscious only of his fear of not reaching the Phokians before the attack.

The gray dawn appeared through the forest and put out the moonlight with its unearthly white.

Aristodemos saw that he had got ahead. Another moment and he broke, torn and spent, into the camp.

Now Herodotos says that the Persians were equally surprised with the Greeks. They were expecting that no one would oppose them on the mountain. And suddenly they saw men flying to arms.

"Those devil Spartans!" they cried out with one accord. How the Spartans should come there they did not reason out. Spartans had not been doing reasonable deeds these past two days. Even Hydarnes went white. But the Malian Ephialtes reassured him.

"Phokians, I think. But not Spartans."

Upon which Hydames set the Persians in order for fighting through.

As for Aristodemos, he flew from tent to tent adjuring the Phokians to make stand in the path. The men were springing up from sleep, reaching wildly for their arms, buckling on corselets with hasty bewildered fingers, running half dressed through the place. Aristodemos had not known how shameful and appalling a panic would be. Everywhere was the cry: "To the peak! To the peak!"

"No—to the Path!" thundered Aristodemos, loud above the tumult. He met the commander; but the commander thrust him aside with an oath.

At that moment came a thick rain of Persian arrows. Whereat with a mighty outcry the whole Greek force made for the higher peak of Kallidromos, just above the camp.

In his rage Aristodemos would not follow them. "Fools! Fools!" he shouted after them, shaking his clenched fists above his head. Then he dropped where he was under cover of a great rock between the fighting lines. Perhaps the Phokians honestly thought to win a battle on the height, or meet death bravely there.

They faced about and formed their battle line, returning a volley of spears down upon the Persians. But though some Persians fell, their column did not pause nor turn aside to grapple with the Phokians. They kept crowding along the path and over down the mountain toward Alpenoi.

Aristodemos where he lay could see the whole foolish battle.

The Persians moving steadily down the path shot sidewise at the Phokians, losing no time in the aiming. They were splendid archers, those Immortals. The reed arrows from their long powerful bows struck with deadly effect. The Phokians after some twenty minutes of such fighting, having suffered greatly from the Persian archery and seeing the unending procession of their foe, broke in confusion and scattered through the wood. The Persian host kept filing through. They were ten thousand men.

Aristodemos still lay behind his rock. To lift himself were instant death. He knew that the slow moments were bringing destruction to all he loved in life. His mind pitched wildly from Hellas to Leonidas, from Leonidas back to Hellas. And with this last hopeless agony came the wild pain of eyes again. He strained his lids apart to see, but there came only a glare and pain that made him faint. He clenched his hands. The right hand closed on Megistias's little dagger.

Megistias! yes—Megistias. He recollected. There was yet one more duty left him. And he was like to be thwarted even of that by his blindness. Yet somehow he must manage to light that fire for Megistias.

At last he moved out from his rock. He crept northward toward the mountain edge where it overlooks the sea. He kept low against the ground, thankful for his brown jerkin and dull tunic among the fallen leaves. But the air around him seemed to grow darker and darker. Strange lightnings played in his head.

Suddenly came a rush of quick feet through the leaves, and a terrified calling. Aristodemos sprang up like a beast of prey, and the slim young Persian straggler screeched like a hurt hare as he pounced upon him. It was only a boy, one of those half-Greek Persian princelings from the Ionian coast. Aristodemos could just discern his thin face, white as chalk. But he threw the boy down roughly, whipped off the gaudy sash from his waist, and bound his arms behind him. The boy screamed with pain, crying that his shoulder was broken. But Aristodemos was deaf to his pleadings. Warfare had transformed him into the very devil the lad believed him. Powerful, dishevelled, with his red streaming eyes, he was terrible indeed.

"Let me go! Let me go!" screamed the Persian with chattering teeth. "I am a Greek. I am a—"

"A damned Greek!" roared Aristodemos, knotting the sash.

"My father will give rich reward! He is Satrap of Karia! He hath much gold! I am his only son!"

"Hush, liar! No Persian hath an only son!" As he spoke, Aristodemos jerked the lad to his feet and gripped his fingers into the tight sash between his shoulders. "Listen!" he commanded sternly. "Silent or I will kill thee! Go straight forward now. Not to right nor left, or I stab thee in the back." The lad shivered and shut his eyes.

"Yes—yes, I will go!" he gasped, and they started off. Aristodemos stepped carefully in the footsteps of the boy. The pain throbbed unceasingly in his eyeballs. As he went the air grew solid black and he saw no longer. But he only stepped the more carefully, taking each little hillock and hollow from the boy. Presently the boy stopped short.

"Go on!" commanded Aristodemos.

"Oh, Master, I can not! This is the edge."

"The edge? What seest thou?"

For the first time the boy realized that his captor

was blind. A cunning look came into his face.

"Persians coming hither. They have missed me at last. Here! Here! Hello!" His shouts were stopped by a blow.

"That is one lie," said his devil. "Thou shalt never make another. Now, wilt tell truth, or go straight to thy gods? Choose!"

"Oh, I—I speak true, true!" chattered the boy in terror.

"Then, what seest thou?" demanded his captor once more.

"The sea, the sea! And the sun about to rise."

"Never mind the sun!"

"And—and islands."

"The shore, boy—the shore! What there?"

"Narrow marsh and some tents, and a little wall—"

"Stop. It is enough." And reaching out, Aristodemos found a tree and bound the boy to it. Then, on hands and knees he began feeling about, raking dead leaves together, now coming upon a twig or dried branch. He soon made a heap. From his breast he drew the flints and struck them, holding them against the leaves. At last there was a low crackling, then a little sharp heat came against his hands. He put a few leaves upon the heat. It grew and the crackling grew. He heaped on branches and limbs, and stayed till the heat grew fervent in his face.

At last it was done. Now he must get down to Thermopylæ and know the worst.

He turned; found his boy easily enough by his sobbing, and unbound him from the tree.

"Go back now toward the path after thy Persians," he said in a quiet voice. "And if thou bring me down to Alpenoi I will set thee free."

CHAPTER TWENTY

Thermopylæ

At daybreak, Megistias sacrificing at his altar in front of the Spartan camp searched anxiously the entrails of the victim for a sign ere the Greeks should go into battle. He looked long and intently; then sighed and slowly shook his head.

Then he looked upward. On a high spur of Kallidromos twinkled as it were a star. It kindled and broadened, then burst into a flame.

"Oh, oh—the signal!" he cried, and looking back into the victims, read there also the fateful portent.

The king stood gravely by, awaiting the issue of the sacrifice.

"Yon is the beacon fire thy Aristodemos promised me!" quivered the old priest to him. "The Barbarian hath gained the upper path!"

The king's face grew dark and rigid. "Careful, Megistias!" he said sternly.

Megistias made a gesture over the altar where the pale entrails confirmed him. Leonidas scarce seemed to heed him, but stood gazing up at the flame upon the mountain as if he would overleap the distance between himself and his friend.

"It is as thou sayest. Then the young man is yet alive."

"Yes, O king. And the Persians—"

Here a scout rushed up from the rear crying the same tidings. And the king, with face as if he had already looked upon death, turned away. "It was fated from the beginning," he said. "I have known it long."

Yet Leonidas marshalled the little army for the last time and standing before them told them that which needed, no telling, which was already graven upon every dark face.

"But it is not the end! It need not be the end, even yet!" he cried to his astonished officers. "Not even yet is Thermopylæ lost! This path of the Anopæa—know about it, every foot. It is a difficult, narrow way, defensible even to within half an hour of Alpenoi. And the Persians can not get there for two hours yet. See yonder!" He pointed to the little white village, Drakospeleia farther up the path, glimpsed on the heights. "There the path is a narrow defile. The Persians can come through only two and two. Ye allies shall march thither. Ye shall keep them out at Drakospeleia. My division shall hold the Pass here."

And did the enthusiasm not catch? Nay, it caught but too readily—too readily for the king's peace.

"We will go!" cried the officers. "We will go!" And Leonidas knew, or thought he knew, that they would go fast and far. Yet he stood quiet before the army.

"Ye Corinthians, march!" he commanded.

At the king's word the men of Corinth filed away.

"And ye Mycenæans—"

"And ye Argives—"

As he named them each band saluted the king and rapidly moved off. The three hundred Spartans on the right seemed to scent the desertion. They smiled grimly and with infinite scorn as each ally departed from their side. They made no sign when the seven hundred Thespians refused to go and cast in their lot with Sparta.

But when Leonidas ordered the Thebans to remain, saying he had no wish to swell Persian ranks, a flash of derision and low laughter lit the Spartan faces for an instant.

And now stood there the little army, all that was left, purged of unsoundness. They went to their morning meal. Leonidas walked among them as they ate.

"Eat and spare not," he said in a clear voice. "Tonight we shall sup in Hades."

They looked up at him with a strange intimate expression, like children of one household. Death was drawing them wonderfully near to one another.

But Leonidas would have purged even his little remnant of all needless death. He begged the holy Megistias to go back. No need to sacrifice one so aged and so wise in the ways of the gods.

"I will not go," answered the old man, almost petulantly. "But with thy leave I will send mine only son to keep my line in Sparta."

Then Leonidas called to him all the youths that were with him and intrusted to each a message, one to Delphi, one to the Ephors at Sparta. The messages seemed important enough; but the youngest spoke out for all with calm disobedience.

"We came to fight, not carry messages, Leonidas."

Then, all things being ready, Leonidas set his little host in battle order and gave to each his last commands. He pronounced to them the battle word, which ran in a low murmur down the ranks. By this word comrade was to know comrade in the mêlée.

About nine of the morning Xerxes drew up his solid square of Persians at a little distance from the outer Pass. He did not intend to make the attack until Hydarnes should appear in the rear of the Greeks. He certainly did not expect what now followed.

The Spartan pipes began to play shrill in the quiet morning. And in the silence, with measured tread, keeping time to the flutes, the Spartan phalanx moved forward. But they did not halt as hitherto to block the narrow Pass. They came on through steadily forward out and beyond, their bright arms glittering in the open, still stepping to the flutes, knowing they were to die. The Spartans were marching in open field into the face of the whole Persian army!

Now their pace quickened with rhythmic rattle of

arms. Louder, faster played the battle flutes. They swept into a run; their deadly line of spears moved level before them. Then broke the fierce battle cry, "Alala! Alala!" Then the phalanx crashed upon the Medes.

The long, last struggle was on.

Three hours raged the strange unequal battle. Again and again the furious weight of the little phalanx drove against the Persian mass and pounded back its huge bulk in bloody confusion. Yet the sheer inertia of numbers must inevitably quench so small a band. Here Demonax fell. White-haired Megistias went down in the crush, and all those youths who that morning had refused to go away. Friend after friend Leonidas saw fall and perish in the ruinous tumult.

Leonidas in the front fought more memorably than all. A wound in his thigh bled copiously, but he was all unaware. Right and left with fatal stroke his short sword thrust and fell. An arrow at close range pierced his cuirass. He drew it out with no pause in his work. But the red life leaped after it.

Alpheos, who fought next him, noted that the king ceased his battle cry and began to fight heavily, breathing out a groan at every blow. Now a splendid Persian warrior fought his way to them, one of the Great King's table companions. He was making for the Spartan king. Leonidas leaped at him and thrust him through. But as he bore the Persian over, Leonidas fell with him and upon him.

So in a moment that devoted life, clean and true as his own true sword, was crushed out underneath the trampling multitude.

Then Alpheos, raging with terrible strength, heaved back the Persians from the body of his king. But again the mass compressed and surged over it. "Leonidas! Leonidas!" was the cry everywhere. The rough soldiers wept as they fought. The whole fury of the battle now centred about the body of Leonidas, which was dragged to and fro as was the corpse of the divine Patrokles before the walls of Troy.

THERMOPYLÆ

Suddenly rose a Spartan shout above the din: "The Persians in the rear! We're surrounded!" And Alpheos, lifting the body of Leonidas in his arms, took command of the little remnant.

"Back," he thundered in his new voice of command. "Back to the Pass! To the mound!" And the Spartans obeyed.

Step by step, with desperate fighting, the little band withdrew into the Pass in their midst defending the precious body of their king. They were scarce a fourth of those who had gone out. It is incredible that they were able to do this. But the Spartans seemed to the very last to have done whatsoever they intended. And now they intended to die. They made their stand upon the hillock near the eastern or Grecian end of the Pass, "where now the stone lion stands in honour of Leonidas." The mountain was at their back.

Here the Persians rushed in upon them from every side. In front the hordes of Xerxes swept in through the Pass as the Greeks retired. From the rear the Immortals under Hydarnes poured down the foothills from Alpenoi along the road. Down the steep path of Alpenoi fell the human torrent of Persians driven from above by the scourgers whose cruel yells and cracking whips sounded even above the din of battle. The poor wretches were driven by thousands into the sea. No one noted that they perished.

But the handful upon the little hill were perishing in a fashion that all the world would remember.

The Thebans had long since thrown down their arms before the Persians and run to them with entreating hands. Most of the Thespians were dead. Less than a hundred Thespians and Spartans remained. They stood back to back circlewise on their small hilltop, their grim bloody faces reeking with sweat, their dark eyes wide and blazing with the death light, dealing ten deaths for one. Two shields were left among them, and not a single spear. They fought with their short swords and as these were broken fought on with hands and teeth.

Few as they were, the Medes shrank from them in terror. "We are fighting with madmen!" they cried. And no doubt they were—with men mad of divine purpose.

Still in their midst the Spartans held the body of their king. Its presence seemed to give them superhuman power. Life after life they exacted for his. But their battle cries rang fewer and fewer in the tumult—fainter and choked as one and one they fell—until at the last Alpheos was battling alone. Then he, too, sank down into silence. And the Spartan Three Hundred were no more.

Meanwhile Aristodemos with his unwilling guide crept darkly down the mountain path in the trail of the Persian detachment and came at length to the deserted village of Alpenoi. Here he loosed the princeling according to promise. The lad bounded off screaming in unexpected joy. Then Aristodemos groped his way alone down the narrow street toward the house where he had left his arms with Eurytos. Now the noise of the battle below the hill began to fill his ears—the confused crash of smiting shields, mingling cries, and the dull roar of contending multitudes—spirited battle cries lifting themselves like victories, only to be submerged under some rival cry from another quarter.

The sound drove him mad with desire for action. To be once more at his dear Leonidas's side, dealing unforgettable punishment to the enemies of his land. He began to run headlong and to cry, "Alala! Alala!"

Quickly and close at hand came an answering cry, "Alala!"

"Alala!" called Aristodemos again, wondering. And again came the cry. He knew that voice. Eurytos must still be here.

He felt his way toward the sound and into the narrow house. Eurytos was on his feet, stamping with impatient rage, cursing his slow Helot.

"The thorax now, thou damned snail!" Eurytos cried, as the terrified slave rose from fastening his greaves.

Then he turned.

"Who answered my call? Who art thou?"

"It is I, Aristodemos. Tell me—the battle! The battle!" and Aristodemos began to creep on hands and knees, searching for his own armour.

"Gods! I think it is the last moment!" responded Eurytos. "Hast come to lead me in?"

"Eurytos, I am as blind as thou! Where is my spear?" moaned Aristodemos fretfully, reaching out his hands.

"Thou blind too? My plague! Because thou didst help me! By Herakles, thou shalt go first!" cried Eurytos in an outburst of affectionate remorse. He pushed his slave toward Aristodemos. "Do on his armour first. But quick—quick!"

At this moment a nearer cry broke upon them, wail after wail in a high, childish voice. A little shepherd boy came running up the way, sobbing forth his bitter lament.

"Leonidas is dead! Le-on-i-das—ai—ai—ai!—is dead!"

Aristodemos rose suddenly erect and tense, and stood swaying. The slave began hurriedly to fasten the greaves upon his legs, but Aristodemos was not aware of him. He was unconscious of being touched. A blackness and a blankness covered his whole mind. Physical darkness was nothing compared with it. Death so embraced him that life itself was unreal, a shadow, a paltry lie. Death, death alone, was real.

Eurytos answered the little shepherd's wail with the customary lament, beating his breast and crying, "O tototoí totoí!"

"Aristodemos!" he cried in wonder. "Dost hear how thy lover the king is dead? Why dost thou not lament?"

"Yes, he is dead," repeated Aristodemos dully from white lips. "My Leonidas, my king!" But he could not think.

Meanwhile the Helot had gone over to Eurytos to fasten his thorax.

"Now," said Eurytos, "Batto can take us both together. Thou knowest, Batto. Down the hill and to the left. Thou wilt not fail."

"Are we going to our Spartans?" asked Aristodemos.

"What ails thee? No, we can not come near to them."

"But we must go to our Spartans," repeated Aristodemos plaintively.

"Fool! They are within the Pass. Ten thousand Persians are between us and them."

Suddenly the whirling mind caught its grip again, and Aristodemos spoke clear.

"Eurytos, art thou going down among the Persians, blind as thou art, to be butchered?"

"I am going down to die. What else to do?"

"What to do? Why, man, thou canst not throw away one sword of Hellas now. Everything, everything is to do. Hellas is tottering to her fall. We must fight, every one of us, fight as never before!"

Eurytos spoke hollowly through his helm and in great amazement.

"What? Dost mean thou wilt not go into the fight?"

"Oh, gods, that I could—into the real fight! Don't be a fool, Eurytos."

"Thou wilt not go into the fight?" repeated Eurytos. "And yet thy Leonidas is dead!"

"Oh—oh!" cried Aristodemos with a sob. The longing to lie dead with his friend swept him overpoweringly. "I must not," he moaned at last. "I must not. Our land—calling, calling us!"

"I don't understand such fine talk. I am a Spartan, and I die with Spartans at the Pass!" Eurytos seized Batto's arm and hurried with him out of the door. But Aristodemos groped after him.

"No—no, Eurytos!" he called. "Oh, the senseless deed! Greece hath such need, such need!"

"Need? She hath no need of cowards! Thou renegade! Thou faithless friend! I spit upon thee!" Right heartily he suited the action to the word.

He was gone. Aristodemos stood in the steep road

alone. He heard for a moment Eurytos's diminishing step, then lost it in the dark. How far away the battle seemed! The awful loneliness of his decision came upon him like an unmeasured sea. The Spartans! Would they also spit upon him? Leonidas—oh, even dead Leonidas!—would he approve of this decision? Was it right after all to stay away from that splendid fighting? What hope remained to Hellas now, that he should keep alive to fight for her?

Unconsciously, as he questioned, he was groping his way down toward the glorious battle din. A very death hunger was upon him, a necessity to find his dead friend though he travel all the corridors of Hades seeking him. He had come very near to the battle. A great sweep of victor shouts came up—Persian shouts. They had got the Pass! They had beaten the devoted Greeks against their hills. Ah, who could defend the hills of Greece as these Spartans had done! Hellas was losing her best. Hellas! Hellas!

Aristodemos stopped. He seemed to see his Hellas through his closed blind lids—a torn bleeding figure with outstretching arms.

"What have I done?" he cried. "What have I done?"

He turned his back to the precious din, and began to grope his way up the road again. He stumbled. He was all confused in darkness.

"Leonidas!" he whispered softly. "Leonidas!" A great sob seized him, and of sheer grief Aristodemos fell fainting in the road. His armour clanged as he fell. And he lay quite still while his helmet grew wet within and slow red drops began to trickle out upon the stones.

CHAPTER TWENTY-ONE

In the Wake of War

Batto hurrying up again from the edge of battle, a very slave of terror, came upon Aristodemos lying there in the road. He stumbled by; then paused. Batto was only a slave. It was strange that he paused at all. Then he went fearfully back, bent over the bronze clad form, and with wretched hurrying fingers unfastened helmet and thorax. He disentangled the shield, lifted the unconscious man upon his back, and staggered on.

From the street he turned into a sheep path that wound up the mountain through the dense green forest. He paused at whiles to rest without setting down his burden, and moved on more slowly as he began to feel secure. After a steep clambering mile from the village he made a sharp turn about a clump of firs and by an unexpected twisting path descended into a cave.

Well had the poor fellow feathered this little nest since early morning, when the keepers of supplies at Alpenoi had fled away and left rich booty to his hand. Bags of meal stood near the dry mouth of the cave. Cheeses and fat wineskins lay far within where a cold spring trickled and sang in the dark.

He laid Aristodemos down.

"Batto's a big fool," he muttered, "—to get a new master!" Nevertheless he brought water and washed clean and pure the wound on the master's forehead. Then he began to examine the closed eyes, uttering short clucks of pity between his teeth.

"Wilt never see again, that's plain," he said. Yet he brought more water and bathed the eyes patiently over and over without aversion for their diseased ugliness. Then he tore off a bit of Aristodemos's linen chiton and laid it wet upon his unconscious forehead.

"Wert such a leaping fellow!" he murmured. "But wilt leap no more. Easy master, thou! I'll leave thee when I will."

Then he sat down with his back against the cave wall. At this moment a hasty footstep crashed in the thicket outside. Batto jumped, crouching double with fear, and hid in the far depth of the cave. A solemn, bearded face peered in, and a very insistent voice scattered the echoes. Batto knew that voice.

"Now Pan be thanked!" he chuckled, running from his retreat. "O gentle god; to send a she-goat, and unmilked!"

He caught the animal, that was glad enough to find a shepherd in the accustomed place. In a few moments Batto was busy. With what a sound of homely comfort did the white milk jet into the wide-mouthed jar! Then Batto's squatty figure moved back and forth in the cave in most delectable industry. He built a little fire to bake the meal cakes he had made, and soon the appetizing smell of cookery mingled with the blinding smoke. Later he sat crosslegged on the floor with the whole repast, in a circle about him, reached for his cheese, his cakes, his milk, overwhelmed with his riches.

O ye nymphs of Kastaly, but this was wine! The kind of wine masters use, not miserable slave wine. Batto had once been made drunk by the Ephors and exhibited to the Spartan boys to disgust them with excess. But no such heavenly liquor as this had the Ephors given him, fit for the blessed gods! He smacked his lips and drank again. Yet even when the wine began to make merry with his legs he remembered to stagger over to the sick man and with infinite pains make him swallow some of the precious stuff. And he took off his own dirty ill-smelling chiton to make a pillow for his head. "I can keep warm with wine," he said proudly.

In the weeks that followed, Batto fared as he never

had fared before. After the Persian army had passed he ventured out farther from his hiding. He milked the goats of the scattered flocks, he ate meal cakes of his own making and drank wine unlimited. Later he even brought back to the cave Aristodemos's armour, and with it some gold and jewelled trinkets of the Persians over which his eyes glittered with greedy joy.

In the meanwhile, for days were long, he tended his patient, saw him come at last from stupor to fever, from fever into weakness, from weakness to memory. And then Batto wondered whether he might not have done better to let him die. For masters make such fuss when the gods visit them with trouble! To them everything's as bad as a whipping! And this man moaned so bitterly! He lay there still for hours with a look upon his face that hurt Batto and made him turn away.

One day Aristodemos lifted his head as Batto came into the cave and began to follow his movements with half-open eyes.

Batto jumped. "Why, Satyrs kick me, thou'rt looking!" he cried, running and kneeling by him. "Dost know me? Say, dost know me?"

"Batto," said Aristodemos weakly. "But what a fat Batto, and what a red face!"

"Thou'rt seeing, thou'rt seeing!" cried Batto, clapping his thighs. "The wine maketh me red," he said proudly. Then he added hastily: "But there's one whole skin left for thee."

Aristodemos smiled at him. "Hast so much care for me, Batto?" he said indulgently. "Why hast thou helped me? There was no need. I could have died there in the road."

"Yes, Master. Wert dying when I found thee," answered Batto, watching wistfully as he spoke the smile that was so rare a thing for a Spartan slave to receive.

"Then why didst thou do it?"

"Because I remembered, Master."

"Remembered what?"

"Ah, masters forget. It was my father's farm where thou didst save the mutton long ago. Eurytos stole it, but thou thought of us, the hungry ones, and gave it back. And thou wast so little, and so brave!"

Batto reached out his hand very timidly, then drew it back again. Even the long weeks of tending did not give him the courage to caress.

"Didst remember that? A thing so little and so long ago? Thou art a good slave, Batto; liker man than slave." Aristodemos reached out and took the rough hand. "Batto," he said, "make me a fighting man again and thou shalt be free."

But weeks passed before Aristodemos, pale, red-eyed, rough bearded, was able to come forth of the cave.

"Batto," he asked one day as he began to be more alive, "tell me of my Spartans. Thou sayest naught of them."

"There's naught to, say, Master," returned Batto. "They're dead."

"Yes; they were crushed. I know that," Aristodemos agreed feebly. "But who escaped?"

"Thou," answered Batto in a word.

"Batto," cried Aristodemos in sudden anger, "thy impudence will kill thee! Come here—here close to my knee. Now tell me what thou knowest."

Batto came trembling, but he did not speak again.

"What is it? There, I see thee better. Tell me the names of those who live. Hast heard nothing?"

"Yes, Master; have heard all."

"Then lie not."

"Master, it is thou—thou only," whined Batto with a kind of awe. "I saw the Helots go, and a few Perioikoi. I saw the Pass after the battle, Master. Only thou art alive."

"Oh, Batto! Oh, Batto!" moaned the sick man as he began to see the truth. Then he fell silent and sat looking straight ahead, fixed in a wide loneliness which Batto could not break in upon.

A week later began as tragic a journey as human heart can imagine—one man and his poor slave trailing back along the way by which the Three Hundred had come out, young, full-lifed, compacted of glorious courage. Aristodemos took the way back feebly. He was unable to support the shield and helm that had once sat so light upon him. He walked bareheaded while Batto behind him carried his arms. They met few travellers, and those generally ran into the coppice before the two could come up.

They passed a little wayside temple. It was but a charred ruin. The masterful wind was scattering it upon the road. Was all Hellas a ruin scattering thus upon the wind?

To Aristodemos his illness in the cave now seemed a long, troubled sleep from which he was awaking upon a strange world—a world which he did not know, whose events he could not guess at—a world of unrelieved sorrow.

The sorrow had a strange trick of meeting him repeated afresh upon the road, thrusting out upon him a new face at each turn of the hills.

It was near this steep little vineyard that Demonax had given him that greeting. He had forgotten about Demonax, that he, too, was dead with the rest. How strongly he had walked that day! How he had lifted those straight black brows of his, with what feigned surprise, to see his friend Eurytos leaning upon Aristodemos's shoulder.

"What, Eurytos," he had said, "art still in the ranks? I thought thou wast sick at Isthmos."

"Yea, dead were I at Isthmos, for all thee!" had the other flung back bitterly. And Aristodemos had added his taunts also. Now those two quarrellers were both gone into the mystery. He wondered if they still taunted each other, meeting in the halls of Hades.

Later, as he neared the village of Tethronion, Alpheos suddenly recurred to him. For here the men had crowded around a spring and pushed and jostled each other from the brink. But Alpheos, that stern and well-nigh unspeaking warrior, had stepped back, still athirst, to give Aristodemos place. It was an unusual courtesy in an older man. Aristodemos had wondered why he did it, but he had not asked him. And now he would never know.

So, one upon another, the familiar figures gleamed forth in his memory and faded again into irrevocable silence. So he walked on solitary through ruined Phokis, over high paths, along lowland roads, through burned little villages and forests dark and still. As he walked his sorrow gathered ever to its focus, fixed itself on that one supreme loss. A threnody was ever beating in his heart. It was all "Leonidas! Leonidas! Leonidas!"

Ah, how clearly Leonidas had gone forth, how fully comprehending what might lie ahead! When in all that north-ward journey had he once smiled or taken ease? Yet he had been their heartener. And never had Aristodemos approached him without midway meeting that glad recognizing look of his, that look of outreach and relief, as if the lonely soul were harboured suddenly in its love and riding free of outer storm.

At the edge of an evening cold and clear Aristodemos came to a well-remembered elm which stretched out great arms over the road, a broad pavilion of shade. Here had been a night's halting place. Aristodemos could even see traces of their camp. In the morning they had sung a pæan as they marched away, the great lusty sound of it reverberating against the hills. No breath more was in those who made that manly music. And now remained this awful, unbroken silence of death, that seemed to embrace the whole world, he alone surviving the world.

With a great anguished cry he sank down upon the road. Batto ran to him. "Master! Master!" he cried. "Ah, I knew the Master was too ill for journeying!" But Aristodemos seized the rough slave hand, pressing it, touching the arm to make sure of its reality. It was real and warm! At least this was living, human! He shook as if in an ague. He called aloud upon Leonidas until Batto looked fearfully about him, feeling that even a ghost must perforce come to answer such piteous summoning. There was a rage, too, at this moment in Aristodemos's heart that would have killed a thousand Persians in payment of his friend.

Next morning on a lonely hillside beside the road Aristodemos saw a bright-coloured heap.

"Batto," he said, "I think yonder is a woman."

"What was a woman," said Batto bluntly.

"But it moves!"

"Thine eyes are yet dim, Master. It's her loose hair lifting in the wind."

They both hurried up the hill. The little face was yet pretty in its gray whiteness. It was scarce more than a child's face, but the clumsy hard-worked hands were tightly clenched and she had torn her hair as was the custom of Greek women. This was still the Phokian land. And right dear had the Phokians paid for their abandonment of the secret path.

"Oh, Batto, she hath terribly suffered!" said Aristodemos. "See her hands!"

"It is only a poor peasant, Master," said Batto. "There be many more have suffered."

"But this one shall have burial. Wouldst anger the gods, Batto?"

Aristodemos knelt beside the little figure and with unsteady hands laid smooth the dress, and the long black locks, which the wind had flung and tossed. They were like a coarse, thick garment reaching to her waist. He and Batto dug a little grave and laid her in it, performing the sacred rites for the dead.

"There, there, poor soul," said Aristodemos. "Thou shalt go into Hades at last, nor wander any longer without rest."

Then he journeyed down the road again, seeing all the way naught but that lamentable sight. Farther on he came upon a rude heap of stones and charred wood. About it sat a family whose home it had been. The mother was trying half-heartedly to put stone upon stone again. The father sat gazing at the place with hollow haunted eyes. As the travellers appeared the children fled screaming to the thicket. But seeing Aristodemos with Batto alone, they came back again stealthily like foxes and began to beg for food. "Bread, Master! Give us bread!" they whined.

Aristodemos asked them whither the Persians had gone. They only looked vacantly at him. "We do not care," the father said at last. "They can do no more to us."

Batto had been looking hard at the mother. "Did ye know a girl," he asked, "with a roundish face? Had lost the tip of her forefinger, and wore a crimson girdle?"

The woman dropped her stone and ran to him, shaking him by the shoulders and crying, "Lanike! Lanike! Where hast thou seen Lanike!"

"Up yonder on the hill," said Batto. "I thought ye looked like kin," he added. "It was my honourable master gave her burial."

Aristodemos thought the woman must faint at so blunt a telling. But she turned to him, clasping his knees and kissing his hands. "It was my Lanike! And thou hast buried her! The gods reward thee!" Then she ran to her husband. "Dost hear?" she cried. "Our Lanike is not left unburied as those others."

But the man only looked stupidly into her face.

"He hath been so," said the woman, "ever since the Persians harried us."

After this Aristodemos lost all hope for Hellas. Even so had the Persians used her to the very end. What was to stop their rage and wantonness? Indeed, was there any Hellas left to save?

He reached Antikyra, one of the ports of sacred Delphi, on the Corinthian Gulf. He wondered at the bright look of the faces in the town. Did they really care so little for the fate of Hellas, seeing that their own town had by some chance escaped? In the market place he found them at their careless talk. A trader passed him, swinging along with sailor gait. Aristodemos ventured to pluck him by the sleeve.

"Tell me," he said desperately, "tell me the worst about Hellas!"

The man stared at him in amazement and pulled away.

"Art thou from the dead," he asked, "or maddened?"

"Oh, would I were dead this day with Hellas!" cried Aristodemos, all his bitterness mirrored in his face.

At this the man tried to flee, fearing some portent. But Aristodemos clung to him.

"Tell me! Tell me!" he pleaded.

"What dost thou want? Hast not heard of Salamis?" Despite his fear of Aristodemos the trader's face took on an exultant look.

"No! What has happened to Salamis?"

"Salamis? Salamis?" The man's voice fairly sang the word. "Why, the gloriousest victory that ever man won! All the gods fought with us!"

Aristodemos's whole frame rang like a sounded lyre.

"Where hast thou been?" questioned the trader incredulously.

Aristodemos could not speak to answer him. But the wild joy of his face was unmistakable.

"Ho, there!" shouted the man to a lounging group nearby. "Here! Here is a fellow that does not know of Salamis! Never heard of Salamis!"

"Not heard of Salamis!" laughed a vender as he leaped over his stall. They crowded about him— loungers, venders, and citizens—overwhelming Aristodemos with their clamour. "Salamis!" roared a burly Corcyrean seaman with a great red scar across his face. "Salamis! Yes, by the gods, the waves of Salamis are red yet with the dirty Persian blood."

"The Persians were at Phaleron—" began a young Delphic pilgrim.

"—But our ships were in a snug hole behind Salamis," broke in another, "and we made the Persians come in after us, into the narrow place."

"The battle was begun by an Athenian," boasted a youth from Athens.

"No; it was an Æginetan!" cried a jealous Corinthian.

"An Æginetan!" retorted the Athenian scornfully. "Ye of Peloponnese would have fled if our Themistokles hadn't trapped you into the fight! Our ships fought in line," he explained. "And when we crashed into the Persians we drove them wild with terror until they fairly began to run each other down. Well, their fleet is a wreck. Our women are piling it now on the shore for kindling wood."

"Xerxes has got him home to Susa, and a sorry time he had coming there again!"

"But they have not gone—not all the Persians!" gasped Aristodemos.

"No. Mardonios is wintering in Thessaly. Oh, but we will thrash him! The gods are with us, man! The gods are with us!" And they clapped him on the back and capered and went quite wild with joy. It was only through questioning that Aristodemos learned how the Athenian Acropolis had much of it been burned.

"The Acropolis!" he cried blankly.

"Yes. But the sacred olive tree in Erechtheus's temple budded anew and sent forth a shoot a cubit long the very day of the burning. And Athens is building it all again." Not even his city's misfortune could damp the young Athenian's jubilation.

At length Aristodemos broke away from them, almost staggering under his weight of joy. Hellas lived! He had presumed to fear for her! And still—for in this the gods were kind—there was work ahead! There would yet be battles for Hellas! He would deal woe to the Persians with his own hand, requiting the death of his love-comrade and king.

The Greeks of the Salamis day did not know that the Western world down all the centuries would be thankful for their deeds. Yet the power of the fact was in them, exalting them with high, fine passion—a passion which outran "Hellas" and was touched with a kind of world prophecy beyond their ken. And it was this world-filling joy which now possessed Aristodemos as he stood looking across the clear blue Gulf of Corinth southward toward home.

He was roused by a timid pull at his sleeve. Batto was there.

"Those be pretty ships, Master. See how they pull at anchor."

"Yes," answered Aristodemos dreamily and hardly aware of him. "They are ever eager to be gone, are ships."

"These ships are for the West. I wish we were going in a ship. Thou canst not go to Sparta in a ship, Master."

"No." Aristodemos did not see his drift.

"Ei! Hateful Sparta!" broke out Batto. "Hateful Sparta!"

Aristodemos turned. It was in his heart to free Batto then and there. But Batto was gone. Aristodemos searched for him through the streets and at the wharves. But there was no Batto anywhere, and he would not put others on the search. He believed that Batto had been about to ask for freedom but at the pinch could not trust his master's promise. Poor Batto!

A ship sailed for Sicily that afternoon with a new man in the crew, a jolly fellow who sang rude Dorian songs all the while he rowed and worked.

"He sings," said the captain, "like a man new free."

CHAPTER TWENTY-TWO

A Mother in Sparta

Salamis wrought upon Aristodemos like some divine medicine. Next morning his eyes for the first time felt well. He washed in the Gulf and started for the south.

Upon the Argos road he fell in with a traveller, a huge Laconian freeman of cheerful countenance who walked with him and began to question.

"Thou'rt a soldier," he ventured. "Hast perhaps fought at Salamis?"

"Would gods I had!" answered Aristodemos. "Know'st thou any of the fighters?"

At this the man started off with the deeds of prowess, of Aristides and his Island fighting, of the Persian woman's ship, of Themistokles—

But as Aristodemos listened a kind of jealousy began to grow in him for those who had gone out to glorious failure at Thermopylæ.

"Yes, every road rings with Salamia-praise!" he burst out bitterly. "But no word—no word for Thermopylæ. And I tell you, man, that was the harder fight." Saying "Thermopylæ" he thought "Leonidas."

"Ay, of course; who knows not that?" The man was puzzled at Aristodemos's sudden wrath. "They gave their lives—those men—every one of them. They were the fore-strength of Salamis. And this is the song of them:

> '*Of those who died at Thermopylæ*
> *Glorious is the fortune, fair the doom.*
> *Their grave is an altar,*

THE SPARTAN

Worship have they for mourning,
A chant of praise for dirge.
No rust shall stain their winding-sheet,
No, nor all-conquering time.'

"All Greece knoweth Simonides's song by heart," said the man, and went on with his exultant chanting—

"'This shrine of valiant men hath taken
For its indweller the glory of all Hellas.
Leonidas is witness, Sparta's king,
Who hath left great glory of noble deeds
And ever fresh renown.'"

Aristodemos walked beside him hearing it, drinking it in. Pride, grief, and envy of the heroic dead contended within him.

"And there's a strange tale about Thermopylæ," the Laconian went on. "They say that one man escaped, one man only."

Aristodemos lifted his head with quick question.

"Oh, the Helots brought the tale. They must always be telling something. If not of men then of demons. Myself, I don't believe it."

"But suppose it had been true?"

"Nay, it's a silly tale, that two men were sick of the eyes; one ran down into the fight and the other ran away."

"But why?" Aristodemos managed to ask. "Why should the other keep away?"

"Oh, no reason that I know of. And some say he was not blind, but was off upon a mission. It's mixed, ye see. But if the man's alive he'll never come back."

"Why not?"

The Laconian gave a short laugh. "Why should he? The world is wide."

At the next road turn Aristodemos made a way of escape from the man.

So this story had come to Sparta, distorted, false. Would the Spartans see through it? Oh, the bitterness of coming back with explanations! Until now he had been too stunned with grief and awe to think of himself indeed, to think clearly at all. But now—would the Spartans see his reason for refusing to plunge after that foolish death? "I was right! I was right!" he said. But he began to explore the Spartan mind as never before. Eurytos said—oh, but Eurytos had been a fool! Aristodemos broke into sweat as he heard again that insult. But Eurytos had been sick, beside himself. Sparta could never be so witless, at home, in calm blood. "I fought with the best," Aristodemos assured himself. Would the Spartans, though, believe that he had fought?

Nay, if the Helots had told so much, they must have told of the good fighting too. They saw him fight. Aye, and the Spartans themselves after all these years knew Aristodemos thoroughly. They knew he was no craven.

Upon this he began to hope and travel on again. So deep in thought had he been that he found himself standing still in the road. Toward the last of his journey Aristodemos grew very lonely, and as he retraced the way by which his beloved captain had first led out the Three Hundred his heart almost burst with the memory of Leonidas. He longed for the sight of some face he knew. He was in a tender mood toward Sparta when he came at last to the town where she smiled on her little hills in the bright sun.

He saw some boys bathing for the noon heat in Eurotas, where he so often had bathed. They looked up toward him. Then he saw them leap out and run off toward the town, flinging their clothes on as they ran.

"Why did they do so?" Aristodemos was at once stung into anxiety again. Still he was not sure whether the boys had recognized him, or whether if they had they might not be racing to be the first with news. With heart tugging at the bitter doubt he strode across the little bridge.

Under a great plane tree sat a woman with her distaff, her babe and slave beside her. She lifted her head to gaze at the traveller, caught a gleam of his shield, a glint of his bowed head. Then she rose up with a breath-less cry and ran to him as only a Spartan woman could run. Aristodemos did not see her until she was close by.

Then his face lightened with joy. He stretched out his great free arm to her.

"Gorgo, Gorgo," he whispered, thrilling at the unex-pected welcome, feeling in his young heart that never woman was so create for loving as this mate of his friend.

As for Gorgo, she laid her widowed head upon his shoulder, weeping her heart out, calling aloud the name they both held so dear.

"Thou didst see him?" she faltered. "Thou canst tell me all that my king did after he left my eyes?"

"Yes, yes," said Aristodemus. "Oh, Gorgo, I saw his heart lift with victory, and I saw it break!"

Upon which Gorgo fell to weeping again. He told her of the march, of Leonidas's masterful strategy.

"But how did he fight?" she asked. "Tell me how he fought!"

"Nay, Gorgo, he was the battle itself. His deeds, his control, were everywhere. He fought like a god!"

"He is a god now," said Gorgo simply. "No? Did you not hear that? The Spartans have deified him. We have a new altar now—the altar to Leonidas!"

But Aristodemos took this bitterly. "Aye," he broke out, "they worship him now as a god, whom they grieved and harried in his life. 'Tis easy enough to honour at home with pleasant sacrifice the hero whom they left to die at the Pass. His death is on their heads!"

"But they do worship him," persisted the woman, with quiet ecstasy. "And this my little son is now the son of a divine one. We bring gifts in the morning, he and I, into the bright new shrine!"

And spite of his first resentful anger, Aristodemos caught her mood. Leonidas—a god! The man whom he had known so close, with whom he had eaten, with whom he had slept, whom he had seen at the day's end weary and forespent, whom he had embraced with devoted love. He was a god! In the twinkling of an eye, one with glorious Herakles, with Castor and Pollux. And no far-off Olympian, but a close guardian god, hovering over his precinct, receiving burnt offering and answering prayer. Oh, what loving, intimate worship would Aristodemos pay him! How close would he find him at that new altar! He felt that he must run to it in his eagerness of adoration.

In those vital days of Greece it was easy to believe. Leonidas's little son interrupted them, pulling at his mother's dress.

"Mother, mother," he whimpered. "Take me now to the river. Thou promised to take me there."

"Yes, little son," she said as she took him in her strong arms. "I will see thee quickly again, Aristodemos. Go to his temple, then come straight to me. Oh, thou must tell me all!"

So Aristodemos kissed them both and walked swiftly onward into the town. He was sure now of the Spartans. Gorgo was queen. Their ways would not be different from hers. She had not even mentioned the Helot story. He passed Lichas, an old friend of Gylippos, who gave him his rough greeting. Aristodemos heard him with a short shaken laugh. Yes, he had mistrusted those Spartans too hastily.

He came in sight of the square. It was crowded. The boys had fetched their news. Aristodemos strode in among the men. "Oh, Tisias!" he cried. "Phileus!" greeting them with outstretched hands.

They surged away from him as if seeing a ghost. Aristodemos looked about startled at their deathly silence. Then a harsh, terrible shout broke the silence. Aristodemos's face whitened like ashes. Something clicked to in his heart like a closed breastplate. Here was a battle such as he had never faced before. But he would face it! A kind of stark courage came into him.

He lifted his hand for silence. There was a dignity and gentleness in the gesture that should have robbed them of their violence. But they only yelled the louder and ran at him, jostling him with their shoulders and elbows. Now he heard more clearly the word which made up that terrible greeting.

"Coward! Coward! Aristodemos the Coward! Coward of Thermopylæ!"

But Aristodemos's clear voice lifted above the noise.

"Hear me! Hear me! Ye shall! Ye do not understand!"

"Oh, yes, speak!" they howled, and they broke into insolent laughter. "Tell us! Tell us—do—where is Alpheos! Where is Demonax? Maron? Why didst not bring them with thee? Eurytos—he was not afraid to die! Where is thy friend Leonidas? Ei, thy lover Leonidas? Ei! Ei! Where is Leonidas?"

So they pelted him with the sacred names of the dead. It was worse than stoning.

"Fools! Ye fools!" he cried in incredulous wrath. "I fought that fight! I bore—"

But their senseless din drowned his voice. With a cry of disgust he broke through the yelling crowd and ran into the temple of Athena Xenia. They thought he was taking sanctuary, and yelled after him:

"The gods refuse thee, thou coward! Go hang thyself!"

But Aristodemos had no fear of them that he should take sanctuary. He was but trying in the quiet of the holy place to get clear of the tumult within as well as of the tumult without, so that he might have strength to brush off this preposterous disgrace. He, the friend of Leonidas, the son of Lykos—oh, it was impossible! Dishonoured!—But first he must still the confusion which possessed him. Gods, how clear, how clear he must keep his brain!

The Spartans soon forgot him there in the temple, and began to go about their various business.

In the afternoon the chorus gathered in its cornel of the Agora and their familiar song arose, well nigh breaking his heart with its melody. But they were singing lamely. They missed their wonted leader.

A MOTHER IN SPARTA

Surely they would listen if he took his right of song among them, that right of Choragos which was his own office. Ah, if he could but sing the story!

He leaped down the temple steps, shouting the song as he came. He had in his heart the full tale of Thermopylæ to sing to that tune.

A moment he swayed them, especially the younger boys, who thrilled under his voice, and all unconsciously took his masterly rhythm. The choral sound lifted as he joined it like a fresh fed flame.

Then the men seized him.

"Thou mad with insolence!" they cried. "Go to thy place!" And they hurled him back beyond the youths, beyond the youngest boys, to the lowest place.

He tried to finish out the song, but his voice choked and failed. Like a wounded thing he slipped away, hurrying with bowed head down the narrow street.

At a corner he came full upon Gorgo herself with her little son.

"Oh—Oh!" he cried. "Gorgo!" Then found that he could not speak at all. But Gorgo seized both his hands. She was full of queenly indignation for his sake.

"I heard them!" she cried. "They gave thee not one chance. Thou art of the bravest. Tell me how thou camest out of battle!"

He told her brokenly of his mission, of his day in the Persian camp, of the belated warning to the Phokians.

"I knew! I knew!" triumphed Gorgo. "It was but slave's tale!"

"We were blind," he told her, "blind as moles!"

"But Eurytos—was he blind?" she asked.

"Yes, and ten thousand Persians were between us and our Spartans. He was led down blind into the shambles. There was no purpose under heaven in the going. It was but a fool's flourish—"

But even as he was speaking he saw, to his horror, Gorgo drawing away, gathering her little one to her, gazing at him in cold wonder.

"Gorgo! Gorgo!" he cried in bitter pleading. "Try to

understand! Do thou not wrong me—do not—"

"I do not wrong thee," she said sadly. And she turned away with a finality that he well knew in her.

His head—his whole body—seemed to sink. He moved slowly down the street and out into the fields.

All day he lay without the town. But, as the cold twilight fell, the longing for some touch with human kind grew very keen. He had not given up his fight. He had no thought to die. It was his right to do battle again for Hellas and for the memory of Leonidas. These dullard Spartans! He would force them to understand. Through the falling dusk he heard the men marching to their evening meal. He determined to take his place among them.

He stood a moment outside the open door. They were already eating, a jolly, hungry crowd, strangely familiar to him though lacking the men he had loved the best. His face looked drawn and thin as he gazed in toward the light, his gray eyes very steady, his lips set in their new, sorrowful way. Then, with head delicately lifted and nostrils just a little stirring with full breath, he walked among them.

He took a vacant place. At once fell silence. The men moved away, leaving him a wide place alone. One of them in so moving brushed against his cuirass and sword. And the look of horror on the man's face as he stepped back recalled to Aristodemos that even the weapons of a coward were of evil touch.

Aristodemos looked about the board and opened his lips to speak. But the captain brought both fists down upon the table with a shout.

"Men! Men! Shall we listen to The Coward speaking in our midst?"

"Aristodemos," he turned upon him, "fill thy belly as thou wilt. But fill us not with lying words, else we fling thee forth."

"I fill thee with no lies!" rang Aristodemos's quick voice. "I speak true. I am no coward. I have fought for Greece. The Helots who came back will tell you. And

A MOTHER IN SPARTA

by the Gods-Who-Know, I will fight for her again!"

He rose, lifting his hands on high, as he pronounced the sacred oath.

There was instant tumult. Some younger men at the table's end shouted:

"Hear him! He has a right to a hearing! Speak, Aristodemos!"

"No!" thundered the leader. "By Pollux, he blasphemes!"

"Don't listen to the blasphemer!" shouted others. And even the young men began to join the shout. "Coward! Coward!" And they pushed him out into the night.

He was neither pale not pleading. "Fools and blind!" he cried. "Your swine's dullness will yet ruin Sparta!"

He plunged madly down the street and into the open. There on Colona Hill, where he and Leonidas had so often held long confidences together, he paced like a frenzied man all the starlit night.

Next morning in spite of wrecking emotions he was boyishly hungry and knew that he must eat to keep strength for this bitter fight. If Sparta refused him he would journey to Athens and fight for Hellas there. He gathered stones and hid behind a rock, whence he soon brought down a hare. He dressed it and made ready his fire. But he had no spark to kindle his fire.

He made his way to the nearest house, where rising smoke showed him that the morning meal was making ready. He knew the man who answered his knock.

"Klearistes," he said with feigned indifference, "I will take a light of thy fire."

The man bristled like an angry dog. "Not thou!" he said, placing himself full in the doorway.

Aristodemos had expected this. For the hearth fire was sacred. He turned with bowed head as if to go away, then wheeling suddenly round he pushed the man full in the chest, toppling him over backward. Aristodemos leaped over him into the house. He seized a fagot from the hearth-blaze and turned with it to get away. The man had risen, but Aristodemos was armed with his brand of burning twigs. With it he parried the man's blows, edged around him to the door and then fled, guarding his precious flame. He had been careful not to hurt the man. He did not want the whole pack of Spartan hounds upon his back.

He kindled his fire and hung his little skinned hare on a spit over the blaze. But the whole incident had been degrading. That he, the son of Lykos, should be a sort of wild man snatching his meat of forest things, sitting alone by his stolen fire, seemed too bitter for belief. Tears welled up in his eyes as he sat there looking at his hare; and he forgot it until it was well nigh past eating for blackness.

There was yet one hope. His mother at least would hear him out. Not that he looked for much affection from her, or even trust. Yet she would want to believe him. Upon Aristodemos hung the whole future of her house. She would listen and she could tell the truth to Sparta.

This morning, however, Aristodemos shrank from contact with anyone. Something within him had been wounded beyond healing, and it was his instinct to keep it hid. And yet—he was the son of Lykos, the lover of Leonidas. It was as if he bore some sacred thing not his own that had been wantonly sullied and which he must needs purify, turning yet away from precious death until that be accomplished.

Death! Ah, what a dear privilege that would have been. The old lament of Achilles kept ringing in his memory:

> *"Straight let me die,*
> *Seeing I might not come to aid*
> *Of my dear comrade*
> *When he lay dying."*

He rose with a sigh and started slowly toward the town. Boys who met him kept the way and made him turn out of the path. Each indignity was like a new blow on an open wound. He grew rigid and cold enduring it. But he straightened himself and hurried on to Pitane to his own house. He looked in at the open door.

His mother sat there in the shadowy room slightly turned away, busy with her task. She was separating bleached wool for the spinning and the snowy heaps of it billowed about her knees and her lap where her fair strong hands moved at the work.

Aristodemos paused. He dreaded to speak to her. Yet as he paused he could not but realize how beautiful she looked there, unconscious with her task, how bright and young the head that his father had loved so well, how broad the bosom breathing restfulness in the shadows. There was in her a thoughtful sadness which he had never seen before. His sorrow had hurt her, too. A great wish was upon him to lay his weary head where it had lain in childhood and, if only for a moment, to forget.

"Mother," he whispered; then found voice and spoke aloud, stepping toward her. "Mother! Makaria!"

She rose and turned, letting fall the wool. Aristodemos never forgot that swift terrible change in her, as she lifted both her hands above her head in a sudden anguish of wrath.

"O-o-oh, thou shame of our race! Thou darest—!"

"But, Mother, thou knowest not the truth," began Aristodemos quietly. "First hear—" But she broke in: "Hear thee, thou impious? Nay, but I curse thee!"

"No, Mother! No, thou wilt not do that!" cried Aristodemos, horror-struck.

"I will! I will!"

He caught at her hands, but the very act seemed to loose the flood of her malediction.

"Thy mother's curse upon thee! Thy mother's curse upon thee!"

Aristodemos dropped to the floor and clasped at her knees. He must compel her, by the binding act of the suppliant from further devastating words. But she writhed away like a lioness.

THE SPARTAN

"Oh, that I had died ere I brought thee forth! Foul shame hast thou brought upon me. May it return to thee—multiplied, multiplied may it return!"

She was full launched now. She began to stamp upon the ground calling the attention of gods below. Her voice rose high like an eagle's. She gathered power of her fury as if her curse were prophecy.

"Pluto hear me! Dark Persephone, hear me! Curse me his way and every path he treadeth! Curse me his head! Curse me his feet! Curse me his song to bitter wailing! When he openeth door, let hospitality deny him! When he offereth gifts and poureth sacred oil blast him from your altars!"

She turned upon his white face and shuddering form.

"A-ah, thou fair promise fulfilled in shame! Apollo—Apollo blight thy false beauty with his plague-shafts! Thou traitor to Leonidas!—thy sword eat thy scabbard, nor ever touch enemy! Ei! Ei! Woes, unnamable woes! Heap them up! Heap them up! O gods! Coming—going—in—in—in—and—"

She became incoherent, gasped for breath and fell moaning upon the floor.

Aristodemos withered under that curse as if it had been some swift pestilence. He stood dry and dumb in the little room. His lips moved, but he could not think this thing. He was accursed—he, Aristodemos. He had done no wrong—yet was an accursed man. Why? Why?

This lightning stroke made Sparta's refusal a trifling thing. That was a moment's trouble; this was living death. No calamity in all the Greek world was so dire as a curse. It searched the uttermost ways of life to life's undoing, to the perishing of whole races. Now was Aristodemos utterly cut off from life. The man he helped would sicken. The country he fought for—oh, even Hellas!—could only take harm of him now! Whole cities had perished because of the presence of one such man unclean.

A MOTHER IN SPARTA

Makaria began to stir and breathe. In a sudden horrible revulsion from her Aristodemos fled from the house. He fled down the narrow street, avoiding the open square, running like a hunted thing by obscure ways until he was clear of the city. At last under a thick leaved plane tree by the deserted road he sank down.

Now he might have died. All reasons to live had been destroyed. But—strange paradox—he was too tired to die, too stunned to remember that he might. He lay with his face upon the earth, not moving nor weeping, but giving forth now and then a low short moan.

He knew not how long he had lain there when he heard a faint sound on the road. He lifted himself, startled as a wild creature, and crawled into the bushes. He would not look around. He had an unutterable shrinking from men. But the sound came nearer, surely directed. Aristodemos lay in the bushes and closed his eyes.

Suddenly there were two little hands in his hair, trying to turn his head, something warm and soft was brushing his cheek, and a babyish voice was crying:

"Demos! Demos! Master!"

Aristodemos had forgotten the child's existence. But as he sat up in dull amaze the little creature quite bubbled over with joyous love. He climbed upon Aristodemos's lap and began to kiss his face with sounding, insistent kisses.

Aristodemos, with a deep drawn unsteady breath, caught the little fellow's shoulders and pushed him rudely off. The child's endearments pierced him with bewildering, sharp sweetness. They made him aware of a strange numbness of soul that felt neither joy nor sorrow anymore.

The little one did not understand. He got down to the ground his face sobering and his aggrieved lower lip trembling at the verge of tears. But his manifest hurt wrought strangely upon Aristodemos.

"Thou shalt not grieve!" he fiercely cried, gathering

him back again. "Grief is too terrible and thou art too small, too young. Come to me!" He put his arms about the child. "Little son, little son!" he said, "why didst thou come to me?" He kissed the child with lips that he could not keep from trembling.

"Demos not go from Mendi, never any more," said the child, quickly comforted. He nestled down against Aristodemos's breast. They sat so for some time, Aristodemos looking dully into space. Then he noticed the child again.

"How thou hast grown!" he said, passing his hand down the pretty body to the bare feet. "Why, thou'rt almost tall."

"Mendi a big, big boy," was his childish boast. "Mendi run away. Mendi find Demos!"

Run away—yes, to be sure; the child had run away. They would be looking for him home in Sparta. And Aristodemos suddenly recalled that his own love—the love of an accursed man—would harm the child. This was no good thing he was doing, to bring down on this little head the displeasure of the gods. He looked at Mendi blankly, with tightening heart. Then he rose and carried him to the middle of the road. He was stern because he dared not be tender.

"Now, Mendi," he said. "Run back the way thou camest. Go to Makaria."

The astonished child looked at him a moment, and then with a great wail sat down flat in the dust.

"Oh, but don't do that," said Aristodemos, much taken aback. He tried to pick up the child, but he was as limp and heavy as a soaked garment. His wails rent the air.

"Wilt not stand on thy feet like a little man?" pleaded Aristodemos. For the dangling feet curled under whenever he tried to set the child upon them.

"Mendi not go to Makaria," wept the boy. "Makaria bad!"

"No, Mendi. Makaria is good." But the words stuck in Aristodemos's throat. "Makaria will give thee honey cake. Run back quick to Makaria."

The child shook his head positively.

"Makaria bad," he repeated.

"But how is she bad?" asked Aristodemos.

The child looked up astonished at his dullness.

"Mendi not like Makaria any more," he declared.

"I wish I knew what thou wouldst tell me, little son," said Aristodemos, troubled at his earnestness. It was harder even than he thought to send the child away. But Mendi seemed to put the whole subject aside. He thrust his two little hands into Aristodemos's hair, pulling it and laughing merrily as Aristodemos shook himself free. Suddenly he sobered.

"Makaria whip Mendi," he said. "Put Mendi out in slave-house." He pulled up his tunic and displayed a chubby thigh ribbed with welts whose origin was plain.

"What? She flogs thee for a slave!" Aristodemos cried, loud and harsh. "Thou, my son, adopted before the king!"

"Makaria put on nasty dress," complained Mendi, holding up his little sleeved arm, and plucking with disdain at the brown cloth. Now, over all Greece a brown garment with sleeves was worn only by slave. Makaria had evidently been prompt to vent her rage upon his adopted son.

"And she dared! She dared!" cried Aristodemos hoarsely. He took the tiny sleeve in his fingers, tore it from wrist to shoulder, and rent it off.

"There," he said wrathfully, "there goes her slavery! Disdainer of the gods!"

There came a day when Aristodemos was rather sorry for having spoiled a warm garment. But just now the anger did him wondrous good.

"For curse or blessing," he said, "thou art mine, Mendi. At least I can save thee from her slavery." And with a wonderful new sense that the child was again his own he caught him in his arms.

"My little son!" he dared to call him. The thought that the child had no other refuge gave him a kind of fearful joy.

"Demos love Mendi now," pronounced Mendi complacently.

"I always loved thee, little one, always, since the moment thou fleddest to me from that vile Phœnician."

But Mendi did not long sustain this height of emotion.

"Mendi have dinner now," he said confidently, looking into Aristodemos's face, while Aristodemos gazed blankly back at him.

"Hungry, art thou? And I have nothing for thee."

The child looked frightened.

"Thou wilt not cry," said Aristodemos hastily.

"No—no," retorted Mendi, blinking his eyes with such a show of hardihood that Aristodemos could not but smile in spite of his perplexity.

"Go home?" asked the child, climbing down.

"No, never!"

"Where, then?"

Ah, where indeed! Was there any whither in the world for an accursed man?

"Oh, Mendi," he cried, "where, where is thine own father? If I could but bring thee to him! Thou must not take a son's curse of me!"

Aristodemos lost himself in the puzzle. What could he do with the child? He dared not keep him, yet he could not leave him on the road. The bitter helplessness of the curse seemed to beat him down. He had never known but that single clue to the child's parentage—if clue indeed it was.

"Mendi," he asked, "where is thy luck-penny?"

Mendi pulled at the string, brought out his coin, and held it toward Aristodemos, saying just as he had said the first day, "Mendi.'"

"Dost remember it so, Mendi? Surely I should get some meaning from thee."

He looked closely at the coin. It was a cunningly fashioned drachma. One side showed a lion with curving back and bristling, mane, the other a beautiful archaic head of Athena. The rim of the coin had been so hacked that it could not have passed for its value, and the city name was obliterated, save a "V E". But on the other side, rudely scratched quite across the body of the lion, were the straggling letters "Π Α Ρ".

Aristodemos did not know the coin. Money was rare in Sparta. The clues were broken, the secret, darkly hid. Who could read it? Diviners sometimes knew such things, saw them in visions or trances. But where was a diviner to be found? Sometimes in temples one could win an oracle from a god. "An oracle!" he mused aloud. Ah, there was one great oracle, one place of all places to seek hidden knowledge. Men came from over seas to the oracle at Delphi, whereas he could win to it afoot. Even the accursed had the right to go to Delphi for questions. "Even the wolves bring gifts to Delphi," was the saying.

"If we could go to Delphi, little man—"

"Dinner at Delphi?" said Mendi easily, slipping his hand into Aristodemos's hand ready for the starting. Aristodemos did not smile. Trustfulness was precious to him just then.

"Yes, it is far. But we will go to Delphi," he decided. But straight arose a new difficulty—money. He would need money for the way and he was penniless.

"Oh, Mendi, little son," he said, the gods are trying us very hard!"

He stood knitting his brows in a puzzle, when there seemed to come a trembling touch upon his arm, the old touch so familiar in his childhood.

"Antiphon's gold!" he exclaimed. "Yes, I will take thy gift now, thou Faithful!" Thou didst well to say that I would have need of it and thou wouldst have it ready!"

He carried the child into the wood. There he found some late berries. He dared not ask for food at any hut.

"Father will get thee something to eat. But thou must wait," he explained.

"Mendi not hungry. Mendi a big boy," he answered. And through the long afternoon and evening he kept to the same word. Aristodemos was between pride and pity, watching him. At dark Mendi fell asleep, and Aristodemos sat holding the little face close to his own, feeling the soft breath coming and going as when he first brought him home from Amyklai. Then he wrapped the child in his own cloak and, laying him in a sheltered thicket, hurried down the road.

It was late now. Sparta showed no light. But as he drew near Aristodemos began to walk more slowly, watching the road. If Sparta had scorned him yesterday what would she do to-day? Word of the curse must have run like wildfire through the town. The Spartans would not suffer an accursed man in their streets: They were prompt at stoning. A dog's death! Aristodemos wondered how long such death would take. "And 'twere a pity" he thought, "to leave the poor child to waken in the thicket alone."

He came first to dark, scattered houses, then to the streets. Here he heard the gruff voices of the sentries changing the watch. He slipped into a narrow alley and lay flat along the house wall. They passed very near. "Ay, he's gone," Aristodemos heard one say. "If the Furies that chase him be as mad as Makaria, he's gone far by now. But the dark Erinyes will get him, far or near."

"Ei, don't speak of the Curse-Maidens! They'll chase thee too!" And so the watchmen passed beyond hearing.

Aristodemos came cautiously out again, shuddering at their talk. Pitane was one of the crowded districts. He paused listening before the turn of every corner. At last he came to his mother's house, threaded the pitch dark alley to the slave quarters in the rear, and found the open door.

Fah, what a fetid place! Its darkness was vocal with the snores of the tired workers. Aristodemos dropped on his knees and began to steal within along the earth floor. He could barely discern the slave forms lying as usual either side of the narrow room. He had to creep with infinite care between them. He shivered as he thought of the howl of terror these slaves would set up if he should awaken them. His great fear was that Antiphon's place might be occupied. But at last he came to it and felt along it in the darkness. He found it vacant. Makaria was not one to keep too many slaves.

Aristodemos lifted the ragged cloth where the tired old bones had rested and began to dig softly in the earth with his knife. It might be a long search, yet he did not think the old man could have buried his treasure very deep. He made one hole, then another, and yet another. The work was slow in the dark. At the fifth digging his knife came against something hard in the earth, and he put his bare fingers to the task. At last he came to the bag itself where the faithful vanished hands had hid it. It was very frail and rotten after these years; Aristodemos had to lift it with great care and fold it in his dress.

The gentle old man seemed to be giving him the gift anew there in the mysterious darkness.

Then he began again the slow creeping out from among the sleepers. This time, in his care for the rotten money-bag, he stumbled against a rough outstretched foot and crouched flat in frozen horror.

"Ho, what's that?" said the sleeper, lifting a tousled head.

"There—there," whispered Aristodemos, "thy snorting woke me. Let the rest of us sleep too." And the man turned over with a sigh to his slumbers again.

Clear of the hut at last Aristodemos with long breath rose to his feet and made his cautious way back through the quiet streets to the open road. Soon Sparta was but a huddle of dark houses behind him.

"Hateful Sparta!" Batto the Helot had called it. And "hateful Sparta" it was indeed to Aristodemos as he turned his back upon it forever. Its spirit of repression had choked him all these years. Now its cruelty had ruined him.

He found Mendi in the thicket safe and warm, lifted

him, still sleeping, in his arms, and with the Curse pursuing him started north upon the Arkadian road for Delphi.

CHAPTER TWENTY-THREE

Through An Archaic Land

Bright dawn looked over the late October fields to Eurotas where he flowed swift and narrow from the hills. Not here the lazy reedy Eurotas of Sparta, but a more youthful stream, near his source and pure-cold with springs. Aristodemos sat on the bank. He had made a long night journey up the riverside carrying the sleeping child. Mendi lay asleep beside him curled close in the crimson soldier cloak. Aristodemos was impatient for his waking. The little fellow had been brave in his supperless hunger. And now a shepherd had just milked a ewe for them and Aristodemos was waiting with the rich bowl. The sunbeams struck across Mount Chelmos in full brightness. Mendi stirred and sat up.

"Little son," said Aristodemos, "wilt have thy breakfast now or fast a while longer?"

"Where is breakfast?" asked Mendi doubtfully.

Aristodemos held forward the great cup cautiously and gave Mendi a peep into the yellow depth. "See what the good sheep hath given thee."

It was a pretty sight to see the boy look up, then down again, incredulously, and with a bubble of laughter draw the cup hastily to him and bury his face over the rim.

"And thou shalt have bread, thou brave little soldier; and cheese too. And this!" He held up a great ripe fig.

Aristodemos feasted his eyes upon the child's feasting.

"Good sheep. Mendi likes that sheep," remarked

the child with a contented sigh as his milk-splashed face appeared again. Then he shook his head. "No like Makaria. Makaria bad to Demos."

"Mendi," Aristodemos spoke very gravely. "Thou must never speak that name again. Dost understand, Mendi? Never again—that name. So long as thou livest."

Mendi nodded with a mouthful. "Yes, Mendi see Makaria. Makaria very dead. Fall down just like Antiphon!" And he added with relish. "Now Makaria all dark in the ground!"

Aristodemos's heart sank.

"No, little man. It is I that am dead, not Makaria," he said half to himself.

"No, no!" cried Mendi with quick solicitude, clambering over to him splashing the milk as he came. "Demos not go in the dark. Stay with Mendi. Mendi give Demos all the milk, all the milk!" He tried to lift the big earthen vessel to Aristodemos's lips and to coax with childish cheer the light back into his face again. Not a mouthful more of his bread and milk would the little fellow eat until Aristodemos had eaten with him. Slavery had taught the child beyond his years.

"Now, little son, we have far to travel," said Aristodemos at last. And swinging the boy to his shoulder he took up his way.

They came in the evening light to pretty Leuktron on the edge of Lacedæmon, where the last mighty ridge of Taÿgetos sinks to the level plain. The little town, pinnacled with high cypress points, sat aloft in delicate relief upon a rocky saddle.

"Oh, Korai, Korai!" shouted Mendi, looking at the cypresses standing tall and still in the sunset. "See the maidens!" So were cypresses called in Sparta.

From Leuktron they turned eastward toward Tegea through a solitary land. This was a weary, dispiriting stage. For it never would occur to a Greek to seek companionship in the grandeur of the solitudes. Nature had been too lately conquered by him. So the mere wildness of the way was bitter to Aristodemos—the stony mountains closing in and rising more inaccessible with every stage of the journey, the stretches of oak forest where sheep paths crossed and recrossed the road. The road itself was so little more than a path that one might easily miss it among the rest. Wolves and wild boars were plenty in the hills, and once Mendi called out joyfully, "Oh, see the big pussy!" when a lusty bear cub lumbered across the way. The region was not that fair flowery Arkady which poets sing, but the rugged Arkadia of ancient Greece—a land of rusticity where men lived in villages or, more usually, lived apart in little huts, a primitive, acorn eating folk clad in rough pigskins.

Aristodemos met these rustics on hillside and in forest: driving their sheep and swine perpetually from place to place with a dull persistency of mere change that seemed to him scarce more directed than the going of the droves themselves. They spoke to him in an ancient dialect with dull, soft sounds of "u" for "o", and they droned a buzzing "z" alike for "d" and "g" and even for "b". Their talk sounded loutish, almost foreign, to Aristodemos.

The land was full of forgotten places. Massive Cyclopian ruins, ancient when Troy was young, sat gray and lonely on their hillocks, unapproachable for tangles of thicket and vine. Here still dwelt archaic and cruel gods, elsewhere forgotten, worshipped in dark forest places. And here lingered strange fables and fearful superstitions. The two travellers spent their nights in the open or in some shepherd's hut. For Aristodemos passed the towns as swiftly as he could. He had no wish to be asked "Who art thou?" or to answer, "That man who came back from Thermopylæ."

Not even the child, whose merry affection had at first so lifted his heart, could now save him from the despair which submerged his spirit. Indeed at times the child seemed to be but the barrier flung athwart his way by angry gods to hinder him from the death he so sorely needed—needed as the weary need sleep.

He was alone in the solitude with Nemesis—"The Watcher." It was her gaze that he felt from the high aloof mountains and the cold down-looking stars. It was the gaze of Fate herself, before whose calm inexorable look men fell like straws.

Sometimes the sharp scream of an eagle above him would curdle his blood, as for the moment he believed the Erinyes were come upon him—swift Erinyes, dabbled in blood, filthy, insane, shrieking, rushing insatiate to fulfill curses. Ah, even as those Spartan sentries had said, the Erinyes must come at last!

As he covered the lonely miles Aristodemos found himself tracing each separate thread of the fateful weaving of his life. Did he stand unwitting in the path of some divine desire? Had his destruction been compacted even before his birth? Or was there possibly some ancient stain upon his race—unknown to him, unknown even to his father? Œdipus had been all unconscious of any guilt until the first blow of divine vengeance fell. Might not some such deadly secret be the clue to his whole frustrated life, his father's early death, his own exile from dear Athens, his separation from Leonidas's death, and now his mother's fateful curse? He began to see his whole life as it were some expert scheme of punishment. His very soul fainted under the awful thought.

Absorbed thus, Aristodemos would quite forget Mendi's presence and let the poor little traveller trudge on beside him until he finally broke into crying for weariness. Then Aristodemos would catch him up in his arms and labour forward mile upon mile without speech.

They had now reached the wide, marshy plain of Mantineia. The sun beat hot upon the humid expanse. Few men were abroad in the heat, and although it was only nine o' clock Aristodemos paused to rest in the shade of a copse. Just over the edge of a hill peeped a square bastion of the ancient fortification, Nestane, Titanic masonry whose very art was lost. Out over the plain the air was a-quiver in the damp heat.

Mendi looked about him for amusement. He had some horse-chestnuts treasured from their forest journeying. "Ballo, ballo!" he cried. Aristodemos caught the little ball and returned it, but forgot to return it the second time and dropped it where he sat. Mendi, with one of those quaint self-imposed canons of childhood, would not pick up for himself the unreturned ball. He stood eyeing it regretfully; then looked at Aristodemos with much questioning.

Suddenly a great idea struck the child. He advanced with outstretched arms, then retreated, held up an imaginary shield and gave a great thrust under it. If Aristodemos had seen at all he must surely have been set a-laughing. The babyish imitation of the battle dance was so stumblingly done, as if the plump dancer would each moment roll over himself upon the ground. But Aristodemos was far away with the real battles yet impending over Hellas or perhaps was facing his own mysterious, hopeless battle.

Mendi was cut to the quick. His lips quivered and his eyes filled. He swallowed hard. Then he turned about and trotted away. "Demos not see Mendi," he complained. "Not see Mendi at all!" He wandered by a little wild vineyard and off upon the plain.

But the silence of Mendi's absence soon recalled Aristodemos to himself. "Mendi!" he called, then rose to his feet. "Mendi! Mendi! Where art thou?"

There was no answer from plain or hill.

Aristodemos knew not how long he might have been dreaming. He remembered with a shudder Mendi's delight at the "pussy bear." The silly child might even run after a bear if he saw one. Or he could so easily be drowned in the marshes.

Aristodemos ran toward the road in real alarm, calling loudly. He met a shepherd with his flock and anxiously questioned him.

"Yez, I zee a little boy yon zide o 'z' road," said the peasant, pointing vaguely.

THE SPARTAN

Finally Aristodemos almost by chance caught a glimpse of him far out on the marshy plain kneeling close to the ground. As he rushed up to him he saw that the child was drinking from a dirty marsh pool.

"Mendi!" he cried so sharply that the little fellow almost fell in. Aristodemos picked him up, scolding and kissing by turns. "Dirty water, Mendi! How couldst thou drink it?" Aristodemos looked down at the pool with disgust. Why were children made so foolish? he wondered.

But Mendi was quite broken-hearted. He laid his tired head on Aristodemos's shoulder with pitiful weeping.

"There, there!" said the soldier-nurse. "Hast thy troubles too, little man. And wast very hot, I know. Come, see, I will wash thee in good water." He pointed to the hillside stream. And soon the little naked body was splashing in a pebbly pool, Mendi shouting with delight as Aristodemos dashed the water on his small strong back. Aristodemos looked at him proudly.

"Art a little athlete already!" he said. "Wilt come to Olympia in thy day!"

The way now led across the somewhat broken plain to Orchomenos. The ancient town could be seen far on its high hilltop which rose abruptly out of the plain. In its encircling wall it looked from below like a little crown upon the peak. Aristodemos was not eager to go up into the town, so he cast about for a shepherd hut where they might pass the night. Between Orchomenos and the farther Mount Trachy ran a deep gully, the only wooded spot at hand. A forest stretched along the gully and spread up the slope of Trachy where it joined the broad pine forest of the mountain. Aristodemos made haste to reach this quiet glen. It was early afternoon, but already in the forest here the air was dark and green and cool. Down in the deep of the woods were places of eternal twilight.

Not far within the forest he came to a wall which seemed to surround a precinct. In the midst stood a noble cedar. The place seemed solitary and decayed.

The wall was green with moss and crumbling, as if its sacredness were long forgotten. Aristodemos began to doubt his finding even a shepherd in this lonely wood. He was standing near the wall, considering whither to turn, when a bright sweet voice spoke behind him.

"Oh, hast thou come to sacrifice to my goddess?"

And turning he saw the eager figure of a little girl not more than ten years old, a little virgin priestess clad in the long saffron robe of Artemis. She was such a blithe little priestess and looked so fresh and sweet in her bright dress that Aristodemos could not resist her unconscious entreaty.

"Yes, I was seeking her," he answered.

The girl clapped her hands in subdued delight, as a childish nun might do.

"Oh, and I was afraid thou hadst but wandered into the wood!" she said, relieved. "For, to speak truly, my goddess hath not had one single worshipper this whole summer. But she is very patient, my goddess. She hath not yet made any sickness or trouble or barrenness of ewes. She stands there in her tree content, and smiles always."

"Perhaps she is satisfied with thy worship," said Aristodemos, smiling down at her.

"But then, I am all alone," she answered, opening her dark eyes wide. "She could not be satisfied with me alone!"

"Alone?" repeated Aristodemos. "Thou, in this lonely place?"

"Oh, my father and mother live behind the precinct. They care for me and I care for the goddess. I alone. Thou seest we are off the road," she ran on, "and there be many priestesses up at the Sanctuary of Artemis Hymnia. The folk go ever there with their gifts."

"Well, I am bringing my gift here," Aristodemos told her. The little priestess smiled happily and reached out her hand to Mendi, who eagerly put his chubby fist within it.

"Come, I will bring thee to her," she said leading

Mendi toward the half open gate. But at the gate she paused again with sudden solicitude. "Thou knowest my Artemis is very old. Thou wilt not think her ugly? She is not like the new and bright gods up in the city. But she is very, very holy."

"I am sure of it," said Aristodemos heartily. "Mendi and I will see only her holiness."

Again she gave him her grateful smile and pushed back the rusty gate.

What a surprise! Within the closure all was order, fresh beauty and care. Everywhere shone hyacinths, blooming beyond their season, in purple masses so close packed that they gave a soft, rich brightness to the place. Two slender cypresses rose spear-like from the carpet of blooms. But the garden was dominated and sheltered as with a canopy by the great ancient cedar which stood in the midst and stretched its arms abroad. The precinct was utterly quiet. Even the birds flitted overhead without a sound.

"I tend the flowers a little," spoke the priestess softly in answer to Aristodemos's look of surprise, "but not much. The goddess loveth wild flowers. See how they bloom! I think the lady goddess tends them with her own hands. Thou knowest at Knidos she hath that name—Hyacinth Nurse."

She led the way through the winding paths. And as she did so a deer lifted himself up from a bed of flowers and came to rub his wet nose against the little priestess's hands. He was very old and frail. His once swift foot stumbled as he walked. Aristodemos saw that he wore a golden collar on which was engraved:

> *"I was caught a fawn*
> *When Agapenor was at Ilium."*

"Thou seest he is holy too," said the little priestess proudly. "He hath outlived many generations of men."

And then, through the broken wall beyond, Aristodemos caught glimpses of bright shy eyes looking in, a

herd of deer and their fawns living close to their goddess who so loved all the wild creatures of the wood.

"She is here!" then whispered the little priestess,
with awe in her voice. And there before them, in a low
fork of the great cedar, stood the small image of Artemis,
like a pillar having head and arms. She was black with
age and dripping with shiny oil from the frequent
anointings of her faithful little ministrant. Poor enough
she was as a reminder of an Immortal. Yet somehow
the goddess had never seemed so real as in this simple
place. Perhaps the gentle worship of her little virgin
had drawn the divine virgin nearer than they knew.
Certainly Aristodemos felt her there with new and
sweeter attributes than he had known before. Here she
was not that goddess in whose honour he had endured
that cruel scourging, but the goddess of all shy and
gentle retirements, lovely as her own fawns, shunner of
cities and the sight of men, the swift wild virgin with pure
moon-cold face. She was the divine, fleet huntress,
running in the untrodden deep of the wood—huntress
and yet protectress of all that was wild grown or had its
life beyond the care of men. Yes, Artemis was here!

"Where can I find my sacrificial gift?" he asked softly.

"There is a goatherd lives yonder across the plain
about a mile away. I know he will afford thee one."

"I will go to him," said Aristodemos promptly. But as
he started away the little priestess said wistfully:

"If the goddess might have a white goat—Yet—
yet—she will be glad of a speckled one."

"It shall be a white goat," smiled Aristodemos
assuringly, and was gone.

When he returned the joy of the little priestess was
pretty to see.

"It is Damon's white kid!" she cried. "The flower of
his flock! And thou hast not forgot to crown her."

The fire was flickering like a jewel on the altar under the cedar. The torch and lustral bowl were ready.
The little priestess herself was crowned for the rite.

"The boy must feed the flame," she said, "for very

kindly is my fair goddess to all that are young, even the sucking young of all creatures of the field, to flowers and young shrubs; but most of all to babies and little children."

And with the tenderest of little smiles she instructed Mendi with his baby hands to toss the sacred fir cones on the flame. Thus they made ready.

"Tell me first thy name," said Aristodemos, turning to her.

"Kallisto," answered the priestess in surprise.

"Kallisto," he repeated. "The prayer shall be for thee."

Then in the forest quiet they made to the goddess their sacrifice and offering.

That night they feasted in the hut with the parents of the maid. Not in many years had that simple household been so gay. And next day, to Mendi's great delight, Aristodemos lingered still. There was a healing in the gentle place and in the unconscious sweetness of the little devotee.

The second morning they resumed their journey. The priestess went with them to the edge of the wood, loath even now to let them go.

"Thou wilt come again?" she said. "Say thou wilt come again."

Then, for the first time since he had met her, Aristodemos recollected his curse.

"No, no," he said hastily. "I am making a long journey. And after that—I think I shall meet death before I come this way again."

But the priestess looked up with so dismayed a face at the change in him that he was instantly contrite.

"And if I should return," he said brightly, "thou mayest be gone. When thou art older, will surely come a goodly youth to persuade thee from thy goddess."

"But I could not leave my goddess. She hath no one but me," protested the child priestess stoutly.

"Thou canst not know. The youth may persuade very strongly. Thy service may be finished and even thy goddess may not fulfill all thy need."

The child did not answer him. She bowed her head, and Aristodemos saw that she was weeping. A moment he bent over her, so close that he touched the fragrant hyacinths crowning her hair. Then once more he lifted Mendi and hurried down the road.

CHAPTER TWENTY-FOUR

The Unsatisfied Curse

Canst tell me which road leadeth north? These mountain paths be hard to hit upon."

The dull shepherd stopped wide-eyed to gaze at Aristodemos and the boy, and pointed vaguely up the mountain. No doubt he was strange to the Laconian speech. He was certainly much concerned lest his sheep wander off, and kept pulling them in with his crook even as he talked. For the place was wild.

But Aristodemos took his directing—indeed he had no other—and swung on up the mountain. They had won now to northern Arkadia. They had passed Stymphalos by its reedy lake, pausing in awe at the wild gorge where the outlet-river plunges from sight roaring into its cavern and disappearing beneath the mountain. Now they were making for Pheneos, traversing the lower slope of mighty Kyllene, the highest summit of the country. For days Aristodemos had seen Kyllene as he walked, its sides dark with pine, its peak already white with snow, and the clouds, now hiding, now revealing its mighty mass. But once upon its side they found the mountain tough climbing.

About two hours up the mountain the path parted. Aristodemos followed the left fork, but it dwindled into a mere sheep track. As he turned to retrace his steps a thick cloud settled upon the slope and he could not see more than a yard before him. Then followed a swift, heavy snow and blotted out the path.

Mendi began to cry from cold and fear. He was a

brave baby, but he had never seen snow before and its stinging whiteness was terrifying. Aristodemos held the little one close under his cloak, though he was himself benumbed with the unaccustomed cold. He tried awhile to find the path but without success. Finally he determined to make the best of his way straight down the slope. But great chasms interrupted him, and he had much difficulty in making any progress around them.

"Mendi, dear," he said, "canst not stop thy crying? Demos will bring thee to a warm place soon."

But Mendi clung close, clutching at him in terror.

"Run! Run!" he pleaded. "Big men in the trees! Mendi's afraid!"

"There are no men in the trees, little man. It is only the white rain."

But Mendi began to point, screaming out with terror. "See! See! Bad men with big catchy hands! Oh! Oh!"

To his dismay Aristodemos saw that the child was sick and delirious. It was the curse! Ghostly and secret, here in this wilderness it had already caught him! It did not occur to him how Mendi had drunk of that stagnant pool by Mantineia.

"Oh, Mendi, Mendi," he cried in anguish, "so soon hath it come upon thee? Is this the reward of thine innocent love? Because in cruel Sparta thou alone didst come to me?"

He wrapped the child tighter in his cloak, weeping without restraint. He ran headlong in desperate search of some way down the mountain. Not Mendi in his delirium was more haunted than he. Moira, that mystic power of evil, that goddess of no conceivable form, void, brooding, terrible, soundless—Moira was utterly come upon him! There was no escape! The innocent little face against his breast, stricken with this sad new torment, filled him with despair.

He came at length below the belt of snow, but here the rain fell heavily. He found a tiny path among the pines which he followed miserably, and soon came out upon an open cliff. Far below lay the beautiful Lake Pheneos, dimly seen through a rift in the cloud. He hurried on, fearful that the path would dribble out and disappear. Finally near nightfall he came upon a little hut so low, so poor, it seemed almost the habitation of some animal rather than a dwelling of man. He could scarcely hope for help from such poor folk, but he knocked at the door.

It opened at once and a little old woman, brown as a leaf, stood before him. She was bent and child-small, as if age had dried her out and left her the diminutive of herself. She scarcely reached above Aristodemos's waist.

"Mother," he cried passionately, "my little boy is dying! For the gods' sake let us rest with thee!"

She peered up at him with her eager, bright inquiry. "Nay, do not ask!" she cried, drawing him with both hands. "Come in, come in!" She drew him over the threshold into the warmth and shut out the rain. "Tht!—tht!—tht! Give me the child," she said, gathering Mendi into her arms. "And don't lament so soon, stranger! Sicker babes than this have got well again."

She took Mendi to the fire and began unwrapping him. The old shepherd hobbled out of his corner and put a stick upon the fire.

"There, there," crooned the old woman to the fretting child. "See the warm fire! Shalt be dry of the cruel rain! And shalt have milk! No? Then water—whatever thou wilt."

The old man moved about the hut, talking half to Aristodemos, half to himself.

"Now Auge there, th' canst trust her—trust her!" he mumbled nodding his head. "Nine times hath Eleutho come o' th' house to her. Ay, nine lusty children hath Auge borne, and well she knew to care for 'em. She knoweth every good plant o' th' mountain. Yea, and that special healing plant that healeth all things this side o' death. Blessed be Asklepios!" he added piously. "But come young man, warm thyself. Thou sure hast need o' fire?"

So very poor and low was the hovel that Aristodemos had to stoop under the smoke-black roof. The rear of the single room opened back into a natural cave, dark and echoing their voices strangely. Yet never had he felt such a warm human welcome. It went to the very marrow with its healing and ready love. He knelt by the fire, lifting his numbed hands to the blaze and watching the ancient woman at her deft ministrations.

"And what have I—what reward for thy good kindness?" he said brokenly. The guilty shadow of his curse hung over him, into whose dread circle, perchance, these also were being drawn by their deed of kindness to him.

"Who asked reward?" retorted the old woman sharply. "It's forty years sin' I had a babe on my breast. Wouldst not give old Auge a pleasure in her age?" She cuddled the child close in her withered arms.

"And thou thinkest—thou thinkest perhaps he may not die?" hesitated Aristodemos.

"Well, he's not dead yet," smiled the old woman shrewdly. "We'll not give thee thy Styxpenny yet, will we, little guest?"

She laid the child upon her couch and, reaching down some dried herbs hanging from the rafter, began to steep them in a little earthen pot at the fire.

"Pretty boy," she sang softly to Mendi. "Here is good medicine. Wilt drink Auge's good warm medicine and go to sleep? Then thou shalt be well."

As she leaned over her work her old eyes caught sight of Aristodemos's hands where he warmed them at the fire. They were brown, powerful hands, but the deft fingers caught her eye. That was no shepherd hand! He had thrown off his broad travelling hat and she saw his easeful muscled shoulders bending toward the fire. Such shoulders the Greeks always spoke of as "godlike."

She rose with a hushed, significant look and gestured to her husband.

He shuffled forward at once.

"Master," he said humbly. "Master, thou sittest at our hearth like a suppliant. Rather wilt thou not receive our guest-honour?" And he dragged toward the fire a rough, heavy bench.

"Thank thee, Father," said Aristodemos, half in dread. He sat down and took Mendi in his arms. "Oh, see," he whispered joyously a moment later. "My little son hath fallen asleep."

But spite of Auge's care and medicines the fever took its way with Mendi, wasting his little body and racking him with pain. His piteous pleadings seemed to break and break again Aristodemos's heart. Watching over him night and day, what would he not have given for one hour's respite to the little sufferer?

The curse seemed a very presence in the hut, a watcher with him beside the little bed. At last even Auge began to lose her confidence, and her face grew dark. Two weeks had passed and Mendi had grown steadily weaker. Auge stood in the door, looking out into the twilight. The weather had changed. It was quite warm again.

Suddenly she turned upon Aristodemos.

"Thou canst save him thyself, an' thou wilt," she said almost savagely. "Thou hast the power we mortals lack. Why wilt not speak thy healing word? See—" she spread her hands—"I have done all I know. I have sacrificed to Apollo, to Asklepios—and to—? Should there be still some other rite?"

"Oh, Mother," pleaded Aristodemos too anguished to note the strange significance of this speech, "dost thou know nothing more—nothing more? Wilt thou let him go to The Dead?"

She looked at him long and incredulously, as though she would say, "What, and not satisfied yet? Why dost thou prove us so?" Then she answered with a patient sigh: "I think there is yet one more help. They say that, when all else fails, the great Mother"—she meant Demeter—"will sometimes take the sick one to her own bosom and give him of her own life."

"How take him?"

"Thou must lay him on a plowed field, and there her life that goeth into the growing corn may even come up into him."

"Oh, then, Auge, quick! Quick! Let us go!"

He bent over the couch and took the poor little body, now but a shadow of itself, in his arms. Then they went out into the evening.

"Do thou tend to him and pray," he said to Auge. "I am afraid to touch him. I may bring him harm."

He sat apart from her as she laid Mendi in a furrow of their small brown field. He bowed his head upon his knees, and sat with tightened hands, hearing the soft wind of the forest at his back, hearing Auge as she went down to the spring now and then for water, hearing— oh, through the long night hours—the low moaning of that dear little voice that surely could never laugh again.

Toward morning the moaning grew softer and fainter, and just before dawn ceased altogether. And in the terrible silence he felt that Mendi was dead.

How swiftly the curse was fulfilling! He was beyond grieving. He thought only of that little boy free from pain, lying there so still in the brown furrow. Mendi, his little man, whose life by unknown Acheron should flower out of its youth—who could never suffer as he himself was suffering now.

And now it came dawn, gray and imperceptible at first, then flashing up golden spears upon distant mountain tops. Auge, sitting like an unmoved fate in her place, lifted a beckoning finger. He went softly to her. She guided his trembling hand to Mendi's forehead. It was moist and delicately warm. The gentle breath which he had thought forever flown was coming and going evently through the parted lips.

"Go thou and thank The Mother," whispered Auge.

"It was to her we should have come at the first."

Aristodemos dared not stay lest he wake the child. He slipped away and ran toward the wood, lifting adoring hands above his head as he ran and pouring out his broken thanks to the blessed Demeter who had given him back the life of his little son.

CHAPTER TWENTY-FIVE

Grecian Hospitality

Mendi's recovery was steady but very slow. It needed all Auge's wisdom and Aristodemos's care to nurse him back to health again. And long before he was strong enough to travel winter had settled down upon Mount Kyllene. Far, far below the valley still kept its green, but the mountain was already deep in snow.

"And now thou art a prisoner with us," said old Auge cheerily, "as close as though thou hadst chains upon thee. Thou couldst never make thy way down through those snow-filled gorges. Ahai! Listen!" She held up her crooked finger as the far off thunder of an avalanche boomed and resounded below their cliff.

"Mother," said Aristodemos seriously, "Some gold I have to give thee, but not enough to pay the living of all winter."

"Gold!" scoffed Auge. "And dost think we would miss a god's blessing by taking gold of thee? Ah, the house is lonely through the months of cold." She turned to build up the fire. "Besides," she added, "art thou not become as our son, and is not Mendi verily my grandson, given to my prayers by the holy Demeter?"

The winter world was a new world to Aristodemos. In his boyhood he had seen snow falling like soft meal in Athenian streets. But never snow that heaped and stayed, making a silent solitude, burying the great pine forest, and bending it heavy to the ground. The roof of the hut was hooded deep in snow. Old Klitor had to dig a burrow to their little spring where they got their water.

"And 'tis not frozen yet, not frozen yet!" he would

proclaim proudly each morning, as he brought in his yoke of water jars. "Known that spring since I was like little Mendi, and it's never been frozen. Always the same, cold in summer, warm in winter. That's our spring!"

And Aristodemos did not smile at his oft repeated praise. There in the mountain the little font was indeed a priceless treasure.

But the snow! "It is marble," Aristodemos said, gazing at it like a wondering child. "What statues Antenor could make of it! But they would perish, even as men."

He went out into the snow and ran for exercise. He would not let his body lose form and firmness there in the narrow hut. It did not occur to Aristodemos that he could even now neglect his training.

As the winter deepened Auge had to take to her bed with rheumatism. Then old Klitor did her work together with his own.

"Mother hath her years upon her—her years upon her!" he would repeat, looking anxiously at her. He was very proud of Auge. "She groweth small and small," he said to Aristodemos, "like the brown leaves. Once she was tall like me. She could lift like a man. Then the gods began to shrink her—smaller, smaller, smaller. She'll blow away some day, like a mist, will my Auge. Look here," he added, turning himself about, "she made me this coat. And the goat's been dead these thirty years—yea, before our children died—that goat she made it of."

Aristodemos thought the old coat looked it, but he did not say so. The pride of the countryman was a new thing to him. He had known only city slaves and Spartan serfs.

The hut was very dark. It had no windows, only the opening overhead which served for a chimney, and the door which on sunny days they left a little open for the light. Sometimes for days together their mountain would be blanketed in clouds and they lived in twilight. And now for the first time Aristodemos knew the cozy cheer of a winter fire. Mendi, whose cheeks were again winning back their ruddiness, would shout and dance with glee as he threw on the pine cones and saw the blaze leap up. All the little room would be filled with the glow, and in the deep curious cave at the back the shadows would play flutteringly upon the rocks.

In the long afternoons they would roast the chestnuts and sweet acorns which Klitor had hoarded like a squirrel. Then Auge, in her cracked voice, would sing to Mendi, leaning against her pillow, the songs she had sung long ago in her childhood

> *"When the north wind doth blow*
> *Home to Hellas we will go."*

She filled the child's ears with stories which, like the Arkadian people, were "older than the moon." And Auge hoarded stories as Klitor hoarded nuts—grotesque folk tales, bred of the dark Arkadian mountains. There were many stories of Pan in his grottoes or haunting the shady groves. Her old father, now half a century dead, tending his flock in Mount Mainalos when he was young, had once actually heard Pan softly piping just over the brow of the hill. "And," she closed the story, "that was the beautifullest music my father ever heard."

"The shepherd man—did he go over the hill and see Pan with his little goaty legs?" asked Mendi eagerly.

"No indeed, child! Dost think a pious man would disturb a god at his music?"

She had a hundred stories of Herakles. For that kindly hero had passed many times up and down Arkadia, the length and breadth of it, doing those mighty deeds of his. 'Twas he and none other had built the monstrous walls of those forgotten cities of Arkadia at which Mendi and Aristodemos had so marvelled on their journey up. No man could have piled them so. 'Twas he had dug the new bed for the river Olbios to drain the lake. Just over that hill to the south he had killed the great Stymphalian birds, more terrible than lions.

But Mendi liked best the story of "Herakles and the

Blue Jay."

"Once on a time," Auge would begin, "there was an old man who lived in a cave on Mount Ostrakina. And he had a lovely daughter whose name was Phialo. And Phialo, wandering alone on the mountain, met one day a glorious tall stranger. She did not ask, 'Who art thou?' She knew it could be no other than the kindly god, and she loved him very dearly and secretly became his wife. By and by she bore him a son. But mean while Herakles had journeyed far away.

"Phialo's old father was very wroth with her, and exposed her with her baby far out upon the savage mountainside. There he bound her hand and foot to a tree and left her to die. The baby wept and wailed, but Phialo could not comfort him, for she was bound.

"Now it chanced that Herakles was returning that way again. And there in the mountain he heard a jay calling and calling. Thou must know, Mendi, that a jay when he wisheth can call just like a weeping child. And good Herakles, thinking some child was alone in the hills, turned aside and followed the voice of the bird. But when he came up with the little bird on the tree he heard yet other cries; for the jay had listened to the wailing of Phialo's babe, and was mimicking its voice.

"So Herakles found the baby lying near a spring, and his poor Phialo bound to the tree. And the god undid the bonds and lifted his own little son in his arms and brought them both safe home again. And thou canst see the very spring to this day. It is called 'Kissa Spring' which is 'Blue Jay Spring'."

But Auge's favourite subject was a more terrible one, —the "Were Wolf."

"When men sacrifice to Lycean Zeus they make a feast," she said, "and at that feast they mingle with the sacrificial meat a bit of human flesh. And whoso by chance eateth of this flesh becomes—a wolf!"

Here Auge would sit up in bed and shake her head, wolf fashion, looking at Mendi with eyes very sharp and bright. Aristodemos was continually astonished at her brightness and quickness, which came so unexpectedly from a body all shrivelled and foredone with age.

"But not straightway is he a wolf," she would go on. "They lead him to a dark pool. There he must strip and hang his clothes upon an oak. Then he must jump, poor man, into the water and swim to the far side where the woods are deep and wild. So in the woods he turns into a wolf. Knowing himself to be a man, he is yet a wolf, and must run night and day with the wolf pack. He howls and scratches with his feet, his belly is lank and hungry for men's flesh. He is like any other wolf. So he must howl and run for nine long years.

"But if he is a good wolf, and never once in all that time eats human flesh, then in the tenth year he may come again to that same pool and jump in and swim back.

"When he climbs out of the water he finds himself a man again. He finds his very garments hanging on the tree. He puts them on and hurries home to his village. But he is now nine years older. Perhaps his father and mother have died, perhaps his wife. His little boy is grown and does not know him. Nine years of precious life are gone, past mending. Strange are ways of Lycean Zeus with men!"

During this tale poor Mendi would back farther and farther away from Auge, and the end of it would always find him between Demos's knees with his head against the broad protecting breast. The scrambling rush of the wolf pack past their own door had often wakened Mendi at night. He had heard them howl afar in the hills. To think of the unhappy Were Wolf among them out in the cold and snow was most dismal to the little boy.

Aristodemos, too, believed the tale. Did he not himself know of a man named Demainetos who had been nine years a wolf and who, as a man again, had practised boxing and won a prize at the Olympian Games?

"Tell Mendi about the Merry People—quick, quick!" Mendi would urge, anxious to forget the Were Wolf.

And so Aristodemos would become the story teller.

"The people of Tiryns are the merriest people in the whole broad world. They laugh and sing and make merry all the time. Even when they would, they can not be serious. I wouldn't be surprised if Mendi here, is a Tirynian. Eh, what thinkest thou, Auge?"

"I'm sure he is," nodded Auge.

"Well, the Tirynians grew tired of laughing always. So they went to the Delphic Oracle and they said:

"'Oh, Priestess, tell us how we may become serious.'

"And the priestess told them that if they would sacrifice a bull to Poseidon and cast him into the sea without laughing, then they would become a staid and sober folk.

So the people of Tiryns went to the seashore, and there they sacrificed the bull. But, just as they were casting him in, keeping their faces long and serious, a little boy—I think he must have been just about as big Mendi—a little boy said something—"

"What—what?" asked Mendi, dancing impatiently.

"I don't know what. But it was something very funny. Oh, very funny indeed! And all the people of Tiryns broke out laughing right there on the seashore. And since then the people of Tiryns can not help laughing and being merry all the time."

But the evenings were never complete until Aristodemos had sung. Klitor in his corner, Auge on her bed, would sit in awed wonder as the little cottage rang full of the glorious tone. And down in the glen even the wolves seemed to stop their howling to listen to the rich, far borne voice. Often he would improvise upon some wild Arkadian legend. Or he would sing them a merry song of their little household happenings. He would sing whole books of Homer, and those odes of Pindar's which he had heard as a child, and many a glorious song sung only the once by an improvisor at some Karneian Festival. For Aristodemos had that primitive bardic memory which men possessed when their minds were yet unspoiled by the use of books.

GRECIAN HOSPITALITY

Even when he was not singing he would sit hour-long, day-long almost, not sounding with his lips, but feeling line by line the great Homeric periods until he came into rhythmic physical oneness with the song.

All this time Aristodemos had never thought of helping old Klitor with his work. Work was for mean men and for slaves. A free citizen never marred his hands or bent his back with it. Not that Aristodemos had any dislike for work. He had never thought of it as in any way related to him. So the old man went slowly about his duties, tending the ewes, cooking the meals, fetching water, while Aristodemos sat by the fire growing ever more irked by the tedium of the hut.

But one dark dawn Aristodemos was roused by groans from Klitor's bed. The young man sprang up and went to him, where he lay on the floor by the fire.

"Oh, we are dead! We are dead!" he was moaning. "Poor Auge, poor Auge! Why did not one child remain to us!"

"What is it, Klitor? Klitor, tell me," cried Aristodemos, bending over him.

Klitor looked up stupidly.

"The pains! Auge's pains, here in my legs, my back. Oh!—I can't move!"

"But if it is Auge's pains thou wilt get well again. Thou art not dying."

"How shall I get well? We will starve. Auge cannot move. The sheep will die. Thou must try to get forth with Mendi down the mountain. We are very old. Many like us perish in the winter."

"Why, Klitor! Klitor!"

Auge awoke and began to wail in low patient fashion in her corner. Aristodemos looked from one to the other. This was a terrible pass. These two old creatures, bed-ridden in their hut!

"I will not leave you, Klitor."

"Nay, thou wouldst sure perish on the way, Master, thou and the child," groaned Klitor desperately.

Still Aristodemos stood. It was dawning upon him

that he could do Klitor's work and save them all. He looked at the yoke standing in the corner. Should he, a Spartan citizen, put that thing upon his neck? Should he milk and tend sheep like a slave? Ah, the gods were humiliating him, perhaps bringing close his curse by a kind of trick! His face grew stern. The curse—perhaps the curse was touching Klitor now. Well, he would fight it! These kind old souls should have the strength of his two hands to keep them from death.

"It is nothing," he said quietly to Klitor. "Am I not strong?" But Klitor did not notice him. "Mother—good mother," he said to Auge, "thou wilt break my heart with thy weeping. I can care for thee. I can do all that thou needest."

"Thou!" cried Klitor in astonishment. "Thou couldst not. I could never see thee do it."

"Shut thine eyes, then. For I will surely serve thee," said Aristodemos, laughing at his amazed face.

"I am ashamed," said the old man. He tried to rise from the floor, but fell back with a groan.

"There, there, Klitor," said Aristodemos, bringing his own covering to throw over the trembling form. Lie still and warm. Ye are both my children and must obey me now."

He went over to the corner, lifted the yoke and awkwardly enough set it on his shoulders. Mendi clapped his hands. "Didst not put on the jars!" he cried.

"Here—here!" and he dragged the wooden jars across the floor. Aristodemos had to stoop while the child, with glee at the employment, hung the jars to the yoke. Then they went out into the bitter cold morning.

"What doth Klitor next?" he asked the child after he had filled the jars. For Mendi had always followed the old man about his work.

"Brings all the sheepies and gives 'em drinks," said the little teacher.

Aristodemos went to the tiny fold that was builded into the cave with the hut and opened the gate for the huddled sheep which were all Klitor's wealth. But the sheep would not come to a strange shepherd.

"Their names, Mendi?" he said.

Mendi pushed among them touching each with his chubby finger. "Lyxo, Erato, Auge, Dike," he called, unconsciously imitating Klitor's very tone. The sheep came at once. The little fellow trotted down to the spring and they followed him in a line down the path. Aristodemos watched the child, his eyes shining with fatherly love.

But the milking was a more difficult matter. Aristodemos tried it long and patiently but with poor success, and at last had to go humbly to Auge for instructions. The two old creatures were lying, still awestruck, on their beds. They had hardly believed Aristodemos would come back to the hut again.

"But thou canst not do it," said Auge, between scorn and reverence. "Thou, with thy hands!"

"Yes Auge, with my hands. Surely not in any other way."

At this Auge laughed, sat up in bed, and with her old knotted hands went through the motions of milking. It was the greatest joke of her life and she chuckled in great delight. Aristodemos was an apt learner and before many days was as skilled as Klitor at the work. Cooking he had often done after hunting in the Taÿgetos. He kept the fire bright with new fuel and swept the house far cleaner than Auge had done, for he had a soldier's neatness.

All tediousness was now forgotten. There was a duty for every hour of the day.

"I have three children to care for," he would say merrily, "and Auge is the youngest of them all."

So the long winter wore slowly away, an endless season to Aristodemos who had known only the short, rainy winters of Athens and Sparta. His round of work brought him wondrous close to Mother Earth, and the kindly influence of forest and sky. He never, indeed, went forth of the hut to look at the stars, and yet he never walked beneath them, folding the bleating ewes or drawing water for Auge, without being keenly aware of them, burning like lamps above him.

At last Auge could hobble about the hut once more. Then presently Klitor grew better. Perhaps the big fire that Aristodemos had kept so constantly roaring had put life again into their old bones.

Then came the month Anthesterion when in the valley the streams begin to leap free. Then Elaphebolion, the beginning of flowers in the low meadows and the first greening of the olives. Still, the snow lay deep on Mount Kyllene. Not until the beginning of Mounychion were the mountain paths free enough, or his two old children strong enough, for Aristodemos to start away.

"But now will our winter just begin," said Auge, looking at him with tearful eyes. "Thou and the child have made springtime in the hut all these frozen months."

It was a still frosty morning of blue sky and bright flitting clouds when Aristodemos made ready to go. He had secretly halved Antiphon's gold and left one share of it on the hearth where Auge would discover it as she worked.

It was very hard to part from these two good simple friends whose hold upon the earth life was so slender and whom he certainly could not see again. Auge had been weeping through the night and was frankly weeping now; but Klitor took on a certain dignity and ceremony at the parting.

They stood outside the door. Aristodemos was cloaked and sandalled for the journey, his broad hat flung back from his neck, his staff in his hand. Mendi sat upon his shoulder digging his heels into Aristodemos's chest for a foothold, his arms waving free. He wore a tiny goatskin coat that Auge had made for him. Not otherwise had Hermes looked with the infant Dionysos when he bore the baby god to be brought up by the nymphs, those ready nurse maids of divine infancy.

Klitor brought out a little cruse of oil, holding it preciously in his two hands.

"Now," he said, "thou goest away. I shall not see

thee at another time. Thy coming was strange and thou hast bent thy back to labour, as gods sometimes do when it pleases them to visit mortal men. This cruse of oil is many times refined and very fragrant. I do not know whither thou art really tending, but take thou it as an offering—perchance to thyself—or—pour it out as thou seest fit."

"An offering? Great Zeus, Klitor, thou hast not thought me—a god!" faltered Aristodemos in astonishment, thinking how intimate they had been together.

"Oh, no,—thou art not," old Klitor repeated, with evident wish not to offend. "Of course thou art not! Nevertheless, take thou the oil as our gift. It is our last. We made it with great care. But we can make it no longer."

Aristodemos put it away from him.

"It would comfort us to know our gift was in thy hand. Dionysos was also unknown," Klitor added significantly, "to those who saw him first."

"But thou didst help us out of the kindness of thy heart, and not because thou thoughtest me a god?" asked Aristodemos wonderingly.

"The child was sick," answered Klitor simply, "and even when this roof hid many children from the rain of Zeus the traveller was always welcome."

"Ah, Klitor, thou art all astray in this matter. But I will gladly take thy gift and give it to the Delphian Apollo. May 'the good god' bless thee!"

Aristodemos would not trust himself to speak longer with them. He put up a hand to steady Mendi on his perch, then turned and went swinging down the path with his wonderful assurance of step among loose stones. The old couple standing at the door watched him go.

"But he could not save the child," spoke Auge's hushed voice in the silence. "It was I had to take him to Demeter and pray."

At this moment Aristodemos came to the last cliff turn and, looking back, waved his staff to them in farewell. As he did so a little white cloud rolling lazily up the gorge, collided softly with the cliff and folded him from their view.

And Klitor, with a quiet, significant look at his wife, turned and stepped with tremulous difficulty over his high threshold.

CHAPTER TWENTY-SIX

An Arkadian Interlude

However much we may love the shyness of spring—her slow, slow coming, each day the added hint, the faint breath of difference— yet after all it is the surprise of spring that we love the best. We love spring because we have forgotten her. Such a surprise, many times intensified, Aristodemos now experienced. This had been his first real winter, his first long months of cold and snow. And now a few hours' swift striding had brought him down from the bleak unaltered heights of Mount Kyllene to the verge of this laughing valley and all the livingness of the awakened year. It was really only March; but in Arkady the power of May was already abroad.

Behind him rose the forest, all aslope, arbutus-haunted, freshly green, the mountain's last declivity. Below him lay Lake Pheneos, clear opal in its deep mountain cup. How the wind blew! It sang in his ears a very satyr-tune to set the heart a dancing. He had to shout to Mendi by his side to make himself heard above its glorious sounding. The blue-green waters of the lake ran like a tide under the wind's merry urging. At the end of the lake a stretch of long-grassed meadow ran on in billows with the waters—all, all under the current wind. The trees, too, bowed and ran. It was as if the whole earth were leaping to some new-imagined goal.

Aristodemos was only twenty-four. The season could not but get into his blood. All that had been inspiriting in his life, his loves, his hopes, his triumphs at Sparta, all seemed to leap again within him. He hugged

THE SPARTAN

Mendi to him with an exulting sense of nearness, as though the child were verily the son of his own body.

He came down to the lake and turned northward along the shore to Pheneos city. He walked swiftly, with a light forward motion, with his hat flung back, his golden head now darkling in the shadows, now gleaming in the sun. There lingered about him yet that subtle immortal look which the Greeks called "youth." Yet he was not a youth, he was a man, and carried his head with a certain calm erectness that would have been deemed over-bold in the Greek Ephebos. His level brows, his deep set serious eyes, were of full manhood—a rich, vigorous face, broad of forehead, even cheeked and strong, with robust chin and full, firm lips. And it was pure with a kind of soldierly purity—had a noble habit of expression. Only as he smiled was it delicate, when his lips played into such tenderness that you seemed to look suddenly quite into his unprotected heart and must inevitably love him as you would a child.

Such a face would be sure of notice at Delphi where those statesmen-priests knew men and recognized power when they saw it.

"Mendi, Mendi," he said in happy excitement. "What was that story Auge used to tell thee about the Aroanios fishes?"

"Eh? Hueh?" asked Mendi—for he always put this birdlike question before making his real answer. Then, as if he remembered, "Oh, sing-fishes!" he cried. "Fishes sing in the river."

"Wouldst hear them?"

"Yes. Fishes sing for Mendi!" And the child began to clap his eager little hands.

"Art so easily gladdened, little man?" said Aristodemos kissing him. "Perhaps we can find them for thee. They are not far away."

They passed unpausing through the small Arkadian city of Pheneos and were quickly out again in the open, turning off from their road southwestward toward Mount Penteleia, beyond which flows the Aroanios.

AN ARKADIAN INTERLUDE

Now this going was not toward Delphi. Delphi meant the parting from Mendi, and that parting was become something from which he was turning his face away and of which he could not bring himself to think. Up in the mountain hut his little playfellow had become his passion. The change had come unperceived. There had been rekindled a kind of second dawn in his soul that was all of the child. Here in these lonely mountains with their unbroken quiet, their secluding snows and now their masterful spirit of spring, the past had been closed over. The great civic life of Sparta, his own tragedy, the impending national disaster—all had grown unreal and far away.

He began to cheat himself with suppositions. Likely enough the child's father was dead, had forgotten or had never cared so very much. Or he had taken a new wife and was rearing to himself a new brood among whom an older son would be ill welcome.

He even dreamed of going back to the friendly little priestess, and felt again with longing that gentle kiss of hers. The youth in him was loving life again, and Hades, peopled with his friends, did not call him now.

Yet, after all, it was a strange, snatching joy that he had. He was really looking at each beauty with the profound searching that one uses toward a parting friend. It was his last springtime. The delicate, starry look of the forest (of leaves very small), the earliest flowers, hanging on threadlike stem, (only deepwood flowers dare venture out with so frail a hold), then the orchards like great festal processions canopied in bloom of snowy pear and flushing wild apple—all, all were his last. He must look his fill now, for he would not meet them on their next return.

Yet all the more he smiled and held to the boy. "Soon," he said, "soon we will come to thy river and to thy fish that sing. But thou art not in haste, Mendi?"

Mendi was in haste enough. But he was not sorry to be set down in a poppy meadow for roaming.

"There gather thy fill," said Aristodemos, and threw

himself upon the turf. He lay with face close to the ground, gazing across to an opposite green slope warm in the sunshine and peopled with feeding sheep. The thin piping of a shepherd came across to him. The tune was quaint and old. The faint, incessant tinkle of the sheep bells made him drowse.

Presently a breeze sprang up and the sheep, stirred by it, began to move down the slope in a tremulous, long, tinkling line. There was one black ewe that walked apart, she and her mottled lamb. The obedient shepherd rose and followed them. Slowly they crossed the little brook and filed up again to where Aristodemos lay. He saw the shepherd's shaggy goatskin coat and heard him as he came, humming a song to himself—not chanting it aloud as a city dweller would, but humming it under his breath as if his much aloneness made him shy of his own voice. He greeted Aristodemos with an old time Arkadian greeting and so passed out of sight, he and his companion sheep.

Still Aristodemos lay and watched the powerful white clouds roll gleaming up the sky from behind the sharp cut crest of the slope, floating clear at last and sailing on, trailing each its shadow over the grass. To his Greek mind such shadows were alive, attendant spirits whose power he did not question. They brought to his mind the Epimeliads, those flock nymphs who dwell among the rocks in lonely grazing places and sometimes challenge the unwary shepherd to a dance. For to him nature was alive and personal, full of greetings and of shy elusions.

At such a leisurely rate it took them three whole days to reach the Aroanios, though it was scarcely fifteen miles distant from Klitor's hut. Here they sought out the place where the fish were said to sing. They sat together on the bank of the deep swift stream, man and child with equal faith in the wonder. The sun sank and the steep forest about them gave forth its sharp evening scent. But still they listened; for the fish, it was said, sang oftenest at evening. A nightingale awoke in the tangle and poured out her sad interrupted song so rich in memory.

"Hark—the sing-fishes!" whispered Mendi in rapture.

"No; little son, not yet. Wait a while," said Aristodemos, with a far away look.

It was not until black dark that they gave up and went back disappointed and hungry to the shepherd's hut.

"For this disappointment thou shalt see Styx," quoth Aristodemos, making further excuse to wander. "Art old enough to remember it, and 'tis a God-touched place."

Aristodemos talked to the child of wonderful Stygian oaths that might not be broken, of the river flowing somehow on, down through Hades itself, and how a man might make oath by the river and drink its water unharmed. But if he should ever break the oath, be it a lifetime after, the sacred water would then poison him and he would forthwith die.

So upon a day of fitful spring showers and sunbursts the two travellers left Nonakris, and took the way—it could not be called road—to the Styx. They had talked merrily in the mountains, merrily among those views of the infinite world and sky. But here they hushed their voices and clambered down in silence. For the Styx flows in a gorge so difficult of descent that Aristodemos had to cling by roots and branches, or leap down and lift Mendi after, or go creeping along ledges where the clammy wall seemed to push him off, while the chasm sheered from the footpath on his other side.

Down, down they went, leaving the broken sunshine and the wind's merry piping. Bottom gained at last, they stood in the chill twilight, the dread cliffs rising above them to the narrow sky. The air was lifelessly still. The gorge was closed at the upper or western end by a great precipice erect as a wall. There, six hundred feet above them, they could see the little Styx itself come tumbling over the top of the wall as if out of the sky and then fall trickling and showering down to their feet. So tiny was the river, so terrible the fall, that only in a sparkle of rain did it reach the deep at last. And as they stood there, its faint showery sound like a meaningful whisper filled their ears.

Aristodemos had no words—even for the child. It seemed to him as though but one more leap would bring the fearless little river into Hades itself. Was the portal to eternal shadows in this very ravine?

A sound echoed through the gorge—a stone set falling by some human foot above them. Then voices echoed in hollow reverberation through the place.

He peered upward and saw a company of men clinging their difficult way down the cleft where he had just descended. The round gleam of a helm, the touch of a crimson cloak, told him they were soldiers.

Ah, he could not meet soldiers even though they were unknown to him. He made what haste he could along the gorge and hid in a cleft.

Nearer they came, great athletic fellows hushed like children in a temple. They stopped in the floor of the gorge where the breathless river gathered itself in a pool. Then one dipped a vessel into the water, and holding it to the others to drink, told off the vows that were between them. Aristodemos could not hear all, only that the vows were of Persia, and Mardonios and of keeping faith with the Hellas League.

But at those few words his long winter shrank into a moment. He was at one again with the old soldier life, with the great doings of the world, and the world danger. Again "Hellas," the Greek master-passion, swept his soul. He trembled in his hiding place. Tears ran down his cheeks—tears of sheer yearning to go out and fight as these men were about to do.

And now he was seized with a very boy's impatience to get out of the gorge—could hardly wait for the men to leave. Soon as they were out of sight he began to scale the cliffs; hurriedly, feverishly.

"Mendi," he said, "Mendi, we were going to Delphi. We have lost time by the way."

AN ARKADIAN INTERLUDE

His purpose seemed to give him chase. He hastened as if under a goad. How less than a man was he
become! How he had dreamed so long, and Hellas trembling on the verge! What though he was cut off and
apart from all the fighting. Hellas! Hellas! still was all
his thought and all his sorrow. And would he have made
Mendi an outlaw with himself, destroying every noble
chance for the child? Mendi must have a country, a
father—his own father. Mendi at least must be a Hellene.
There was no other way. To get Mendi that father was
the one straight manly deed left for Aristodemos. And
over this he was dallying like a woman!

In such high mood he sped toward Delphi, to give
up his last sweet hold of life. Beyond Delphi he did not
think.

No loitering now—only haste, haste!

This was not renunciation. Renunciation would
have seemed a strange foolishness to him. It was no,
question of doing right or wrong. He did not think of it
so. He had a half-conscious reasoning about it which
sounds strange to modern ears, but which to his Hellenic mind was simple and inevitable. "Life is sad," he
said, "and to-morrow we die. Therefore, let us be noble!"
This was the strange "therefore" that came to the mind
of every noble Greek.

A strange sequence indeed. But the minds which
thought those beautiful forms out of the marble, that drew
a veil of lovely mythic wonder over their hills and valleys
and ennobled even the simple wayside flowers—like-
wise thought nobly upon life. The beauty that they loved
in outward things they loved also in things within. As
they loved a beautiful temple, a swift stepping youth,
even so they loved a just law, a logical system of thought,
a high deed—loved them with a curious intensity. It was
not the moral side of goodness that appealed to them
but its sheer beauty, its harmonious fitness..

"Let us be noble!" they said lovingly, doggedly.

It was in religion that they went astray. Their gods
were but so many enigmas. There was no real good-

ness in the heavens, no real kindness in the powers that ruled.

"But if the universe is confused and ugly, then all the more," cried the intrepid Greeks, "let us be noble!" Even in such brave fashion did they fling back at their puzzling gods.

Yet Aristodemos, for all his high mood, found that the sorrow of parting with the child ate into his heart more than he would have confessed. And as he came to cities once again, to the abodes of men, as he passed smoking altars and foot-echoing temples, he could not but be sensible of a shadow upon the very gods themselves. He did not in any wise doubt the reality of the gods, but he accused them in his heart. Those bright beings, so fair, so sure themselves of life, what right had they so wantonly to vex and fret man's little day, which must so soon go down in darkness! It was the shadow of that sorrow which forever was to trouble the Greek race that now crossed the mirror of Aristodemos's soul. For while, from first to last the best in the Hebrew heart beat up-ward with irrepressible joy toward his God, the best in the Greek heart through all the centuries contended bitterly with his. We hear the Greek pleading pitiful-wise with his blessed gods that they would be only as good as he himself, only as just and fair and kind as he himself could be. Perhaps the fact was that in the story-telling childhood of the Greek race, Homer and the unknown writers of the Theogonia had fixed the character of the gods forever before they could come to their own at the hands of the sensitive worshipful Greek maturity. However that may be, as the Greek awoke he looked out upon his Zeus, his Athena, even his Apollo, with sad and troubled eyes, questioning and trying them until after some centuries he found refuge in his own calm philosophy.

In Aristodemos's day such bitter questioning was as yet only as the hovering of dark wings over Greece.

But already the deep spirit of Æschylus was stirring. Pindar was becoming a high voiced prophet. No thinking Greek could escape it.

And so the vague, high questioning assailed Aristodemos in the wild gave hurry to his feet, drove him for refuge to the Delphi place, there to hide like a wounded bird in its temple eaves. There surely he would find some wisdom, some clue and higher calm.

As he journeyed, those stories which had amused his childhood, which he had heard among the slaves and from Antiphon, came back to him distressfully clear. How helpless sometimes were the gods themselves, how foolish and headlong in their sudden loves. It was well enough for Zeus to be amorous—he was by nature the father and begetter of men. But Apollo, his boyhood's love! It hurt Aristodemos that Apollo should be other than pure. That amour of the god with unwilling Kreûsa the daughter of Erechtheus, there in the cave at the Acropolis. He had seen the place often. He remembered it now with a swift, involuntary scorn. Leonidas or Lykos would never have so demeaned themselves!

His youthful devotion to Apollo had been a kind of friendship, a familiarity, a natural pleasure daily renewed by acts of ritual. But now! What had he to do with that face of calm, ineffable brightness, that god of joy, to whom even the winter season was a discomfort not to be borne? And the god's image, so easily vivid in his boyish days, was faded now, and far.

Once, indeed, he almost felt an access of faith in Apollo. He had awakened upon the mountain side before sunrise, when earth and sky lay in the bright quiet of dawn—the pure twilight which with all its likeness to the evening can never be mistaken for it, because of its subtle difference of growing and of hope. Mendi lay waking beside him, his warm cheeks flushed with his sleep.

Then it was that a small cloud was blown softly across the valley, and stole like a presence toward him. It was not taller than the trees, and very defined. It moved in delicate silence, nearer, nearer, until the heart of Aristodemos burned within him.

"Thou immortal god!" he said, not daring to speak Apollo's name. His voice trembled with something more like love than fear.

He cast down his eyes not daring to look. He glanced toward the child hoping he too had perceived it. At last he lifted his head again, feeling—ah, the cold breath of the fog. Here was his cloud torn among the laurels, melting to naught. Foolish heart that he was, why had he hoped?

At length, after several days of almost silent journeying, Mendi and Aristodemos came out of Arkadia into the mountains of Achaia—and found themselves upon the ridge of a long headland flanked by gorges on either side. Thence they looked down far below upon the blue Corinthian Gulf, and saw the white fingers of the surf running and returning on the gentle beach, sounding their deep fresh music. Beyond the Gulf rose the mountains of Phokis folding and hiding away the sacred Oracle of Greece. Next morning Aristodemos found himself with Mendi at his knee in a little bobbing boat, with coveted Delphi growing slowly nearer across the dancing distance.

Thus, sorrowing, groping, loving, he came to Delphi at last.

CHAPTER TWENTY-SEVEN

The Place of Golden Tripods

A band of pilgrims were hurrying along the steep way that mounted to Delphi. They were eager to reach the precinct before nightfall.

Among them Aristodemos carried the tired Mendi on his shoulder. Of all these questioners he perhaps bore the bitterest question. He was nearing the goal of a long, anxious faring. But the gods were capricious. He began to wonder how the Pythia would receive an accursed man. For some Olympian reason, hidden from him, his very presence at Delphi might be a sacrilege which Apollo would wrathfully resent. It might be a part of the very curse that he should come hither to be damned. Others might ask cure for themselves, but with so many chances of refusal and the almost certainty of wrecking the whole purpose of his coming, Aristodemos dared not ask cure of his curse. And even Delphi, he reflected, could not cure a curse until after some fashion the dark Erinyes, those insatiable ones, had had their will upon the man. No, he would keep silence and run his chance.

The road led here through the Krissaian Plain, a steep-walled vale, rich and fertile, full of yellowing corn. In moist places oleanders and pomegranates flamed, generous of red bloom and far flung scent.

Now the road turned to the right and made northeast for Delphi, mounting above the fields and up through the steep olive groves until Aristodemos could look back over grove, field and plain and out upon the Corinthian Gulf which he had crossed that morning. In the Pleistos

Ravine below the road were the famous potteries with their hovering haze of smoke. The potter slaves, their day's work done, flocked carolling along the road and mingled with the travellers. Among them Aristodemos saw a dream-eyed vase painter with his arm frankly about his sweetheart.

Higher and still higher climbed the way. It was a happy way toward Delphi. The throng grew momently more talkative, eager, expectant. They began to point out distant places, clear seen on the high mountain sides. But Aristodemos was so absorbed in his own thoughts that he forgot the famous turning of the road until, at a step around a little spur, suddenly he found himself within a vast amphitheatre of hills and the whole of sacred Delphi, stem and beautiful, open before him. There lay the precinct of the Oracle, contained within its wall, quadrate on its sunny slope. Crowning it upon its far side was the pure great temple of the god's own voice, very clean and chaste at the foot of savage cliffs.

The precinct was crowded with little coloured temples all in a golden mist of sunset light, those bright treasuries of the god, uncounted and precious. Amid them Aristodemos caught a confused gleam of brazen tripods and far famed statues. He could see the white zig-zag of the Sacred Way winding upward through the sloping precinct, among the thick set fanes, to lose itself from view around the Great Temple's eastern front.

Close beyond the Oracle rose the two yellow, shining cliffs, almost a thousand feet high, catching full face the setting sun. They were a great curve of golden wall, cleft midway by a narrow gorge of cascades. Phaidriades "the Shining Ones" the loving Delphians called them. They likened them to the bright pinions of the sun, as if Phoebus himself were some glorious hovering creature stretching vast protecting wings about his Sacred Place. Back of the cliffs the mountains soared, their stupendous circle enclosing the whole vale. And still above these, hidden by the cliff, he knew that Parnassos lifted its gleaming snows high in the blue.

THE PLACE OF GOLDEN TRIPODS

Ah, "Sacred Delphi," "Navel of the World," "Earth's Deep-Murmuring Seat," "Voice-Place of Prophecy," "Presence of the God." In all Hellas what is like to thee!

Pilgrims and populace swept on into the town. But Aristodemos stood still at the turn breathing like a runner. He lifted supplicating hands above his head. He was not praying. He was only sensible of the vivid exaltation of the place.

"We will not go in to-night," he told Mendi, "not to-night. There is no place for us in the town." So they slept near the roadway under the high stars and escaped the sordid haggling of a Delphian inn.

They awoke with the lark's first notes and clambered down into the Pleistos ravine for their morning plunge. Then the two pilgrims, fresh from their dip in the cold stream, climbed up to the road again and made toward the "Place of Golden Tripods."

The road led along a terrace. Below at his right huddled the roofs of common Delphi, in steep downward succession. Above the road, in the sacred Delphi where the priests had their homes, the pleasant houses rose aspiring, tier after tier, to where the splendid New Stadion was building close to the cliff. Statues of victors stood at the street corners, mostly music victors holding lyre and plectron. Now they passed along the high precinct wall and came at last to the sacred Eastern Gate.

Here Aristodemos paused, and lifting Mendi to his face gazed so closely into his eyes that he saw him all blurred and dim.

"Kiss me, my dear son," he said gently.

The child kissed his cheek. But Aristodemos looked away lost in struggling thought, as if he had forgotten the child in his arms. Then his gaze returned, and even Mendi understood that it was in some sense a parting.

"Demos not shut Mendi in the big house—No, no!" he cried, clinging to him.

"No, little son, Demos will never put thee anywhere save in thine own father's arms."

He put the child down, and with sudden, grave self-mastery stood erect in the serene prayer-attitude of the Greek.

"Hail, Paian, healing God!" he said. "Good luck to thee and blessing, Child of Latona!"

The porter opened. Aristodemos washed hands in the white lustral basin, dipped Mendi's chubby palms, and so, from defilement free, they entered the sacred place. As says the Delphic proverb:

> "Oh, stranger, if holy of soul,
> Enter the shrine of the holy god
> Having but touched the lustral water.
> For lustration is an easy matter to the good.
> But an evil man
> The whole of Ocean can not cleanse with its streams."

"Comest thou a visitor or a consultant?" asked the porter.

"A consultant."

"Then thy way is there." He pointed to a doorway at the left of the paved court. For they were not yet within the Precinct, but in a vestibule of the gate. The door led into a short corridor, this again to a courtyard open to the sky and surrounded by a pleasant colonnade. This was the receiving place of the priests.

The white robed men there gathered looked more like a group of statesmen than the devotees of a god. And statesmen they really were, a little sacred tribe of them, each born into the noble race and bred in the proud traditions of the Oracle—its greatness, its responsibility. These men felt the broad destiny of Hellas to be in their hands.

As Aristodemos entered the chief priest was speaking, an old man remarkable for a beautiful white beard and a humorous brightness of eye. The younger men had turned toward him with interest and respect. They did not at once notice Aristodemos as he stood near the door half dreading that they should see him, awed at the dignity of the place. Then one of the priests started eagerly toward him.

"Hast thou been waiting?" he said courteously. "Come where we can speak alone. I am Nikander."

He led Aristodemos to the colonnade, looking upon him with kind but very observant eyes.

"Thou art in trouble, my son?" he said when they stood alone. "What wilt thou have of the god?"

"Nothing for myself," answered Aristodemos hastily, and fancied that Nikander looked a little disappointed. "It is for this boy here—not my son, save by adoption. Will the god direct me to the boy's father?"

"Undoubtedly he will, for thy purpose seems simple and good." The priest took out his waxed tablet. "Who asks the question?" he said, preparing to write the name.

Aristodemos felt his heart tighten in the pause.

"The question is—is from the boy himself, Mendi a Chian."

"Of Chios?" asked the priest, looking up doubtfully from his writing.

"That is where the trader said he bought him," Aristodemos hastened to explain. He had not known that he would be questioned thus. "It is probably not his birthplace. That is what I wish to know."

"Tell me all the story." The priest drew him to a sunny seat. And there Aristodemos began to tell him Mendi's story, warming to the task, freeing his tongue at the last.

"And oh, Nikander, look at him! Is he not pure Greek? Was it not a sacrilege to enslave such a Greek?"

"Yes—he seems well born and thou didst well to free him. But, having adopted him dost thou not wish to keep him for thyself? But—perhaps thou hast now a firstborn of thine own."

"No. I am not even married. But the father, if he be living—think of the sorrow, the loss of such a son!"

"And thou wouldst restore him, then, for that, father's sake?"

"Yes, and—and—" Aristodemos hesitated again,

"and for the child's sake."

The priest sat awhile in silent thought, observing now Aristodemos, now Mendi who was playing knuckle-bones on the floor. Presently he said:

"And thou sayest there is a charm he wore?"

"Yes. Come, here, Mendi."

Mendi rose, and the priest quietly slipped the string from his pretty neck. But Mendi forthwith burst into angry tears. "Naughty man! Naughty man!" he cried, struggling and grasping after his luckpenny. He did not ask Aristodemos's help, but made his own fight. The priest, laughing, held the amulet out of reach.

"Not much slave spirit there!" he said merrily, while Aristodemos, greatly shocked at Mendi's disrespect, tried to quiet him. "Leave the coin with me," said Nikander. "We priests like to discuss such matters before we go in to the god with the question. 'Know thyself' saith Apollo, and he loveth the understanding and open mind. Not readily doth he give answer to the ignorant or witless questioner. And when he doth, the mortal never followeth it aright.

"And now, as thou perhaps knowest, there are three days to the seventh of the month, our lucky day, when the Oracle is like to speak. Already the Pythia hath begun her purification that she may be able to receive within her mind the prophetic spirit of the god. Go about the Precinct and take thy fill of looking. For never again will thine eyes behold such riches of beauty. Unless," he added smiling, "it be thy happy fate to visit again the Oracle of Apollo."

He accompanied Aristodemos to the inner gate, and pushed it open with a pleasure in his welcome that made the welcome very sweet to receive.

"Loxias fare with thee!" he said. "Ask for Nikander when thou hast need of anything."

The portal clanged to and Aristodemos breathed free again. He found himself shut into a spacious treasureland. A moment he stood bewildered. Then he felt rise within him that excitement which the Greek always felt in the presence of art. He started eagerly toward a near group of statues. Well might he turn to them—Athens's thank-offering after glorious Marathon! There in gentle dignity under their light-roofed canopy stood Athens's peculiar gods and heroes, those who had so filled Aristodemos's mind in childhood, and happily had never been dethroned. Erechtheus was there, and Cecrops, and Pandion from whose loins he himself was sprung, and Pallas, his own goddess, virgin pure. It was like a "Welcome home." Aristodemos swept out both hands to them.

"My gods!" he cried. "My own heroes, keepers of my father's hearth!"

But he was fairly beyond speech. He began to go from one to the other close and eager. And now he perceived in the old familiarity something mysteriously new, a living quality such as he had never seen in stone before. Pausanias, seeing these noble statues centuries later, said Phidias had made them. But Phidias was at this time but a twelve-year boy. The statues were of the simpler, yet really as beautiful, art of the generation before his.

They stood erect, planted on both feet. The simple artist knew no other way. They had a tightness of figure like lusty buds close-folded. Not yet quite free of archaic bonds, they nevertheless were alive. The foolish archaic smile had suddenly given place to a preoccupied seriousness. The square faces, grave full lips, deep eyes, broad brows and low yet lovely heads, all prefigured the glorious Parthenon frieze. But the full outflung divineness of the Phidian Immortals was as yet withheld. Instead there breathed from them a spirit of dignified innocence, the strength and reserve of a noble immaturity.

Aristodemos had never seen such statues before. The art had grown suddenly—overnight, as it were. While he had been shut away in Sparta, patient hands and dreamful hearts had been at work. In the midst of all the tumult of the war Greek art had been growing toward that marvellous Phidian climax which was to come, that vision of gods and perfect men which still to-day lights the heart of humanity.

Aristodemos lifted the wondering Mendi from one to another, crying:

"See, see, Mendi—thy Demos's own forefather. And see here, the Maiden Pallas, how pure, how serious! She looks at us as if she knew us for her own. Look well, Mendi. Some day thou wilt hear of Marathon whose glory is as yet too great for thee."

He lavished the bright moments here like a spend-thrift. It was long before he could break away to look about the splendid Precinct.

Before him was the Sacred Way, paved and white, mounting the hillside in its great triple zigzag to the Temple. On its either hand, rose the brilliant-coloured treasure houses and colonnades, the painted statues standing all about in the open, like people. The Way Side was however not so crowded as it later became. There still were open spaces full of laurel, now just abloom. Bees boomed everywhere. They were espe-cially associated with Apollo. For it was the bees, with their wax and gauzy wings, that were famed to have built the first temple at Delphi.

The morning was a great heartful of sun. A fresh spring wind was blowing. Ah, the Way was before him. Is it any wonder that to the sore-burdened Aristodemos it seemed a kind of divine holiday?

He began by turning back to look at things in their order, and saw standing near the Gate the famous Corcyrean Bull. He told Mendi the story of the bull leav-ing his herd and bellowing on the sea-shore until the Corcyreans, heeding him, had gone down and caught the countless shoals of tunnies, the beginning of their great sea wealth. Wherefore the grateful Corcyreans had offered this bronze effigy of their benefactor to the Delphian god.

The great fellow stood on his pedestal with that quaint animation and intelligence which the art of early

THE PLACE OF GOLDEN TRIPODS

Greece bestowed upon animals—perhaps because the simple sculptors believed them more capable of thought than we do. He was truly modelled, spare and sharp-cut like a Japanese-bronze.

Now Aristodemos resumed his progress up the Sacred Way. He saw the Tarentine Victory Offering, whose story also he knew. Indeed, as he mounted, the wondrous Way seemed to Aristodemos a path of visible victories, each telling its own brave familiar tale.

Further up the hill Aristodemos now noticed a high projecting bastion or platform flanking the Way and looking out over the Precinct walls. Atop of it in the sunshine stood a tiny bright temple. It was the far-famed Siphnian Treasury. Truly the little fane in its gemlike perfection deserved to be so uplifted. It was old Ionic, exceeding simple of form, a mere chamber with two slender columns in front forming, with the forward-reaching side-walls, a little shady portico. But upon this simplicity was carved a richness of chaste ornament that even now in its ruin is beyond compare.

Aristodemos mounted its tower-like platform for a closer view. The frieze showed a living procession cut with the depth and delicacy of a master hand. Herakles, Pelops, gods contending with giants, a whole scene from Homer. Such sculptures were the open story books of the Greeks. On the front pediment Apollo was fighting Herakles for the Dephic tripod—seat of prophecy.

Looking on this pictured contest, Aristodemos suddenly realized how deeply anxious Apollo was to speak with men. Had not the god thus battled with each successive possessor of the Oracle back to its original owner, Gaia, —Mother Earth—until at last he had made it wholly his own and could speak without hindrance to men of asking-hearts? With a new depth of reverence toward his boyhood's god, Aristodemos entered the little fane to worship. Mendi walked silent beside him holding his hand.

When he came out again the sunlight had broadened into mid-morning. The place was filling with people all a-gaze and excited. The great day of the year was at hand, the Springday, Birthday of Apollo, the first day on which Apollo was like to speak after the winter silence.

For Delphi was all winter the possession of Dionysos and those strange practices which that passionate god compelled. But now, in the blessed springtime, Apollo was returned to his own from his far wintering in the Hyperborean land. Now ceased the dissonant flute playing, the frantic worship, the ranging of wild, ecstatic women over Parnassos. Now succeeded the high worship of the law-giving and law-obeying god. It was the triumph of civilization, the mastery of thought and order over chaotic and barbaric conditions. And civilization was not then so old that it could be taken for granted. It was a novel and uncertain heritage, a matter for pride and emotion, as with it the Greek faced a barbarous world.

The very music of Apollo set forth the change. From hillside and temple Aristodemos could hear it, the sweet quieting music of the god, the sounding lyre, the clear, well ordered paean, the discreet song. It was very stately, like a confident music of victory.

Aristodemos came down from the little temple to the Way and mingled with the crowd. It was a quiet crowd, yet throbbing with controlled emotion. He moved slowly on gazing eagerly as he walked, the weary little Mendi trudging it at his side holding fast his hand.

But near the Way's first turn Aristodemos stopped, wide-eyed. Whose was that familiar back—that man there on the neighbouring temple porch? He should know that back, for it certainly was Spartan. Aristodemos hastily recalled the old men he knew. Ha, it was Tisias, the father of Demonax—a man who had lost an only son at Thermopylæ!

A heavy trembling seized Aristodemos. He snatched Mendi up and darted behind a group of statues. What to do?—run now from this temple place, throwaway the whole purpose for which he had journeyed so far, be the coward that they called him?   But he had gained on the road a kind of needful imprudence that served him now.

"No, Mendi, no!" he said, so fiercely that Mendi wondered, open-eyed.   "We'll get thine Oracle, cheap or dear. Tisias can do no harm that is not already done!"

He stayed behind the statues, though, until he saw the old man come down from the shrine, go down the Way, and enter the Siphnian Treasury which he himself had just quitted.

"Good gods!" he said, with a laugh that frightened the boy.

They came out again upon the Way, rounded the turn, and there faced a marvellous sight—a colossal marble Sphynx, brightly coloured, topping a lofty column, uplifting her wings on high. How she startled him with her wide outlooking eyes, smiling that grave mysterious smile. The sight gave change to his mind so that he went on up the Way, gaining interest again in what he saw. He passed the rugged natural rock where the famous Sibyl had once chanted her prophesies and dark sayings. Then he came to the ancient threshing floor, where every eighth year the great ritual drama, "Apollo Vanquishing the Python," was performed. Then he made the last turn of the Way and began to mount steeply along the eastern face of the Great Temple's foundation. At his right stood the gifts of the early tyrants, the golden bowl of Lydian Crœsus, the golden lion of Cretan Midas, and huge silver craters, the rich metal-work of the East, so splendidly engraved that not a fingertip could touch where the wondrous graver's tool had not moved.

Here, too, at the most conspicuous part of the Way, stood crowded multitudes of statues, Zeus, Herakles, Latona the Mother, Artemis the sister of the Delphian god, Achilles on horseback with Patroklos running beside the horse. Here were votive chariots and countless bronze animals, wolf, goat, dolphin, bison, ox, and many noble horses. And here stood the famous bronze date-palm, with its lifelike roots and the frog squatting at the base.

And here, most prominent of all, stood the Apollos, statues so ancient that their very artists had become mythical. And side by side with these stood statues fresh from yesterday. Here were Apollos of pure gold, of gold and silver mixed, of bronze and of marble. Here Apollo contended with Herakles, seized a leaping deer, talked with his mother and sister, lifted up in victorious hands the figureheads of captured ships of Salamis.

Here at this Crown of the Way Apollo's worshippers might see him in all the acts of his unending life, might greet him in every aspect that they loved and knew. Later Apollo was to become a kind of poet-dreamer, with lax garments and flowing hair. But when Aristodemos climbed the Way to the temple Apollo was the young prophet, the god of vision alight with the high power of song, the "Stern Avenger," "Strong helper," "Phœbus of the Golden Sword," "Far Darter," "Healing God." Such names they called him, and with such attributes they revealed him here.

Aristodemos's starved nature grew riotous of feasting. He was conscious of nothing but the pure joy of beholding. His heart was full. No place was left in him for hunger or for dread.

In such high mood he climbed the final steps to the temple platform. A strange fragrance met him. Then upon the broad outspread terrace, he found himself facing the great Temple front—the Temple of the Oracle, robust, calm, and strong like the god whose home it was. A noble Doric colonnade marched full around it, and all was overlaid with the rich elemental colours which the Greeks loved, red mastering the rest. Atop the roof the winged akroteria gave their lightness and flying aspect to the whole. Above the temple, the great cliffs soared to the sky. Aristodemos drew a long breath.

Suddenly an eagle swooped down from the height toward the great open-air altar to snatch at the sacrifice. Then Aristodemos heard the sharp twanging of a

bow and the cry of the wounded bird as it fled screaming into the blue.

"Wilt steal from the great god himself?" cried an indignant young voice, and Aristodemos was aware of a
young altar-defender, who now laid aside his bow and,
taking up a fresh laurel, began to sweep and purify the
temple threshold. He was a blooming boy, his hair yet
moist from the ceremonial bath, his white robes fresh
upon him.

The place was very quiet. And now the boy was
bringing out a golden ewer filled, as Aristodemos knew,
with the sacred water of Kastalia. He began to sprinkle,
as it were, dew upon the place, singing softly to himself,

"With hands from all defilement free."

Aristodemos watched him, longing ardently to go
himself within the Temple, yet not daring to do so. He
took out his coin irresolute. But it was only enough for
his single offering at the receiving of the Oracle. No; he
must wait the three days. He turned away. But the
gentle boy hastened after him.

"There has been offered this morning a general sacrifice for strangers," he told Aristodemos kindly. Delphi
was never grasping of gifts. Her welcome was equal
for rich and for poor.

So Aristodemos, with Mendi asleep on his shoulder, stepped over the threshold into the great shadowy
temple.

The lofty temple chamber was the place of the "very
holy" things, objects which had been familiar to Aristodemos all his life. Could he be actually looking upon
them now? In the middle of the room rose the great
Omphalos Stone, "Navel of the Earth," dome shaped,
shining with oil and hung about with bright woolen fillets.

An eagle of pure gold stood on either hand. Here
had met the two eagles which Zeus had sent flying from
the ends of the earth to find the centre. Near it was

Apollo's hearth, where leaped his eternal fire, filling the lofty place with flickering light and setting the eagle-wings aflutter as with life.

Aristodemos stopped to spell out the famous "Maxims of the Sages," set in golden letters on a pillar:

"Know thyself."

"Nothing in excess."

These were tokens of the age-long bond between Delphi and the Wisdom-Lovers. For Delphi had her philosophers long before Athens. She was in close touch with the philosophers of Ionia and of the far Italian coast. Even now their deep questioning was exerting its secret uplifting influence upon Delphi, pruning away her crude Doric ceremonial and giving her an authority of actual moral law, which she in turn was teaching to all Greece. To Delphi men came to be made clean, and Delphi was learning to make them really clean. It was in this great, solemn chamber that consultants received their Oracles. Few but kings and ambassadors ever entered the adytum in the crypt, beyond, where the god spoke.

But now Aristodemos came upon an object which was entirely new to him—a large iron chair near the Omphalos. A lyre lay upon it. With childish impulse he reached out and touched the strings. Then he noticed how polished it was. Evidently it was a "companion of many songs."

He lingered long in this holy place. Then he thoughtfully left the great chamber, came out into the bright sun and made his way down from the temple steps toward the new offering of Gelon.

He was looking deeply absorbed at this splendid group when he heard a voice near him suddenly cry out. It was a cry of amazement and emotion. Aristodemos turned fiercely to face Tisias. But he faced another instead. The man started toward him. He was an unforgettable man of about middle age, shorter than Aristodemos, but beautiful and very strong. His large, eager eyes searched Aristodemos with wonderful brightness.

"By holy Apollo!" he cried again, seizing Aristodemos's wrist. "Lykos again in the flesh! Whence art thou? Of Athens—of Athens?"

"No," stammered Aristodemos.

"Of Sparta, then? The boy went to Sparta."

"Yes."

"Then art thou Aristodemos, son of Lykos? Answer! Answer!"

But Aristodemos did not answer. He stood silent and white, appalled at the sudden meeting. He knew at once his father's friend. He felt the man's outreaching joy. Yet in all his confusion he had but the one instinct— to hide from Pindar the shame that would tarnish Lykos's memory. He could never wrap his curse like an evil garment about that clear, bright, honoured figure.

"There was an Aristodemos, son of Lykos," he slowly answered at last, "but he is dead."

The man dropped Aristodemos's hand as if in sudden awe of him.

"Then have the gods made Lykos over again because of his beauty," he said.

He stood gazing at Aristodemos, his face quivering with emotion. Aristodemos, fearing to trust himself, turned almost rudely away.

"No—no! Do not move!" cried the other. "So—thy head turned aside! Oh, I could embrace thee for my friend!"

Aristodemos darted a startled, appealing look at the man.

"Forgive me," said the stranger, "I have taken liberties with thee. Thy likeness is so marvellous. Good luck to thee, and free joy of Delphi!"

He was gone. Aristodemos stood helpless on the spot. Then he clasped Mendi to him and hurried out of the Precinct down across the wild ravine and out into the hills beyond.

But the other man hastened off full of purpose. He strode in among the priests.

"Which of you received that young man this morning, —the beautiful one with golden hair, the one with the child? Who is he?"

Nikander rose and came to him smiling at his vehemence.

"Who is he?" urged Pindar. "What is his name?"

"He gave no name," replied Nikander. "He made his request in the child's name—a rather unusual and noble request."

"And who the child?"

"A Chian, he says. But I do not believe it."

"Nay; but answer me more fully, I beg. If I could only know whether he be Lykos's son! Can you not tell me something?"

"Would that I might, dear friend. The young man hath great need."

"Think you so? Oh, think you so indeed? I too read sorrow in his face."

"It is the look," said wise Nikander, "of a man under a curse. I have seen it before, and it is like nothing else—the curse-look in the eyes."

"Oh—oh!" cried the other under his breath, as if Nikander had struck him. Then he added, "That explains! That explains! But Lykos's son! I must find if it be he. Will I lose him, think you? Will he stay for the Oracle?"

"He will certainly stay for the Oracle," answered the quiet priest.

CHAPTER TWENTY-EIGHT

The Pythia Speaks

Before sunrise on the day of the Oracle Aristodemos re-entered the Precinct by an obscure gate and threaded narrow byways to the grove above the Great Temple. Even now he could hardly believe that he was come again, his contest within had been so sharp against it. This sudden meeting with Pindar had stirred him to the depths. Before, he had seemed to have something of the unmoved quality of Fate herself. He had faced Fate so long. But Pindar! Pindar! How Aristodemos loved him! Yet he must not meet Pindar again. A public stoning at old Tisias's hands could never break him, but Pindar's kindness might. He must not meet with Pindar!

Aristodemos sat among the laurels breathing the sweet air, looking down to where the crowded temple roofs brightened in the morning sun. Footsteps presently broke the silence. It was Nikander mounting the path. Were these priests omniscient! How had Nikander known that he was here? Aristodemos started anxiously to his feet. Then he saw that Nikander was smiling.

"Is all well with thee?" he said as he came up. "Thou hast not let me do thee any service."

Mendi, with childish impulse, ran to him, reaching out his little hands.

"Mendi loves thee!" he said frankly.

The priest lifted the child in his arms.

"Hast a little boy at home, too?" questioned the child.

"Yes! How knowest thou that?" answered Nikander, a swift happy light in his eyes.

Then Mendi suddenly recollected.

"That little boy wear Mendi's luckpenny now," he said ruefully.

"No, indeed, he will not, thou Shrewdness!" laughed Nikander. And taking out the amulet he threw it over the baby neck. "Thou art full of humours. Yesterday thou foughtest—today thou lovest."

He looked over Mendi's curls, watching Aristodemos's face. Indeed, through all the colloquy Aristodemos had felt that Nikander was keenly watching him.

"Thou must find it very hard to part with this little lover of thine," he said to him.

"It is necessary—" began Aristodemos, then turned away his head so abruptly that Nikander hastened to add:

"It is time for our sacrifice. We must be going. The Pythia will be early at the Tripod."

He turned, still holding Mendi, and the three hastened down the slope.

First they sought the Kastalian Spring under the foot of the Phaidriad Cliffs just where the mighty gorge cleaves them. The gathering worshippers talked softly, but the gorge gave back mysteriously the murmur of their voices. The precious water of Kastaly stood crystal in its square basin, with broad marble steps leading down. Here all consultants must wash their hair before approaching the Oracle.

Aristodemos divested himself and Mendi of their garments. The priest never forgot the beauty of the unnamed suppliant who, "in the ripeness of golden crowned youth," descended with his child into the clear water. Then the two re-clothed, crowned their wet heads with laurel, binding them with bright fillets, and went on to the Fore Temple, where they made their sacrifices. Afterward they returned in the full morning sunlight to the Temple of Apollo.

On the way Nikander said to Aristodemos:

"Thou art bidden down into the very Sanctuary, the Place of the Tripod. It is a rare privilege, but Pindar hath desired it for thee, and with us a wish of Pindar is almost law."

"He is very kind," stammered Aristodemos.

"He is very great. Here in Delphi we honour him as no poet hath been honoured. He is close to the god. Didst thou not see his iron chair in the temple? There by the hour he sits and sings. We Delphians are honoured by his presence and his songs. For he hath visions. Pindar hath taken a strong liking for thee."

"No, no," corrected Aristodemos. "He hath fancied some resemblance."

"Nay, young man. It is thyself."

"Myself?"

"Yes. So he hath told me."

Aristodemos trembled inwardly. How little chance there really was to avoid Pindar. And how impossible to compose himself for a meeting. He scanned the group of consultants about the Great Altar on the terrace. But Pindar was not among them.

The company was a mixed one—a sailor who had had a dream and feared to make his voyage; a farmer asking about the planting of his field; a pompous ambassador with a secret inquiry from an Eastern king. There was also a young ambassador from a distant Western colony desiring to settle a dispute with the mother city. And last of all a sunny old Athenian who, being white haired and near his end, was come to free his slaves.

"'Twere a pity to sell them," he whispered aside to Aristodemos. "And I am sure they won't go with me to Hades. So I'm selling them to Apollo." And selling them to the god he actually was. The documents were already signed and sealed by which Apollo bought them for a price. And the god would set them free. No dishonest master or heir would ever claim a slave again in face of such a document. In such wise Apollo protected the weak.

But as they were talking a sudden silence fell upon the crowd.

THE SPARTAN

The Pythia led by the white-haired Hosios had appeared upon the terrace. She was dressed in a long robe, was laurel crowned and had loose flowing hair. She was only an ignorant peasant girl and went to her task docile, but visibly unwilling. She had fasted some days. She had run through the purifying laurel smoke. She had chewed the laurel leaves. And now, even before entering the shrine, she was upon the verge of ecstasy. A year ago she had doubtless been a wholesome country maid. But her sacred duties had been severe. She lifted to the Hosios a pale pinched face with pointed, trembling chin, keeping her eyes upon his and seeing naught else. He seemed to lead her by that gaze of his rather than by the hand. He himself was silent and intent. So they entered the fane.

The consultants followed, an awed procession, halting in the main room of the temple. Only Aristodemos and Mendi with the Eastern ambassador went onward with the priests.

A rude ladder led down into the holy place, a gloomy cave partly roofed over by slabs of stone. The roof was thick hung with fresh laurel. In the floor was a narrow rift of black depth. Astride this rose the Tripod, golden and tall. Near by stood the very ancient golden statue of Apollo and the altar whose low clear flame played with unearthly glitter upon the golden things and sent the shadows starting among the laurel.

Mendi convulsively clasped Aristodemos's neck and hid his face. Aristodemos himself was in awe beyond measure.

In the tense silence they gathered about the Tripod. And the little Pythia, with eyes still fixed and held by the eyes of the ancient priest, lifted her hands to him like a child to be taken. She was very thin and light. The priest lifted her easily to her high perilous seat of prophecy.

Then for the first time her eyes wavered. There came into them a look of comprehension and mute appeal. Aristodemos thought she would have spoken. But the old Hosios lifted his finger before her, slowly waving it. Her black wide eyes followed its waving, move for move. Again she was still. So they waited.

Above them the laurel boughs gave out the smell of green woods in the cave-like place. The awe-stricken worshippers fixedly watched the Pythia on the Tripod as men watch the sacred face of death. Aristodemos began to feel strangely sleepy. A dreamlike, floating sensation almost overcame him.

Then in the heavy silence he heard, or thought he heard, a murmuring from beneath. The watchers stirred uneasily and glanced into each other's white faces. On the face of the-little Pythia came a look of mortal fear.

A cold vapour puffed up from the cleft, filling the place with its clammy damp and smell of caves—

Then, with a sharp cry, the Pythia was seized.

It was a terrible sight. So strong was the onrush of the god upon the frail spirit of the girl that it twisted and convulsed her with the fury of its inner stress. It seemed to flood away every vestige of her own tiny conscious-ness and leave her but the vibrating, well-nigh breaking instrument of Apollo's will.

She swayed, almost fell from the Tripod. Then her girlish body stiffened upright. She leaned forward, one arm outstretched, her black eyes brightening to a glassy stare.

"O Apollon! 'Pollan! 'Pollon!"

The place rang with her terrible, never-to-be-for-gotten cry, as if all the weight of all the past and future of the world lay upon that little maid.

At first the cry was naught but the god's name. Then she began to form words.

"Oh, I see—I see—" she repeated many times. Then, *"I see—a ship. It carrieth a whole city upon a sea of storm. I see—I see—It is war—it gleameth—red— red! And the man—he giveth laws to a people. Laws— not like the laws of other peoples.—I see the man—I see—I see—I see—I—"* Her shrill voice grew fainter, dying upon her lips.

THE SPARTAN

The old priest stirred. Aristodemos saw him lean forward with eyes as glassy as the Pythia's own, and with terrible, uplifted hand.

"Whence? Whence come they?" he commanded. "Thou knowest! Speak!"

She fell a-moaning and wringing her hands. Then quite suddenly, and in measured tones and swaying to the rhythm, she began to chant:

> *"Phokaia—Hyele*
> *Phokaia—Hyele*
> *Phokaia—Hyele."*

What could the priests make of all this?

Yet at her words a gleam of delighted faith lighted the Hosios's face and was answered in Nikander's. Was it not a marvel that to the utterly ignorant little Pythia the god should give this vision of a long-past battle in far Ionia? Nikander understood that vision. He knew how that the citizens of Ionian Phokaia, rather than submit to the Persians, had sailed away far to the West, and how the remnant of them had founded the now thriving young city of Hyele upon the Italian Coast. He knew also of the brilliant young philosopher and leader whose fame was growing so great and who had given to the new city its good laws. Indeed, for the past three days the priests had been eagerly discussing that same young philosopher, whose name was so like the child's name, and whose city's coin was the child's luckpenny.

It never occurred even to these clear-thinking men that the ecstatic Pythia might somehow be reflecting in a vacant mind their own intense thoughts. They were dealing with powers which they did not understand. And who shall say that the god did not guide their simple faith?

But now the Pythia was rambling on about a palace by a broad river, a palace of golden doors and gardens and cypress trees, until the eyes of the stout old ambassador started from his head.

THE PYTHIA SPEAKS

"The King's own royal gardens!" he whispered.

Then the Pythia swooned. The kindly Hosios caught her in his arms and bore her tenderly away, white and dishevelled as her own trailing robes.

CHAPTER TWENTY-NINE

The Singer of Delphi

Aristodemos came out strangely shaken, looking on the light of day as if he too had been away from earth. He hurried from the temple. He felt that he must be alone with this vast experience. He had beheld what he believed to be the active creative force of all Greek song and all Greek civilization. He had seen the fount of it bubbling up in chaotic strength too full to be articulate. But to him it was not a blind force. It was the exuberant expressiveness of the intelligent god, of Apollo himself.

So overwhelmed was he by his thoughts that he hurried up the slope and along to where the stadion was building. There by chance he came to the rock-cut steps that led to the long and dangerous way up the cliff. He bounded up, swinging Mendi to his shoulder, glad to vent his strength upon the difficult climb.

He reached the top of Delphi's lofty cliff. It was the first step in the grand Parnassian staircase, a thousand feet above the Orade and three thousand above the sea. He found himself upon a broad plateau broken with clumps of fir, and bounded on three sides by mountains. He swiftly followed the track across the level to a place marked by a statue of Pan. Then he began to mount the path to the farther heights, a still greater climb, until he came suddenly upon a cavern in the mountainside. The sun struck glittering into the forest of stalactite columns within its shadowy depths.

"Oh, pretty, pretty!" cried Mendi. He had enjoyed the mad climb with gales of laughter.

THE SINGER OF DELPHI

"Why, Mendi, we have found the Korykian Cave!" said Aristodemos, as he caught sight of the rough stone at the entrance bearing the dedication to Pan and the Nymphs. It was indeed a place for nymphs to sport in, so cool and away from the world. He wandered in among the shadows, then sat down to rest, letting the child play about him and looking out through the columns to the bright opening.

Mendi was in treasure land. He picked up the bright stones, bringing them one by one to Aristodemos. "For Demos," he kept saying. "All for Demos." Aristodemos was monotonously thinking, "The Oracle! The Oracle!" To-day perhaps, he would receive it. What difficult mandate would it lay upon him? What would it reveal? One thing at any rate it must reveal—the parting from the child. "Oh, Mendi, Mendi!" he cried, catching him up as he came with gifts and fondly kissing him, then hiding his face for very bitterness of thought.

At this moment the air outside the cave was swept with a sweet, wild strain of music. He lifted his head, intently listening. Was it some god in this mountainplace?

Aristodemos seized Mendi's hand and rushed out. Now he heard it clear, the song and the strong-swept lyre. He saw a man wrapped in a thick shepherd's cloak sitting at a little distance at the cliff-edge over-looking the great dip of valley.

If he had stopped to think, he would never have approached that music. Such an uplifted column of song only one man could rear. But in his bitter mood he reeked not who the glorious singer must be. The music sounded like a god's, and he drew near as dumb animals follow the music of Orpheus. He did not speak, but when he had come quite close, the singer felt his presence and turned. Ah, how quickly he did all things!

Aristodemos began to back away with foolish, blundering apologies. But Pindar looked straight into his face and silenced him. Then he said seriously:

"Young man, why dost thou avoid me? What evil

word hast thou heard of me?"

"Oh, no—no evil!"

And yet," said Pindar darkening, "thou dost avoid."

Aristodemos stood silent.

"Oho!" said Pindar quickly, "Some natural dislike! I had not thought of that."

Aristodemos had been too absorbed in his own bewilderment to reflect that he could in any way affront or grieve the poet.

"No, no, Pindar!" he cried in great distress. "Thou whom all men hononr and love! O thou—"

He seemed so desperately wrought upon that Pindar, fearing he had gone too far, laid a quieting hand upon him.

"Well, well," he said. "I will not accuse thee. That is," he added with a smile, "not if thou stayest. There are not many who would deny Pindar a pleasure, and I greatly desire it. It is thy likeness. My friend Lykos was exceeding dear to me."

Aristodemos dared not speak. There was so much that he was in peril of saying. He stood gazing at Pindar, half-haunted, yet so hungrily eager that Pindar almost wept beholding him.

"Thou wilt stay?" he asked gently. "For the sake of the likeness. For the sake of my dead friend."

Aristodemos stood long as one dazed. Then he bent down quickly to the child.

"Sit here. Mendi," he said, "here in this safe place," giving him his bright pebbles. "Here are thy little toys."

Pindar could not but notice how tender he was with the child.

Then Aristodemos sat down at Pindar's side, perturbed, wondering what difficult question he would next have to face. But the poet did not speak again. He sat silent awhile, looking off southward into the illimitable distance that lay below, where the Gulf of Corinth stretched blue and far, and where rose the shadowy mountains in Arkadia. At length he absently reached for his lyre and began to play.

THE SINGER OF DELPHI

He played wanderingly, carelessly. Yet Aristodemos was astonished at the masterly grasp of the tones, like strength at play. He forgot his anxiety and caution.

Then Pindar, as if he had gathered his thought together, began to sing:

> *"In a little moment*
> *Groweth up the delight of me;*
> *Yea, and in like sort*
> *Falleth it to ground.*
>
> *"Things of a day—*
> *What are we and what not?*
> *Man is a dream of shadows. Nevertheless, when*
> *   a glory from God*
> *Hath shined on him,*
> *Clear light abideth upon man,*
> *And life serene."*

Aristodemos listened breathless. What did it mean? What wonderful song was this? Life immortal was not often spoken of by the Greeks.

But Pindar took up another strain:

> *"For those below shineth the strength of the sun,*
> *While in our world it is night.*
> *And the space of crimson flowered meadows*
> *Before their city*
> *Is full of the shade of frankincense*
> *And fruits of gold.*
>
> *"And some in horses and bodily feats,*
> *And some in dicing, some in harping*
> *Have delight;*
> *Among them thriveth all fair, flowering bliss.*
> *And fragrance streameth ever*
> *Through the lovely land,*
> *As they mingle incense of every kind*
> *At the Oracles bidding*

THE SPARTAN

Upon the altars of the gods."

There he stopped. The exalted calm of the song had worked its will with the younger man. He had never heard anything like this.

"What does it mean?" he cried. "Of whom singest thou this?"

It was the question Pindar had hoped for. He was by no means unconscious of his power, and he was now exerting it with full intent.

"I sing it," he said quietly, "I sing it of the dead. But there is one, always one, whom I think of in singing it. He was my sworn brother. Since him I have had no friend. Never lived there one like him."

He paused, dreaming himself into the past.

"He had a son that I could almost have loved in his stead—a manly boy."

He heard Aristodemos take a troubled, deep breath. "I talked with the child as we came from the burial of his father. I held the little mourner in my arms; and he questioned, oh, so deeply! After that I was summoned suddenly to Thebes. And when at length I came back the boy was gone. Ah, but he was his father's true son!"

"But he too is dead," said Aristodemos.

"Yes. And thou didst really know him in Sparta?"

"When he was a boy."

"And so he is dead," said Pindar. "If he were living how I would love him! Yes, even if he had come upon some great evil."

Aristodemos looked up with dismay. How much did Pindar really know or guess?

But Pindar was inscrutable.

"Well, well," he said after a long silence, sweeping a broad chord upon the lyre. "Hear this!" and he struck into a high-sounding strain, not of the dead but of the living:

"I pray thee, lover of splendour,
Most beautiful among the cities of men,

Page 300

THE SINGER OF DELPHI

Haunt of Persephone,
Thou who by the banks of Akragas stream
Nourishest thy flocks,
Thou inhabitest a city builded pleasantly— "

So he sang on and on, of things splendid but not significant. Then gradually his tune changed. Aristodemos heard now a curiously familiar strain, now a wandering approach to an old haunting melody. At last Pindar was openly singing:

"Let Hellas join, let Hellas join together, _
Drive them with shouts and with our glittering
spears
Across the wine-dark sea!"

It was Lykos's old Karneian song, first sung at Sparta. Aristodemos held himself motionless, clasping tightly his knees. The song raced over his heart, tearing up the precious things he had so long kept hid. He grew cold. He broke into a sweat. Then like a flash his palm swept out and rudely struck the vibrating strings to silence.

"Not that song, not that song!" he cried. "I can not-
"

Restraint was gone. Pindar might have had all his story of him now. Yet Pindar still pushed him cruelly.

"That was my friend's song. He used to say that his boy was born of that song."

"But he was ill born, ill destined!" cried Aristodemos, covering his face with quivering hands.

"What? The son of Lykos—ill born?"

"No, no! It is of another I spoke—another! There is no stain on Lykos's memory!"

Aristodemos uttered the words, but he faltered over them. His soul was in revolt. Another moment and he would have turned and claimed his father, claimed his father's friend—yes, and all the love that was his right.

But now, with the light of certainty in his eyes, Pindar

quickly spoke again.

"Well do I know it," he said. "There is no stain on Lykos's memory. Nor ever hath been stain on Lykos's memory!"

The words caught Aristodemos like a trumpet call. He steadied himself, lifted his head and kept silence. Then the impetuous Pindar threw both arms about him. For the ardent Greek had no reserve in his affection.

"Ah, dear stranger," he said, "my music hath a strange power. Often and again it striketh a sorrow to men's hearts—yea, even to hearts that have no proper sorrow. Lykos indeed is dead," he cried, "his son also, even as thou hast said—his son is dead. But, before the gods, I love thee who art so like to him I loved!"

"Thou dost not—thou dost not know me!" urged Aristodemos.

"No, I do not know thee," repeated Pindar, as he proudly gazed into the set, brave face. "But I have seen the Lykos look in thee, and for that I love thee."

And Aristodemos closed his eyes and hid his face on Pindar's breast, even as he had done when a little lad at Athens.

CHAPTER THIRTY

At the Oracle's Bidding

It was late afternoon before Aristodemos and Pindar reached Delphi again. They went at once to the place where the oracles were given forth. In a closed room beyond a pleasant portico the priests were sitting in deep consultation, trying in all faith to find the will of Apollo in the chaotic words of the swooning priestess. They pondered over their oracles with infinite care.

Nikander came to meet them.

"Thy oracle is ready," he said. "Sooner than all the rest. It was very clear." He smiled, seeing the two together, wondering how the wise Pindar had fared with the nameless young man.

Aristodemos reached out a quick eager hand for the tablet and read:

The Oracle

"Follow the path of the ship
> *that fleeing the wrath of the Persians*
Carried a city afar Lacedæmon
> *to the uttermost coasts of the sunset.*
Touch thy far-wand'ring keel
> *in the mud of the dark-flowing Hales.*
There is a town, Hyele,
> *though some have otherwise named it.*
Find thee a man, of wisdom profound:
> *profounder his sorrow!*
If unto him thou deliver thy charge,
> *long kept, he will bless thee."*

Aristodemos read the lines through, and then again more slowly, knitting his brow and holding his nether lip between thumb and finger—an old gesture of Lykos which caused Pindar's heart to leap with memory.

"I don't understand it," he said. "Where is Hyele?"

"It is sometimes called Eléa," said Nikander.

"But where in the world is it?"

"It is one of those young colonies of the far West, on the Italian coast above Sicily."

The Delphians had a masterly knowledge of coasts and indeed had directed most of the colonizing of the Hellenic world.

Aristodemos wrung his hands in despair. "How the gods are against me!" he cried.

"What is it? What ails thee?" cried Pindar, eagerly taking the tablet.

"You see," said Nikander, "how clearly the place is pointed out, and the man."

"Yes, but how to get across the broad sea! On land I could walk—" Aristodemos was bitterly ashamed of his poverty.

Nikander and Pindar exchanged glances.

"Thou dost not think, my son," said Nikander, laying a friendly hand upon his shoulder, "that the god would send thee a-journeying, and yet give thee no faring? The gods are not foolish. And the gold that the Oracle shall give thee is not to thee but to the child's father. Will he not repay a hundredfold, having his boy again?"

Aristodemos turned away his face.

"It is not thine," concluded Nikander quietly, "to question a transaction of the Oracle."

It was planned that Aristodemos should embark the next day upon an expected ship for Sicily. But the vessel did not arrive. So he remained at Delphi, while Nikander daily sent down a slave to the port for ship tidings.

The waiting was no barren time. It was Pindar's time, and Pindar filled it. Aristodemos's whole nature seemed to lift and blossom. He drank of that kindness as a dry field drinks the rain. He felt strangely safe. Pindar's love seemed to shut out even the curse, which must be waiting somewhere dry-eyed for its fulfilling. Strong and absorbing was that poet of the splendid fresh life of Greece. Pindar drove Aristodemos to the full length of his own daring thought and speculation.

Every morning he sought the young man. Sometimes the swift joy of that waiting young face moved Pindar so that he could scarce give him greeting. They walked together about the Precinct or sat in the quiet grove. Pindar was learning him, not his history; for to that Pindar did not refer again, but to himself.

"But if Attica had been at once given over to the Persian," Pindar argued one day, "the struggle would have ended long ago."

"Ended! Yes—in shameful ruin!" cried Aristodemos hotly. "Wouldst thou give up Athens?"

"But wouldst thou," urged Pindar, "lose all in trying to save Athens?"

The old fire lighted Aristodemos's eyes.

"Pindar," he cried, "we must save all—Athens, Bœotia, even Eretria! Oh, Pindar! what smallest state of Hellas wouldst thou throw to the Persian dogs?"

Then Pindar, the first great Pan-Hellenist, threw back his head with delighted laughter, crying:

"Not one, dear friend—not one!" And Aristodemos saw that Pindar had been trying him. "Ah, would that there were other Spartans who could see as broad a Hellas as thou seest!"

"There was one who saw. Leonidas saw—" replied Aristodemos. Then he stopped short, nor could Pindar win from him another word concerning the war.

And with what eagerness did they discuss the great questions that burned the hearts of ancient men. Are the gods moral? What is the orderly world? And life itself? For Pindar was forever trying to reach beyond death. He talked out his ventures with heedless freedom, grasping and clarifying his thoughts by contact with the fresh keen mind of the younger man. Thus one day he turned upon him with great earnestness.

"Spend not thy desire upon the life immortal, but seek of the gods such gifts as are suited to thy mortality. Use such tools as are at thy hand!"

Yet the next day, after a long, musing conversation which had grown ever and ever more earnest, he cried:

"Yes, the body is indeed subject to the great power of death. But there remaineth yet alive the shadow of life. It must be so, for this only is from the gods."

"The shadow of life!" repeated Aristodemos wonderingly.

Pindar mused on, the vision within him growing as he talked.

"Whosoever hath been of good courage and hath had pleasure in keeping oaths and hath refrained his soul from iniquity, he shall travel the way of Zeus to the Islands of the Blest. There:

> *"Evenly ever in sunlight night and day*
> *An unvexed life the good receive*
> *In that new world.*
>
> *"There ocean breezes waft,*
> *And golden flowers are glowing,*
> *Glowing on splendrous trees.*
>
> *"And other sweet flowers the water feedeth,*
> *With wreaths whereof the blessed ones*
> *Entwine their happy hands."*

He was lost, singing.

"But," blundered in Aristodemos, "yesterday thou wert saying, 'Desire not—' "

"Yesterday I had no vision. Today I have," said the seer. "Not desire a life immortal?" he repeated scornfully. "But I do desire it, and thou desirest it. We venture not to ask this from the gods. But—today I see it! I see it plain! The steadfast in courage shall surely live—

shall surely live. Heed what I say, my friend; for, by the gods, it is true!"

At these times not even the Hebrew prophets were more commanding than Pindar.

With such startling contradictions he stung Aristodemos into immortal aspirations. He seemed to swing him out of this contentious world into his own clear spaces of thought.

But at last the ship came which would take him to Corcyra, and Corcyra was a great port for the West. The poet and Nikander both went down to Kirrha with him. Nikander carried Mendi, who through these days had lived among his own children. The priest had grown very fond of the little fellow so happily snatched from slavery.

In the harbour rocked the ship *Thetis* at anchor.

"Thou art going a far journey," said Pindar, throwing his arm over Aristodemos's shoulder. "But thou wilt come back again when the quest is done."

"No, I think not."

"Nay, thou must come back! Whither wilt thou go?" Pindar was full of anxiety for him.

"Oh," said Aristodemos with sudden weariness, "then the gods will have done with me!"

He was finding it very difficult to part, still unrevealed, from his father's friend.

The sailors began to stir along the deck and to heave up the cable.

"They are ready!" cried Nikander, hurrying Aristodemos into the little boat and kissing Mendi as the slave dipped oars. Pindar ran out deep into the water, insisting ardently: "But thou must come! Here or at Thebes thou wilt always find me. Thou must come to me!" A few moments later Aristodemos had clambered lap into the busy, moving vessel. And Pindar and the priest were already distant figures on the beach.

All that day Aristodemos lay stretched upon the deck, while the shores of the Gulf drifted by—the retiring hills with their blue rifts and valley shadows. Mighty

Parnassos seemed scarce farther away at sunset than in the morning. He hardly knew why his mind should feel so enlarged, spacious as the wind-blown Sea. But Pindar's spirit was potent with him.

At nights the ship put in to shore, for merchantmen with valuable cargoes were discreet sailors. They would build a fire upon the beach and sit around it with brown faces to the light, talking loud, drinking deep, and sleeping under the stars.

At Corcyra, after two weeks of waiting, he found a vessel carrying Cyprus copper and Chian wine to Tarentum, in Italy. The *Boar* was altogether boarlike in shape, was furnished with a snout and tusks and had upon her bows two great eyes. How else could she see her way? She carried a broad low sail upon a central mast and was painted bright red.

With the weighing of the anchor Aristodemos saw the last of Greece. No more skirting of coasts. The clumsy vessel rounded the northern point of Corcyra, squared away her sail, and laid a direct course across for Italy. Now he was alone with his quest in that circle of sky-met sea, with the ship pointing unremittingly toward the sunset. He felt himself sailing out toward the world's end, toward life's end, so far as he could see. Beyond this last commission was nothing for him but the waste of the sea and to face his curse to the end.

Mendi was his stay. Aristodemos talked with him by the hour in low, musing tones, nervously grasping his little hands. But there was a doll-maker aboard with whom Mendi had fallen in love on the dock at Corcyra, a stocky man with a broad wrinkled face and a bald head, save for gray tufts at the temples. He had small eyes with drooping folded lids, which when he smiled radiated wrinkles as if his whole face were twinkling. He had fashioned the child a doll of clay. Aristodemos had never thought of a doll for so sensible a boy as Mendi. He had always treated Mendi as an equal. So Mendi would wriggle away, and when Aristodemos would go after him he would always find him in a circle of laughing sailors playing knucklebones or sitting upon the doll-maker's knee.

"Mendi, boy," said Aristodemos imprudently one day, as he brought him back for the fifth time, "dost not love thy Demos any longer?"

"Yes. I love Skyllis too. Skyllis made Mendi a—"

"Skyllis be hanged! He is an old slave dog!"

"Look," said Mendi contentedly, holding up his wretched doll.

"Child, child, what a hideous thing!" cried Aristodemos, pushing it away. Presently however Mendi trotted off again, and Aristodemos soon heard his silvery laugh amid the loud guffaws of the men, while he himself sat brooding foolishly alone.

But Mendi belonged to him! No one, slave nor king, should have one moment of the child until—

He rose with a sudden sweep of anger and strode forward to where Mendi sat among his merry comrades. Aristodemos's face silenced them. He snatched up the child and marched him back in disgrace. But there his silly anger melted.

"Do not leave me," he pleaded, holding him fast. "Do not leave thy Demos now. So soon I will see thee no more." And Mendi, awed by what he did not understand, crouched whimpering against Aristodemos's breast.

The *Boar* soon sighted Italy, crawled south around the heel of it, and sailed up into the Tarentine Gulf, landing at Tarentum. Here Aristodemos was very impatient at first, but as the days passed he lost his sense of haste. After all, was not each day as the last that he should keep his little son? For he now began more boldly to call Mendi his son, ignoring the anger of the gods. He played marbles, knucklebones—whatever Mendi commanded. He began to dread the coming of the Elean ship. But it did finally come, nevertheless, and aboard it the travellers began the longer portion or their voyage.

They sailed down the Leukanian coast, putting in at Herakleia, Siris, ruined Sybaris—now a byword for luxury—and Croton, where Pythagoras was still living and held to be well-nigh divine by the devoted Society about him. They also touched at Skylakion and Kaulonia.

At all the different ports Aristodemos went about the docks astonished at their noisy traffic and crowded shipping. He noticed in the streets how few were the old men he met, and how many the young, active men who walked swiftly and wore rich dress, like men who have lately grown prosperous. They talked with him readily. He noted in them a certain disposition to break away from old customs and to speak and act in their own original ways.

For Italy was then the new, untried land, "The West," the frontier of civilization. Hither came the adventurous blood. Here, as if blown across the sea, a new Hellas was blossoming. Yet, notwithstanding its prosperous activity, the chief strength of this early fifth-century "West" was really spiritual. It was new and lofty ideals of living, bold guesses of thought, fresh poesy, that these young colonists sent back to the mother land. The "Music of the Spheres," the noble "Pythagorean Brother-hood," the "Parmenadean Life" and its famed "Countenance of Peace"—these were the commerce of that ancient "West."

The voyage was not without its danger. Some months before this time Gelon, the tyrant of Syracuse, had conquered the Carthaginians at Himera and the sea was still strewn with that human wreckage of war—desperate men turned pirates.

As the ship rounded the southernmost cape of Italy a gale blew them off from the protecting land. Then the south wind seized them and blew them back again. It was then that they saw on the horizon a pointed sail that steadily drew near them. In spite of the high wind the crew ran to the halyards, hoisted the yard and shook down the whole great sail. The bulky merchant ship heeled and groaned under the unaccustomed urging. Aristodemos ran out from the cabin to find the deck standing aslant like a slippery wall, and the mast leaning almost level with the waves.

"Pirates! Pirates!" ran from one sailor's mouth to the next, and, fearing rude men more than the rude seas, they were trying the utmost power of their vessel. It was an unequal race. The long Punic warship, refitted for her disgraceful enterprise, leaped over the water like a hound.

Aristodemos stood clinging to the latticed bulwark, looking astern across the foam-flecked flood at the growing sail. The possibility of battle made his blood tingle. He waited with steady pleasure for the moment when the ships should grapple and he should use his sword again.

But that moment did not come. Under her labouring sail the merchantman still kept ahead of her foe. Then the storm closed down with rain and fog. Under cover of this they changed her course and escaped. But they lay hid several days in a narrow inlet before they ventured out again.

Then, hugging the coast of Italy, they crept past smoking Ætna, where the great earth-giant slumbered so uneasily, past Scylla and Charybdis and so sped north-ward toward their port of Elea.

CHAPTER THIRTY-ONE

A Philosopher in His Garden

There it is! Elea! Elea! Ee—lee—aa!" cried the lookout from the masthead.

The sailors on deck cut merry capers and shouted a noisy sea song in delight over the prosperous end of their long voyage. The uproar brought Aristodemos to the prow. But his landsman's eyes could make out nothing but the same low coast that they had been skirting for days. It seemed impossible that he could have arrived thus suddenly at the goal of his interminable journey from Sparta.

He dully watched the two headlands slowly open, revealing at last the obscure entrance to the Hales. How ran the Oracle?

> *"Touch thy far-wandering keel*
> *in the mud of the dark flowing Hales."*

"Far-wandering"—surely!

The ship made her way, with much laborious rowing and warping, up the little river into the artificial basin that was the port of Elea. From here they could see, still further up the stream, the white houses and red-tiled roofs of the town itself mounting the hill within its encircling walls. Far away from the world and the world's warring it seemed, and very secluded on the western coast of this western land. Here, if anywhere, men could practise undisturbed their own high virtues.

And in this town, at this very moment, was really

living—Mendi's father!

A sailor beside Aristodemos was looking along the wharf to another ship discharging there.

"Hello!" he cried. "If there isn't the 'Dolphin', already unloaded! And here comes the corn!" pointing to a line of slaves who were trotting up with full bags on their heads. Corn was the great return cargo from the West. "They'll be off again for old Cyprus tomorrow! Wonder if they'll run afoul of our Carthage friends! Tell 'em to keep a lookout!" Sailors from the world's ends are all neighbours in their own fashion.

Aristodemos led Mendi ashore and pushed his way up the crowded, clamorous wharf. The landing of a Tarentine ship was no small event and brought an eager swarm of humanity to the docks. Fruit and water vendors clamoured in his ear, hired-out slaves snatched at his luggage, shouting, "I carry for you! Carry for you!"

Piles of merchandise blocked his passage through the sheds—sacks of salt from Daunia, ironware from far Pontus, jars of Cyprus wine, oil of old Hellas and of the new olives of Italy, spices from the East, pottery, smoked and salt fish, tar and coils of rope. And back of all were the great mounds of corn-bags awaiting shipment, all piled so close that a landsman must wonder how ships or men could find their own. And oh, the smells of it all!

Aristodemos pushed through the press and hurried on past the bazaars of the port. But how was he to find Mendi's father?

"Find thee a man of wisdom profound:
profounder his sorrow!"

It was after all but a vague description. And he was utterly weary of difficulties!

A lusty merchant hailed him from his little booth.

"Come here to live with us, Master? Ye couldn't do better. 'Tis the town of the whole coast!"

"No, I'm' only a traveller," said Aristodemos. Then he realized that he had best begin his search at once.

THE SPARTAN

He turned to the merchant and asked clumsily:

"Was this town ever attacked by pirates? Or did you perhaps ever hear of a dame and her son being carried off, two or three years ago?"

"What—what's that?" The man began to bustle indignantly among his wares. "By Plutean Hermes, no! Pirates! I'd have ye understand, stranger, that this town is just as safe and civilized as any in old Hellas—aye, and better governed! And look at the trade—"

"I'm not a tradesman, I say," interposed Aristodemos impatiently.

"What be ye then? I tell ye we don't have pirates here! No, nor women-stealers! What be ye after, anyhow? What be ye after?"

Aristodemos began to see trouble ahead. A stranger was very much an alien in a city where he had no citizen rights. Men about them were beginning to stop their trade and listen.

"It was but a story I heard," he said.

"And a lie it was!" shouted the man. "A lie to ruin trade. Never you believe it—not for a moment!"

The man evidently was of a quick temper and uncertain tongue. Yet Aristodemos caught at his words with a sort of hope that he was really ashamed of. Perhaps after all Mendi might not have come from this town. The Oracle might have had some meaning which even the priests had misunderstood. And, should the father not be found, Mendi would remain his own son.

Aristodemos and Mendi now left the port and approached the city gates. He was not without misgiving as to their reception. For the merchant had been testy.

But once within the walls all his doubts vanished. The spirit of the community could be sensed like an aroma. Pleasant streets led up the hill whereon a temple fashioned like the temples at home and holding the home gods, smiled out over the western sea. The town was not close-crowded within its walls as an older town would be. Orange trees ashine with golden fruit stood about the low white houses.

A PHILOSOPHER IN HIS GARDEN

In the streets the young citizens strode past each other as though the whole world were unweighted with years and full of a glad vigour like their own. They greeted Aristodemos with free and friendly looks, as men who had dared the unknown western oceans and had caught the mood of mental and social bigness.

Toward the hilltop Aristodemos touched one of the young men on the arm.

"Canst thou tell me where I may look for a lodging?" he asked.

The Elean gave him courteous direction, and added: "We do not see many strangers here in Elea—that is, save traders. And thou art not a trader."

"No."

"Thou'lt like our city," said the man with a touch of welcome and pride. "There is no city in all Hellas that hath so enlightened laws."

"Enlightened laws—and so far away?"

"Hast thou not heard?" the Elean asked incredulous. For to the colonist his own colony was all the world.

"I have not been where I might hear," said Aristodemos.

"We have our laws," went on the Elean with a quick ring in his voice, "because we have our Lawgiver. He indeed is Elea. Every year it is the Elean custom for the citizens to swear afresh to keep his laws. For they are not like the laws of other men. They are like the words of the gods."

Aristodemos's face went ashen white. The Pythia's wailing voice rang in his memory -

> "He giveth laws to a people
> Not like the laws of other peoples."

"What is thy ruler's name?" he asked quietly.

"But Parmenides is not our ruler," answered the young man joyously. "He is our philosopher and he guides the city out of the wise kindness of his heart. Young man, thou art a brave dissembler, but art expressly come, nevertheless, to sit at his feet. Be thankful that thou mayest. Men come even from Croton, from the divine Pythagoras himself, to listen to him. For he hath the secret beyond the secret."

> "—of wisdom profound:
>   profounder his sorrow!"

sang the insistent Oracle.

"Tell me," broke out Aristodemos, "hath this Parmenides some sorrow, some great sorrow?"

The Elean caught his arm.

"Do not speak of it so plainly, here in the public street. We who love him never talk of it at all."

"But I must know," said Aristodemos in his deep voice, so earnestly that the young man led him to a quiet place apart.

"I will tell thee," he said hastily. "But never think that this sorrow is the displeasure of the gods. They do not so. They do not harass men."

"But what is it?" quivered Aristodemos impatiently. Moralizing was not his need just now.

"It was two years ago. Some Tyrian merchants came displaying choice silks and brazen wares upon the outer beach. Everybody went to see. But that evening Parmenides's little son was not to be found in the house. Parmenides and his slaves went out to search for him. And the mother must have gone out afterward. She was not like a woman, for she could think and was not afraid.

Someone saw her running alone down the beach road, calling for the child. But we know nothing more, save that in the morning the merchants were gone and the woman as well as the child had disappeared."

Oh, the Oracle—the Oracle! How had he ever dared to doubt it?

He had yet one more question.

"Hath the philosopher—perhaps—a new marriage?—a new heir?"

"Parmenides? Oh no. Honourable and rich fathers have offered their daughters. I do believe that, philosopher though he is, he is secretly eating his heart out in longing for his wife and son." The young devotee sighed. "It is difficult to put by the things of this world."

Aristodemos's eyes suddenly filled. But the tears were for himself and not at all for the sorrowing father.

"I see that thou art near to this matter," said the Elean. Aristodemos seized both his hands.

"Yes, yes—I am near to it. But for the love of the gods, be silent. I will do well, not ill, I promise thee. Do not speak of me!"

"I will not," said the young man, wondering at him. "Thy secret is thine own." But before he could speak further Aristodemos had caught up Mendi and hurried on.

The inn was at a corner of the market. On the way thither Mendi stopped him before a toy booth, wanting to buy.

"Whatever thou wilt," said Aristodemos, setting him down before the booth. Mendi choose a little rolling wheel, and Aristodemos gave the man a gold coin. The merchant returned the change in silver. Then Mendi, dropping his wheel, drew down Aristodemos's palm to look within.

"O-oh!" he shouted. "Many, many luckpennies! All my penny! Demos—look! All my penny!"

Aristodemos looked with amazement. They were indeed the self-same coin—the Athena head, the lion—quite the same. "But no—not quite the same," he told Mendi, as with shaking fingers he lifted the child's well known piece. "Thine saith, 'ΠΑΡ—'"

"'ΜΕΝΙΔΕΣ,'surely Parmenides'." Put in the grinning merchant.

"The gods are pursuing me!" thought Aristodemos, and he hurried to the inn.

They had a cell-like room and a narrow couch. For the Greeks never learned the comfort of sleeping spaciously. Aristodemos lay all night open-eyed. Once he leaned over close to the child in the darkness, smoothing the cover, and Mendi threw out a hot little hand, murmuring, "Demos—Demos." Was he indeed so constantly in the child's mind? He re-lived that last evening in Sparta. "Nobody followed me," said Aristodemos, "nobody but thou, little man."

And now Mendi's unconsciousness of the parting began to smite him in the darkness with a sense of his having deceived the child. It seemed the last refined cruelty of the gods, to take away his son so unpreparedly at the last.

"He is mine! He is mine!" he kept repeating to himself.

Gray dawn at last crept into the room. Then the golden sunrise.

Aristodemos rose, washed Mendi's whole body and combed his hair. He dressed him in a little white chiton which he had bought yesterday of the merchant at the port. Then he gave him food. He lingered with exquisite care over these services.

"Demos makes Mendi beautiful!" said the child, delighted.

"The gods have made thee beautiful," said Aristodemos, kissing the fresh little face. "When thou art a man thou wilt be more beautiful still."

"When I be man, I be like my Demos," laughed Mendi, running his two hands into Aristodemos's thick hair and pulling his head down beside his own.

They went out into the staring sunshine. Men were passing to and fro, even as yesterday.

"Where will I find Parmenides?" he asked.

"At this hour," they told him, "he walks in his garden." So, following their direction, Aristodemos passed out through the farther gate of the city and along a ridge where he soon came upon the garden. It was enclosed in a luxuriant hedge, a pleasant place, with shadowy trees and many flowers, grown evidently for use in the garden's tiny temple. For the Greeks, lovers of flowers though they were, never had gardens or used flowers for themselves. Gardens were always sacred, always planted to pleasure the Immortals, and were enjoyed only as casual privileges by mortals entering there.

Aristodemos holding Mendi's hand crept into the hedge and peeped through. He seemed to be fulfilling some blind obedience of which he scarce remembered the meaning. He could see near at hand a grassy space with a small altar. Farther away was the little temple among the trees. He could hear voices, but the speakers were hidden from him behind flowering oleanders.

An eager, youthful voice was saying:

"But, Parmenides, the earth moves in a perfectly meted path, and the measured stars circling in heaven give forth their divine chorus of ordered song. As saith Herakleitos, 'The invisible harmony is better than the visible, the unheard than the heard.' Is not this subtle potency of number immanent in all the universe? And is not this the First Principle? Surely, Parmenides, you can not go beyond this?"

Evidently this was some young disciple of Pythagoras newly come from Croton. Aristodemos was startled out of his dullness by the strange, far-searching words.

"But I do go beyond it," came a rich deep voice, the very essence of quietude. "Beyond number itself is the thought of number. Thought is pure reality. And 'Thought' is one and the same with 'That-to-which-thought-is-directed.' It is indifferent," he added, "where I begin; for thither I shall return again."

"But 'Thought'?" came again the boyish, troubled voice. "Dost thou mean my thinking and thine?"

"Yes, and all thinking. But beyond 'Thought' again is 'Being'," said the authoritative one, "for without 'Being' thou wilt find no thought. 'Being' is birthless, deathless, knows no 'was' nor 'shall be' but ever 'is'. Go tell them that at Croton. Ah, Polykritos, such thoughts as these are like immortal charioteers. Sometimes they bear me aloft to the uttermost parts of heaven, to the gates of Day and Night."

Parmenides spoke with inspired conviction. Even philosophers were young in Italy then, and did not doubt but they might win the very essence of all truth. This man, shut away from other sages, undiscouraged by others' failures, thought with an almost childish directness unhampered by sidelong speculation and with a poet's glow of imagination. The note of bitterness that sounds through the questions of Socrates was not in him.

The Pythagorean youth, Polykritos, lifted once more his argumentative voice. But Aristodemos did not hear him. Under his laurel hedge he was opening a clear, unspoiled mind like a chalice, to the fulfilling wisdom which he had heard. Could it be that behind the changeful procession of the glorious Immortals was "The One?" His thought grew dizzy with the uplift.

Mendi began to move restlessly.

"Be still," he commanded in a whisper. "Thy father is speaking! Thy father! Dost not hear him?"

But the discussion was already ended. Polykritos was now taking his leave. Presently a slave boy appeared and set incense and barley by the altar, making ready for the sacrifice.

Then along the green path with bent thoughtful head, came the Philosopher himself.

Aristodemos had not expected to see a man like this.

He was not beyond thirty-five years, and he had a look of out-of-doors and of abundant life. Yet withal there was the scholar's gentleness in his bearing, and his eyes had the look of deep inner absorption which comes of dwelling with the invisible. His slender face was one to move the soul like a great quiet song, for in this young man had grown up the imperturbable virtue of the wise. Socrates, that ruthless old scrutinizer, who saw him fully sixty years later than this, says of him:

"I have a kind of reverence, not so much for Melissos and the others who say that 'All is one and at rest' as for the great leader himself, Parmenides, venerable and 'aweful' as in Homeric language he may be called. Him I should be ashamed to approach in a spirit unworthy of him. I met him when he was an old man and I a mere youth, and he appeared to me to have a glorious depth of mind. And I am afraid we may not fully understand his language and may fall short even more of his meaning.

The young philosopher was busying himself about the altar. He lighted the incense and the dim blue smoke rose among the quiet trees. Then, standing back from the altar, he lifted up his hands and began aloud, as was Greek custom, his morning prayer.

My God, who art the One Being, whom men have not known, worshipping the beautiful fleeting images of thee—My God, Indivisible, Birthless and Deathless, take me to Thyself! For I like thee am a thinking being, and thought to thought unites, as flame to flame.

"Oh, keep me from the all-incredible path that leadeth backward to confusion, for now I am grievously like to stumble into it. Relieve me from this my sorrow. Love first of all thou didst create. But love confuseth and shattereth the mind. Whom I have lost, I have lost. Keep my thoughts from her. Let me not still forever like a fool expect her, putting, with every footstep, every sound, the sword afresh into my heart."

He began, to pace back and forth before the altar, more at struggle with himself than at prayer.

"Where is my strength?" he cried. "Where is my wisdom? They flow from me like water! I lose them! Day by day the vision departeth from me! And my son— oh, my little son! Must he wander and suffer afar, his sweet mind darkened by the words of foolish men— dumb, unreasoning cattle? Or hast thou snatched him from degradation by swift death?" He stopped suddenly. "Oh, God, let me know him dead! A sign—a sign!"

Tears broke his voice. Tears ran down his rare dispassionate face. Aristodemos heard him breathing like one in pain, and lowered his eyes. To see that lofty, calm mind breaking with sorrow was beyond his daring. So, turning, Aristodemos saw Mendi close at his knee and fast asleep. He lifted him.

"Demos will go now?" said the sleepy little voice.

"Hush, child." Aristodemos as he spoke was aware that he was weeping. Yet he was very deliberate.

He stripped off the single little garment, so that Mendi was clothed upon only with his luckpenny and his own childish beauty.

"Now!" he whispered, kissing the plump shoulders. "Thou must go out to that man yonder; Lift thy luckpenny thus in thy hand, and say to him, 'Father, I am thy son. I am come from Delphic Apollo.' Oh, but canst thou say it?"

But Parmenides had heard the stirring in the bushes and now began to look about, confused. Aristodemos quickly thrust the child out of the hedge with the stern, unwonted whisper, "Go straight to him. Else I whip thee!"

And Mendi, scared and stumbling, ran to the altar and his father's knee.

For a moment Parmenides looked upon him unchanged. Then there fell upon his face such a light of joy as Aristodemos had never seen. Nor even then did Parmenides cry out, but fell upon his knees before the child as if suddenly bereft of all strength.

"Ye gods! Ye gods!" he said in a ringing whisper, as he laid his hands upon the little body. Their two faces, brought thus together, were wonderfully alike.

Aristodemos thought that Mendi would forget all his message. Yet his last sight of the child was to be that of his obedience. He lifted the luckpenny as bidden, and began to repeat the words, "Father, I am thy son. Come from Delphi 'Pollo."

But Parmenides kissed the speaking lips and laid his cheek over the amulet against the little breast.

"My son!" he said with infinite tenderness. "What need have I of a token. Thou art all token. All my son, my son, my son!"

With that word ringing in his ears Aristodemos crept

out to the road. He started dazedly toward the city. He was seeing nothing—nothing but that blessed joy in the face of Parmenides. Over and over again his memory kept performing that change until the transformation became his own. The happiness of Parmenides swept utterly through him.

He stopped in the road, amazed. To his Greek mind this just and reasonable joy was quite inexplicable. It did not occur to him to connect it with the restoration which he had just accomplished. He had undertaken it in despair, knowing that upon its completion he would be barred forever from every honourable activity by his curse. Ah, the curse—could it be alifting? But no, curses never lifted; they fulfilled—fulfilled to the end.

Yet again the happiness flooded him.

"Apollo, Oh, Apollo!" he sobbed in, desperate doubt. "Why dost thou entrap me? I obeyed thine Oracle. What art thou doing unto me?"

Word and prayer died upon his lips in the agony of his questioning. Suddenly he seemed to hear actual words.

"Was not I, too, once unclean? And hast thou not borne the yoke upon thy shoulders even as I, Apollo, bore it in the fields of Admetos? By the yoke was I cleansed!"

The yoke—? Why—yes, the yoke in Klitor's hut! Aristodemos had quite forgotten how, from ancient days, the Bearing-of-the-Yoke had been the ritual-cleansing from blood guiltiness and curse.

"Is it that? Is it that, dear Son of Leto? The little yoke I bore for Klitor?"

Suddenly he knew his answer:

"Thou hast fulfilled thy sorrow.
Apollo makes thee free!"

He stood there in the road, trembling, convinced, quiet, tears wetting his face, yet his face aflame. He could not comprehend this freedom!

Suddenly he loosed a mighty war-shout alone there on the country road.

"I can fight for Hellas! Paian! O Paian!"

Then he leaped and ran headlong, not through the city but down the rough hill and along the river for the port. The "Dolphin," that ship for Cyprus! She was to be off to-day. He might yet win to her!

He reached the wharves, pushed shouting through the confusion and the crowds. The "Dolphin" was already out in the stream floating down with the current. The sailors were shaking down the sail. Aristodemos called wildly to a boatman and offered him such a fare as made him spring to his oars.

"Ahoy! Ahoy!" shouted Aristodemos from his skiff, while the swarming labourers and sailors crowded the edge of the docks and swelled the laughing uproar—"A passenger! A passenger!"

The seamen heard. They loosed sheets, turned their flapping sail into the wind and lost a little headway. In a moment the breathless rowing boatman had brought Aristodemos to the ship's side.

"What's this?" roared the captain. "Just a madman? I thought the whole city must be afire!"

"No, it is only a soldier!" said Aristodemos still in a voice of shouting. "A soldier who is going back to Hellas and to fight!"

CHAPTER THIRTY-TWO

Through Unwilling Seas

That night he slept as he had not slept for a year. He lay at the prow between sea and stars. One deep long breath, and day surprised him. He awoke refreshed as a child. It was as though he had been long ill without knowing it, and now was suddenly well.

He saw the sun spring up out of the sea—not Phœbus's self, yet in some sort the splendour of his power, the flaming signal of the God of Purifications.

"Blessed Son of Leto!" he cried. "Thou, even thou, hast lifted my curse and given me wings!"

The ship beneath him was leaping its way onward through the bright sea. He took up his fresh gift of life. He would go to Pindar. Now he could confess himself Lykos's son. He would take to himself this good love of his father's friend. All life he would take to the full. He would hurry to the Athenian army. Sparta was out of the question. Ah, he had always been an Athenian, never a Spartan. He would go to his birthplace among clear-thinking men.

As he lay there on the deck the deified Leonidas seemed to be with him almost visibly at his side.

"Dost not see, Leondrion," he whispered intensely, "I am going into battle. Come, fight with me again for Hellas as our Kastor and Polydeukes fight among the host. Hellas hath need of thee!" So he persuaded the hero-spirit of his friend.

Then, roused by his surging thoughts, he rose and strode among the men. The sailors who had brought him to Elea would never have recognized their wan-faced, silent passenger in this full-lifed young man. He talked and sang with the crew, spoke cheerily to the slaves, and told merry stories by the camp fire when they bivouacked ashore at night. On days of calm he would stamp the deck with impatience. Yet, even then he would laugh at his own bad temper.

The "Dolphin" rounded southern Italy, coasted up into the Tarentine Gulf with the usual landings and interruptions, made out again and, free of Iapygia, spread wing at last for Greece. But oh, the journey was as long as a life! How could it be otherwise, with his heart so leaping out of him toward Greece; and his body lagging in a half helpless ship at every caprice of the delaying sea?

Two days of favouring wind brought them across to Corcyra, where, barely touching, the little ship flew down the island-guarded shore of Akarnania, past the broad opening of the Corinthian Gulf and southward still, skirting the shores of Peloponnese, where faint and far inland, like white Titans against the sky. Aristodemos could discern the pure peaks of Taÿgetos.

When the morning was calm he would dive from the side, vent his strength upon the sea, climb in again puffing and laughing, shake his streaming hair out of his eyes and take breath for another day. It was thus he put off his consuming dread that the battles might be fought before he could reach the army.

They touched at Pylos. Aristodemos questioned breathlessly. Here was news at last!

Mardonios had wintered in Thessaly. He had kept with him the best fighting troops of Persia—a vast host still, and the more powerful for the pruning away of the rabble. Mardonios was expected to march upon Athens. But whether he had yet marched they did not know.

Aristodemos ran back to the ship.

"O, ye gods," he cried as the ship weighed anchor once more, "bring me there in time!"

But at this first contact with Greece he had come once more within the dread circle of the great Persian Shadow. Pindar had called it, "The Tantalos Stone that is hanging over us." For ten years it had hung over Hellas. There had been no real relief. Marathon. Thermopylæ, Salamis—all these were but heroic incidents in a useless resistance. Hellas lacked still the conclusive achievement that was to render all these battles victories.

Those meagre, half snatched tidings at Pylos must suffice Aristodemos until the "Dolphin" should reach her haven at Cythera. There he could easily get swift ship for Athens. But he felt as if he could not endure the suspense another day.

They rounded Cape Tænarum. Already the barren gray outline of Cythera was rising from the sea, a desolate birthplace for the tender goddess of love. But there under those treacherous high promontories a quick northern blast swept down upon the little ship with blinding rain, driving her helpless down the Southern Sea in instant fear of foundering. Then the wind abated and left them with huddled sail, unknowing where they were. Once more they turned northward and the fourth morning sighted Crete stretching like a long and lofty wall across the entrance to the Ægean. Based in the purple sea and soaring with billowing peaks into the snows of upper air, it seemed set there in the buoyant morning gloriously to enclose Greece and her precious islands from the world.

And is that Crete?" asked Aristodemos of the captain, shading his eyes for the brightness of those snowy summits.

"Praise Aphrodite, it is!"

"And then we will soon make Cythera?"

Cythera! Not he! He could better market his corn in Crete, now that he was so near. That he was consigned to Cythera mattered little to a Grecian captain. And the trifling consideration of a passenger's convenience was of no weight whatever. So Aristodemos together with the corn and the other merchandise was dumped on the wharf at Lebena, the port of Gortyna, on the southern shore of Crete.

THE SPARTAN

Aristodemos quickly got him across the Cretan ridge to Knosos on the northern shore. Here the citizens were full of rumours of the war, how obtained it would be hard to say. But sailors have far-hearing ears.

First of all, Mardonios had marched south from Thessaly. To the restless Aristodemos this news was harrowing to the last degree.

And—"the tempting of Athens!" had the stranger heard of that? No? Then was he to hear a most glorious thing! Mardonios had sent envoys and tempted Athens with an overwhelming bribe. He had offered them the security of their own Attica and the possession of any other land of Hellas which they might choose, if only they would ally with Persia.

"And Athens's answer?" burst in Aristodemos, his blood suddenly singing in his ears.

The famous Athenian answer had already passed into tradition.

"There is not gold enough on earth, nor under it, nor any land so goodly, that we should consent to take them and enslave Hellas by making any alliance with the Medes!"

"Oh, ye gods, what a city!" cried out Aristodemos.

"Of course Mardonios is in a fury. And he has marched straight upon Athens."

Aristodemos's face grew stern with the sudden realizing of the terrible cost Athens was paying for her fidelity to Greece.

"Have not the Spartans come to Athens?" he asked sharply.

"I have heard that the Athenians are expecting them. If only some ship would bring us news! Perhaps they are fighting now!"

"Fighting now!" groaned Aristodemos as he turned and hurried to the shore. Only now did he begin to realize the calamity of this Cretan stoppage. In time of peace he could have got ship for Athens almost any day. But the long Persian war had swept the Ægean as clear of sails as an undiscovered sea. Day by day he haunted the docks, straining his eyes for a sail until his sight grew confused and he saw sails where sails there were none. There seemed some wild thing in his breast trying to leap out across the Cretan Sea. The men about the wharves grew familiar with his restless pacing figure.

After three weeks a single ship appeared. Aristodemos was aboard her before she could anchor. She was a merchant vessel of Eubœa and the captain calmly announced that he was going home. The Cretans cried out against such folly. But the man had had a long and terrible faring. He was going home, he said, and to stay. He was minded to see whether he could recognize his wife, and whether or not his little lad had grown a beard. Aristodemos threw his arms about the stubborn sailor-man and kissed him. He saw from his very jolly reck-lessness that the man was not to be restrained.

So the next morning Aristodemos was away with him on the purple, crisping sea, sail to the wind, keel to the foam, both singing the steady music of a ship before the breeze. The second morning Melos grew great before them, and shortly afterward they glided in among the Cyclades. On all sides in the expanse of the Ægean lay "The Islands," delicate ashen gray upon the violet sea.

Night fell, and still the ship sped on. Blessed winds, blowing so steadily from the south! Blessed homesick captain, who for his homesickness would not loiter! On they sped in the moon's full light, leaving a silvery wake heaving upon the sea. Soft sea mists lay about the Islands' bases, but their summits rose clear in the moon-light—there and there, and there. Aristodemos could number them as if it were day.

Rest he could not. The going! The going! It was to him like the satisfying of hunger.

Another day they sped, and presently rounding Keos, entered the quiet waters between Attica and Eubœa. The captain had promised to set Aristodemos on the Attic shore.

Night came at last. The captain put in under the

shore, lowered a boat, and rumbled him a hearty goodbye. Then Aristodemos was in the little skiff creeping alone in the misty dark, the shore looming larger, larger before him. Could it be Attica thus stepping at once into reality, after the long years?

He leaped ashore and made his way up the silent beach. He was strangely quiet of heart. The rising moon showed that he had landed in a little bay almost circled by a rocky headland where in the midst lay a small peaked island, sharp against the moon. Then with a flash he recognized the place. By a strange chance he had come ashore upon the very region of his father's tribal land. Yonder were the fields that Lykos had been visiting the day Aristodemos was born. That dark opening beyond was the glen where Aristodemos as a boy had used to hear the nightingales. And oh, the smell of the stubble giving forth its fragrance to the dews! He could see no more for the sudden tumult and the tears.

He hurried forward along the well known path. Oh the fair land, the fair land! How it sang to his heart in the moonlight! How infinitely sweet was the road's every turning—the expectancy of what lay beyond and of finding it unchanged, eloquent of memory. All the loves of his life seemed to sweep into the one love of homeland.

Tomorrow he would be in Athens. Its familiar streets, temples and sunny colonnades shone bright as day within his mind. His love was like sight.

Then of a sudden the desertedness of the land smote him. He began to see that the region was changed. The Persian had been here. His mark lay everywhere upon the wasted fields, upon the broken farm huts whose doors hung open vacantly. He passed little groves of pine trees, sacred and still, whose very stillness made the menace more oppressive.

His course, however, was plain. He must get around the Persians to the Athenian army wherever it might be. Was the enemy at Athens? Had the Athenians fled? Had they fought that day? Would they be fighting to-morrow? He had not a single clew. Nor had he met a soul upon the road. The peasants must have fled to the hills. He must be quick. An hour's delay now might lose him his battle-chance. He hurried on under the brightening moon, looking keenly for some indication.

As he neared the base of Hymettos he saw beyond a field a faint gleam of light from a thicket. Peasant or Persian would afford him some knowledge of his way, and knowledge he must have. He crept across the field.

In the thicket he perceived a low hut with open door. No peasant, surely, would be so foolhardy as to keep a light. He drew near and listened. All was quiet. Making ready his weapon he cautiously looked in. The place seemed empty. Then in the corner on a heap of straw, he saw no man, but a woman asleep. A woman? A mere slip of a peasant girl pale and lean, a black tangle of hair half hiding her face.

Without a stir her eyes opened and gazed wide upon Aristodemos, two black pools of terror. He tried to speak low to her, but she broke in with her cries:

"O—oh, oh! I thought the Persians were gone! Don't take me off, Master! Master; don't take me off!"

"Hush—hush!" commanded Aristodemos.

But she flattened herself against the wall and kept whispering on, "Don't take me off!"

"Woman," he cried with rising impatience, "use eyes and sense! I am an Athenian! Where is the Athenian army?"

She opened her mouth and gazed at him. "Athenian? But the Persians be all about!"

"Are they at Athens?"

"Yes, at Athens."

"When were they here?"

"Fore yesterday. They came on a sudden. They killed my man in the field. And his father and mother got off to the hills, and took my baby. Oh, they took my baby away with them! They would not leave him to me! They took my baby off to the hills!"

She began to cry again, putting her rough peasant fists into her eyes like a child.

"But where are the Athenians?" he urged again.

"Oh, how do I know?" she sobbed. "But all the Persians have gone back to Athens. And why don't the old mother bring me back my son again? He hath no fit food in the hills, and here my breasts are full with the milk that is his!"

Aristodemos was turning hurriedly away. But the misery of the little mother-figure made him pause upon the threshold.

"Why not go after the Child thyself?"

"He is only two days born—my first born!"

Aristodemos knew the sturdy ways of these peasant mothers.

"Still thou couldst follow," he said.

"Nay, Master, I would follow," she urged, "but my leg here is broke."

He stepped quickly back into the hut again. "Great Zeus!" he said with that deepening of voice he had when suddenly moved, "and hast thou been alone here in pain?"

She did not answer. This question was beside her point.

"They will come back," she pleaded. "Will they not? See. I have set the light. They will see the light and know that the house is safe again. Won't they come, then?"

"Art thou not afraid to lie here with the light that anyone may see?"

She shook her head. "I have oil. Oh, I will keep it burning! They must see it soon. It is so hard to wait!"

"Zeus be merciful! And thou naught but a child!"

At this she took offence. "My son will not call me a child."

"Nor will I! Nor will I."

Aristodemos had seen the wellspring outside. He hurriedly refilled her jug and set it beside her. Then he opened his wallet and gave her well nigh all his store.

THROUGH UNWILLING SEAS

And while she still dumbly wondered at him he left her.

"I am a fool," he told himself as he strode along the road again, "to give away my bread. I have grown soft with much wandering!" But his heart beat to the high tune, and he could not put by the ragged figure with the generous breasts and the childish waiting eyes. The incident greatly intensified his sense of the bitter danger he so longed to lift. Her patient, perilous waiting seemed one with the waiting of Hellas.

As night deepened he began to climb the well remembered pass of Hymettos. He held his Cretan sword bare in his hand. For Hymettos Pass would be sentinelled. If he could get across Hymettos perhaps he could see the situation of the armies on the Attic plain.

The moon set as he climbed. He climbed on cautiously in the darkness, making his way from height to height. He reached the top. But still he saw no sign of Persian guard or any trace of man. He crossed the ridge and made his way down the more gradual slopes of the Athenian side. Presently he left the travelled way and keeping to the hills made for a high, projecting spur overlooking the city. At last he knew that Athens must lie beneath him. He shaded his eyes, but in the first gray of dawn could see nothing. The suspense of this last impatient moment was insupportable.

The day broke slowly. It was the roads that first grew visible, the Eleusis road and the straight road to the sea. Then the olive clumps pricked through the mists of the Ilissos. Then suddenly the whole sky was a-sail with soft pink clouds and the Saronic Gulf ran in ruddy fire and little Salamis, only a year old to fame, rose like a purple hyacinth from the sea.

But what was this appearance in the plain below him—this wheel-shaped space of blackness? A breath of smoke drew from it, fouling the delicate mists. A ragged hill of ruins rose in the midst.

Athens! Oh, crown of woes! Not Athens burned as a year ago; but Athens ruined, destroyed, changed like a face of death. He trembled so that for a moment he could not look. He stood dull with whirling mind. Athens—destroyed! Athens—destroyed! Then where were the Persians? He brushed his confused eyes and began to scan the plain for her destroyers. But to his amazement he saw no sign of them anywhere. Still he stood upon his ledge, gazing, gazing! He was astounded and astray.

Then he took his decision, and plunged down the mountain. The Persians would not be in that burned city. They must have destroyed because they were about to depart. But the Athenians—why, the Athenians would cling to Athens. He was sure to find some Athenians there—if not the army.

He reached the little valley of the Ilissos and recklessly made for the Olympieion. The great temple, still unfinished, stood outside the city wall, its huge columns silent in the morning. Aristodemos crept within. From here he could watch the spring, Kallirrhoë. If any Persian garrison remained, the men would show themselves here at the city's chief water supply. Or, if the city held Athenians, they too must come. An hour he watched. But neither Persian nor Athenian came down the worn path. At intervals a thrush in the thicket scattered the silence.

He was deeply puzzled. He stepped out, resolved to take his chance. A section of the great city wall had been pulled down. He clambered over, and saw—oh, what he saw!

At first he recognized nothing. Then he could make out that the place of fire-blasted trees below him had been the Precinct of the Lenaian Dionysos, and those tumbled blocks and columns the god's little temple, the broken wine jars telling of its merry spring festival where the freemen had tasted the new vintage.

A lame, dwarfish slave was skulking among the jars, but catching sight of Aristodemos he cried out in a sort of gibberish and fled hobbling away. Aristodemos sprang down from the wall and caught him, only to find that he was deaf and mute as well as lame. No wonder the

Persian had left him behind.

Then Aristodemos ran on headlong toward the mid-city, crunching with his blackened sandals the cinders of precious things, leaping the fallen house-walls in his way. Was it for this that he had come so far? He began to cry out as he ran:

"Athens, O Athens! Art thou no more, and can I yet be alive!"

He came to the little valley between the Pnyx and the Acropolis. This was one of the oldest quarters of Athens, where the early population had crowded like confined waters between hills. Here had stood the huddled dwellings roof to roof, rude ancestral homes proudly owned by families of old Athenian blood. Here had wound the tortuous, narrow streets, full of neighbour-folk, obstructed with herms at the corners and with door-way pillar-gods. It had been a busy place, difficult to thread without many a stoppage and delay. But now he could walk straight across the quarter as across an open field. Masses of charred timbers, low walls, quadrangles curiously small filled with ruin of thatch and household wreckage—these were all that remained of the homes he had known so well.

Oh, the aloneness of the place! Only the fountain at the foot of Pnyx Hill broke the silence with its continuous pouring. The waters gushed cheerily from the familiar lion mouths. Ah, generous little fountain. No one to drink of thee now!

Aristodemos turned and ran up the Nine-Gated Terraces of the Acropolis height. Up there surely there must be some little faithfulness, some priests who had remained hid in the temple.

His dear temple of Athena, the bright Hecatompedon, was a row of blackened pillar-stumps upholding nothing. The whole shrine lay open to the immodest glare of the sun. Even the aloof, dim chamber of the goddess was ravished of its privacy. The morning breeze swept wantonly through, whirling the ashes along the marble floor. The brilliant sculptures lay heaped in fragments all about him—Herakles down-hurled from his lofty pediment lay among the broken coils of his gorgeous Snake—Athena herself, her arms off at the elbows and fallen erect among the ruins, seemed still to menace the broken Giant at her feet. And everywhere, everywhere his childhood's favourites, the Korai, those delicate maiden statues, smiled up to him from the littered ground. And—oh, horror!—was that his mother's face there among them? Was she pursuing him here? But it was only the statue he was used to think so like her in his childish days.

Aristodemos was crying now like a child, unrestrainedly and aloud. It was the broken crying of a man who has lost his grasp and is bewildered. His Athens was obliterated.

He stumbled blindly down the steep again. Just within the Nine-Gates his foot struck something that rang out. It was an Athenian cuirass, a spoil dropped by the Persians. Its crested helm lay near together with its shield, a splendid thing blazoning Athena's owl, emblem of the beloved, vanished city. The sight brought him to himself. He lifted the shield to its place on his arm. The touch of it was like a draught of new wine.

He came to his own quarter, the Inner Kerameikos. But here he turned away his head as he ran, lest he see his father's house and be again unmanned.

But where—where were the Athenians? He must find them, if only a remnant of the army. He must find them if only to die with them, now that this last struggle was come. But where? Where?

Suddenly he recalled as an almost forgotten dream that he had heard the sailors of Antikyra say: "Before the Salamis battle all the Athenians retired to Salamis Island." Salamis? Had they perhaps gone thither again? His heart lifted with the hope.

He now found himself at the Thriasian Gate, upon the Eleusis Road. He would hurry to Eleusis, where he was sure of a boat to cross to Salamis. His road ran through the Outer Kerameikos. Here he suddenly came face to face with his father's tomb. "Father, my father!" he sobbed, for a carven portrait of Lykos had been set there. The tomb had been changed. Someone, Pindar no doubt, had carved upon it the old epitaph:

"Pity me, who was so beautiful and am dead."

"No, my father!" Aristodemos spoke aloud to his dead. "Rather pity me who must live and see what I have seen."

Did the grave speak, or was it his own booming thought that answered him? Suddenly the whole vast wrong and ruin seemed to sweep through and infuriate him.

He sprang away with face terrible of expression. He rushed down the road heavily yet swiftly like a maddened bull. He was filled with a wrath that was in itself a strength. Mile upon mile he ran, feeling no weight, though his new armour was heavy upon him. He ran through the olive wood, leaped the Kephissos at a bound.

Familiar things he passed unseeing. There was in him a battle-hunger which drove him. No restraint was left in him. He must find the army. He must fight now, or go mad.

At the hill of Aigaleos he slowed a little. Then he climbed on with incredible strength. At last he found himself at the well known turn of the hill that would reveal to him Salamis and its bay and Eleusis on the low, curving shore. He paused, dreading to look. What if they had destroyed Eleusis also?

He swept around the turn.

Merciful Zeus! There they were! There they were! His dear Athenians! They were crossing back from Salamis to Eleusis. The shore was thronging with them. The bright armour of their moving forms was flashing in the sun. The whole bay was white-winged with ships plying from Salamis. Tossing row-boats were making their way among the sail with hurrying oars. Every coming craft, big or little, was loaded to the gunwale with men. And far down along the Isthmian Road he could see the oncoming phalanxes from the south. At last all Greece was meeting in full force. And he, Aristodemos, was come in time!

Even as he looked he hurried toward the place, down the rough hill and along the old shore road. Fleet with joy, he sped around the curve of the Bay like a wing-footed Hermes, his upturned face as bright and expectant as the face of the god-messenger himself. He began to hear the general bustle of the landing, then the great hearty shoutings as boatload after boatload made the shore. Then a new and louder clamour! Another troop had arrived from the north.

Nearer and nearer he came to them. He could hear the greetings, the mingled voices, the grind of moving shields, the hammering of armourers, the neighing of horses—all the din and roar of busy moving thousands. Louder it grew, and louder. Now it was all about him. Again and yet again the stupendous shouting of the armies drowned all voices in one valorous roar.

Then suddenly, oh, wonderful! above the tumultuous noise, clear and powerful, with glorious swinging step, sounded the old Spartan marching song. The Spartans! The Spartans had come up! The welcoming Athenians joined their song. Surely it was but yesterday that Aristodemos had marched to those same mighty choruses.

These joyous battle sounds of united Greece wiped out his bitter year as though it had not been. Some living source within him welled up unscathed from trial. His readiness to love, his readiness to hope and to believe, was fresh, unstained and new.

Now he was elbowing his way through a press of shouting, noisy Athenians. He came to the water's edge where the Athenian officers stood. Only now, when it became necessary to make himself known, did he recollect himself.

Would they drive him off, these exuberant, life-full

men? Would they snatch his chance of action from him? Well, let them stone him, now, where he stood! "I will have death or I will fight for Greece!" he thought doggedly.

A tall, quiet-voiced officer was standing at the shore, directing the landing and ordering the disposition of the camp. Aristodemos went to him.

"May I join your company?" he asked. Spite of himself he began to tremble from sheer solicitude and ardour.

The man, who was Aristides, bent upon him a searching look.

"I have not seen thee in Athens."

"No. I have been long an exile. But—I was born there. Lykos of Pandion's tribe was my father."

"Join the company of Olympiodoros yonder," said Aristides. "That is thy deme."

"May I? May I?" whispered Aristodemos, suddenly unbelieving.

"Yes, my son. Why not?" said the general, looking kindly at the flushed, glad face. Then he turned quickly to his business.

Aristodemos bounded away to help with the boats, and, as he did so, broke into glad song with the rest.

CHAPTER THIRTY-THREE

Hellas in Arms at Last

Oh, the exuberant companionship, the glad activity, the babble of Athenian talk, the bursts of laughter, and the shouting! Already his long solitariness seemed to Aristodemos but a dream.

"Come, lend a hand here!" called a big-bearded Athenian as he caught a rope from a landing boat. Aristodemos sprang to haul with him, but before they could bring the craft in her eager passengers had leaped overboard and were scrambling ashore through the surf. Already the rowers were pushing off for another load.

"See how bright my shield is!" childishly called a boy who had just got ashore. Evidently he had recently been admitted to the ranks.

"It will be dulled enough when thou comest back," said Aristodemos, with the smile of an old soldier. "A shield gets battered when a brave man carries it."

"But the Spartans! The Spartans are with us at last!" the Athenians kept telling the new-comers. They had reason enough to rejoice over it. For it was only at the last minute, and after fierce persuasions and threats, that reluctant Sparta had sent her army north of the Isthmos.

"Here come the Eretrians down the Athens road, and the Styrians after them!" As the new troops came in, great shouts of welcome went up from the soldiers on the beach.

Hardly had this shouting died down when the Leukadians and Anaktorians came in sight on the mountain road. The united army rose to honour them, for they were come from the farthest west, of Greece, from the shore of Akarnania and from an island lying off the shore. How dusty they looked after their long march, and how they grinned with pride at the welcome they got!

So through the busy afternoon and far into the night they kept coming in. Greece was draining herself for this last effort of freedom. Never in her whole history did she assemble so large a force. Already a hundred thousand men were marshalled at Eleusis. Aristodemos watched the swelling ranks with unutterable satisfaction. The heart within him seemed filling, filling with the coming of every new troop.

All the while he was very busy, here helping a youth with his too-spirited horse, there adjusting a shield strap, or sharing the evening meal. Everybody spoke to him and everybody took his presence for granted. Now he stopped to watch a man coming out from a plunge in the sea, his long hair dripping, his fine shoulders glistening in the sunset light. The man stumbled over something in the water.

"Holy Mother of Kore!" he cried with a wry face. "How will I look, now, limping into battle!"

Then he bent and lifted something out of the water. It proved to be an iron boat-anchor with a chain. "Here's the crab!" he called out, dragging it out with him. "Come out of the sea. Thou art my lawful captive. Thou shalt serve me in battle!"

His comrades gathered jeering around, evidently expecting some piece of drollery. He dressed, put on his corselet, and began to fasten the anchor chain to his belt.

"What! Thou'rt never going to lug that thing into battle!" laughed Aristodemos. For the man seemed so extravagantly in earnest.

"Won't I though? See here!" And picking up the anchor he ran forward a few steps with it, then cast it and began to fight an imaginary foe.

The soldiers laughed uproariously. "Anchored in the fight! Ho, Sophanes! They may sink you, but they won't drive you! A new warship! Oh, Sophanes! what next?" And they put him through his performance again for the benefit of the newcomers who crowded up. He was evidently a whimsical favourite among the men.

Yet it was from this same boy-hearted giant that Aristodemos got the clearest account of the Persian movements and of Aristides's probable plan. The two sat on the moonlit beach and talked far into the night with the quiet gravity of men upon the eve of battle.

"You see," said Sophanes, "the Persians left Athens several days ago, made a raid over here on Megara, and when they heard the Spartans were coming, marched back again through Attica up into Bœotia. They went through Dekeleia on the way. I wonder what they left of it!" Sophanes was quiet for a while, thinking of his home. "And that was the move," he went on, "that fetched those Spartans out of their good-for-nothing despicable Peloponnese. Embassies and arguments never would have brought them!"

Aristodemos knit his brows.

"Don't you see?" explained Sophanes, "Mardonios means to found an empire in Bœotia and to include all northern Greece. Ei! the Spartans suddenly woke up when they saw a Persian frontier on the Corinthian Gulf!"

"The gods be thanked they're here, from whatever cause!" said Aristodemos.

"Now," said Sophanes, "we'll march into Bœotia and fight the Persians there."

"And renegade Thebes will be their stronghold, I suppose?"

"Thebes will be their dinner-table, and the north their market-garden. We must manage to cut them off from Thebes and the north. But Thebes isn't big enough to hold them. No; to my thinking we'll storm no city. It's a wrestle of two armies in open field. He that beats the other hath the prize—and the prize will be Hellas. Great Zeus, what an army we've got!" cried Sophanes with enthusiasm. "We'll settle with those Persian beasts for destroying our Athens!"

"Athens!" breathed Aristodemos with sudden recollection. "I passed through Athens to-day!"

"Today? Alone? Oh, how did it look?"

Aristodemos covered his face with his hands. Sophanes laid his arm heartily about his shoulder. "I thank the gods they spared me such a sight!" he said.

At midnight the army was drawn up on the beach, while the priests set up their altars and made sacrifices.

"They stood in deep silence, until at last the exultant word came down the waiting line:

"The sacrifices are favourable!"

Then they set out on the Platæan Road. And how the battle pipes sounded in the darkness! Aristodemos had heard them last at Thermopylæ. He found himself once more in the moving column, breathing men close about him, his sword tapping its familiar click upon his thigh. He had a glorious sense of being with his own.

Sophanes marched beside him. He was still undaunted of his whimsical purpose and lugged his anchor. He would not even trust it to his slave. The noisy cheer of the afternoon had given place to a great seriousness in the ranks, a weight of purpose which kept the men silent as they marched.

They passed through the blackness of an olive wood, blindly stepping in each other's tracks. Then they came out among low, starlit hills, and marching steadily, presently began to climb toward the mountains. Then with gray dawn they came to the pass leading over the Kithairon range into Bœotia.

"Ha—there is Eleutheria!" called Sophanes. "Like an old gray eagle on her nest! Couldn't we touch up those traitor Thebans with a bit of Athenian deviltry?" But the gray-towered fortress standing like another rock upon its rocky precipice gave no sign of life, and the army shouted derision as it passed.

Up the steep defile they wound from height to height. The brightness of the morning air seemed to warm their blood, for as they climbed the column burst into song. And what should they be singing but the old doggerel that Aristodemos had sung in his childhood!

> *"In a myrtle bough shall my sword lie hid,*
> *Thus Harmodios and Aristogeiton did,*
> *The day they struck the tyrant down*
> *And made our Athens a freemen's town."*

In its strength of eight thousand Athenian voices the merry banquet song took on a thunderous dignity. Aristodemos joined in with a mighty joy. The air echoed, the pine clad slopes gave back,

> *"A freemen's town!—A freemen's town!"*

Yes; a freemen's town had Athens ever been, from the time when Erechtheus had builded it. And now, though the city was no more than a cinder heap on the plain, the very mountains were still undauntedly proclaiming it,

> *"A freemen's town—a freemen's town."*

They reached the top of the pass and began to pour down over it. There the wide Bœotian plain, sun filled and generous, sweeping to its far blue mountain horizon, lay suddenly spread below them. There was the birth-place of Dionysos and Herakles, and there in the far distance Helikon of Apollo and the Muses with its twin peaks. That great white mass in the west was beloved Parnassos, beyond which Delphi itself lay hid. Oh, who would not, with his last blood, defend this crying Hellas-land!

The tired fellows stood there, grimly smiling. "Shall the Persian dogs hold this Bœotia?"

Then they marched silently down. On the last declivity they came to Erythrai. Here the scouts reported that the Persians were encamped north of the Asopos

River, only two miles away, and were about to attack.

The Greeks made ready. They stretched out their battle line across the road by which they had come, and upon the low hills on either side. The Spartans took the post of honour on the right flank, the Athenians took the left, on the last outreaching spurs of Kithairon. The other allies held the centre on the lower ground where ran the road.

"There lies our battle-field," said Sophanes, gazing down upon the two miles of plain rolling north to the Asopos River. "The Persians are using the Asopos as their barrier. And we shall have to keep open the Kithairon passes—our men and supplies have got to come that way."

Now their long, living line stood complete, its grounded spears glittering erect, its white crests tossing above the level helms, shield touching shield down the brazen length. "Walled in with shields of bronze," says Homer. And not a man in all the line but knew that phrase.

Aristodemos stood there in his rank by Sophanes, with all Thermopylæ surging in his veins, with all those heroic souls, swept then out of life, rushing back into him with their pervading strength.

"Here they come," he said quietly to Sophanes.

"No; not yet!" answered the other, looking down from their elevation.

But Aristodemos's eyes had caught what seemed a mere dust cloud on the plain. It was moving.

"Oh—I see!" cried Sophanes breathlessly. For now the white bodies of the horses began to gleam out from the mass, tumultuous with motion, now the flurry and glitter of spears, now the tossing of thousands of gay-capped heads. And still over all the flying mass ever that cloud of yellow dust, closing, rolling, lifting—"the voiceless herald of the army." Mardonios had sent against the Greeks the whole body of his Persian cavalry.

At a little distance they halted and formed their vast

battle line, their restless horses neighing and stamping. Their commander, Masistios, was conspicuous even at this distance in their front.

There was an intense waiting.

Then, "It's the Megarians!" went up the cry. "They're upon the Megarians!"

One Persian squadron had separated and was hurling itself upon the narrow Greek front that held the low ground near the road.

"Oh, they will break through—they will seize the pass!" groaned Aristodemos. For the Megarian line was giving back like a bended bow.

"No—they hold! They hold!"

But Aristodemos, stamping the ground with impatience, knew that they could not hold. As the first Persian squadron circled off another beat forward against the same narrow front. This time the Megarians, struggling, fighting, shouting, began to give way on the road.

None came to their support.

As for Aristodemos, only his lifetime discipline kept him standing in his place, while the fortune of Hellas ebbed below.

Then he heard the long, wailing cry of the Megarian herald as he ran along the hill.

"O Allies, we can not hold! Help! Help the Megarians!" And straight followed Pausanias's mounted messenger, clattering in haste. The Greek commander-in-chief was calling for volunteers from his own Spartans.

But the Spartans would not go.

Now the messenger was calling to the Athenians.

How clumsily the ancient army did its work! And all these precious minutes the unequal battle was raging in the road below.

But the Athenians responded with a quick, glad shout. To Aristodemos's inexpressible joy, it was his own company that made answer, the three hundred men under Olympiodoros.

The face of the Athenian captain gleamed. "I must

have a company of bowmen!" he cried, and was off.

Down the hill ran the mighty fellows in their clattering armour. They reached the Megarians just as the Persian horse were wheeling off from their last charge. A quick, disciplined movement, and the fresh Athenian phalanxes were through and in front of their bleeding allies. They were hardly in position when with trilling thunder of hoofs a new Persian squadron was upon them.

The Athenians with levelled spears braced themselves to receive them. Sensitive Ionians they were, quick of laughter and of tears, imaginative, tender; yet every nut-brown face of them was set as granite, and not a muscle shook. Aristodemos was sensible of a strange power within—the deed instinct at the deed moment.

Then fell the torrent of javelins—then the wild confusion, the hot breathed galloping horses and yelling men. Aristodemos's spear drove deep into the horse before him. He heard its wild human shriek, saw it rear high and throw its rider back into the living deluge. Then the battle rage was all about him. Then began the steady labour of fighting, too intense to be remembered.

Finally the Persian squadron made off, and he stood panting among the panting bloody men, the sweat rolling down his armour while he gathered breath against the new onslaught.

It came—passed again like some incredible agony and again came.

"Hellas! Hellas!" he groaned when at moments he seemed overcome with the breathless weight of exertion.

So far there was no decisive advantage.

And now the Persian leader, Masistios himself, took personal command of the attacking squadron, riding in advance, his white Nisian horse leaping responsive to his hand. He was a large man, a masterly horseman, splendid with crimson and gold—a superb barbaric warrior.

As he reached the Athenians an arrow struck his horse's flank. The frightened animal plunged and threw its rider. Masistios leaped to his feet; but the Athenians were upon him. He was gigantic in strength, and made a terrible fight for his life. He flashed and wounded everywhere. Aristodemos almost pitied him, so superb of skill, so desperately over-matched with numbers.

But presently the spear of Masistios stuck through a lithe Athenian boy who lifted his arms before him with a wild, struggling cry.

"Persian hound! Wilt thou gather Greek lives for thine!" Aristodemos struck a staggering blow to the Persian's breast. He felt the shock of metal on his sword point, and Masistios turned unharmed upon him, with a grim triumphant smile. The man was clad in some rare armour beneath his tunic.

"At his eyes! At his eyes!" shouted Aristodemos. But the others did not for the moment comprehend, and seeing Aristodemos's skill, gave him opportunity. Closer and closer he pressed to that giant form, and its play of lightning strokes. The others wondered that he did not thrust.

Then suddenly he made a feint at the man's belly, and as Masistios lowered his shield but a hair's breadth, Aristodemos sheared over the rim straight through his eye. It was a quick, thorough deed. Leonidas had not taught him that master-stroke in vain. But dearly had the Athenians to pay for it that day.

The Persians had drawn off without at first perceiving the absence of their leader. But now the Athenians could see the messengers furiously flying back and forth. Presently the whole vast Persian line began to concentrate. Then the mighty, compact mass of horsemen, many ranks deep, drove forward, coming, all together, for vengeance and for the body of their leader.

The three hundred Athenians sent up a great cry to the whole Greek army for help, standing, the while, their ground as the black tempest cloud swept up upon them.

It was no longer human. Men and horses were

merged in elemental tumult. On it came, a hurricane of screaming men and crashing armour, a vast uproar. The very ground beneath their feet began to shake with its myriad pounding hoofs. Ahead of this tempest came its bitter rain of arrows.

Who can tell what keeps men firm in the face of such an impending crash?

"After all, it is only death!" thought Arisiodemos standing above Masistios's body. It was this they were coming for. Then the struggle itself seized mind, soul and body.

The awful impact pushed the Athenians bodily back. Aristodemos found this labour infinitely heavier than the most desperate fighting he had ever known—to be crushed back among the mass of men, to stumble over the fallen yet to keep blows steady and shield everywhere. Aristodemos, moreover, was dragging with hands or feet the heavy body of the Persian general.

The battle was losing! What stupidity kept the allies still delaying?

The battle was losing! Even submerged as he was he was conscious of it.

The battle was losing!

Now they had wrenched Masistios's body away! He heard the barbarian scream of delight. He sprang among the Persians after it, shouting, "Follow! Follow!"

He found himself surrounded, parrying blows from all sides. The Athenians had ebbed entirely away.

Then he became sensible of a mighty surging tide behind, a pressure that bore him forward like a breaker.

Then he knew! It was the whole Greek army behind him driving irresistibly. Now how swift the battle moved! How easily the Greeks won back the body of Masistios and left it secure behind as they charged victorious down the slopes!

At last the Persian cavalry clattered away and away over the hills to their camp, wailing the loss of their leader and leaving the field strewn with their dead.

Aristodemos felt stupified with joy. That he should

have fought in the front of victory! That he, the accursed wanderer, should have dealt great blows for Hellas!

"Hey, wake up!" cried the jubilant Sophanes, shaking him. "Thou art a very fiend of a fighter! Didst not hear me call thee to drop that Persian carrion and run back with us? If all Greece hadn't pushed in at that instant thou wert a dead Greek now!"

"No," said Aristodemos quietly, "there was a chance."

"By the gods, you took it! And who taught you that sword play? I never—"

Here a shout from the excited Greeks brought them both to their feet. The body of Masistios was being carted down the line. Men were leaving the ranks to wonder at his barbaric beauty and splendid dress.

"But who killed him? Who killed him?" they asked.

"One of Olympiodoros's men," the cartman answered. "But he hath not come forward for honours yet."

CHAPTER THIRTY-FOUR

The Saving of Greece

Victory! The Greek camp was all "Victory!" The men sang "Victory!" drank "Victory!" They were jubilant, tearful, tender toward their gods. Prudence was not in them. Had they not scattered the Persian locust to the winds? "Ohe!" they cried. "The campaign is as good as ended,"

"You Greeks are always children," once said a half envious Egyptian to the Greek historian.

Even the generals seemed utterly jubilant, and made their further plans with naïve confidence. On the morrow they would circle westward around the southern borders of the plain, concealing their march among the foothills. Then they would cross the Asopos River about two miles west of the Persian camp, and surprise it from the rear. This move would cut off the Persians from their northward Theban Road.

Thus lightly did the Greeks leave their hills where their superior position had been half their victory, unmindful how easily the swift Persian cavalry could deal with their heavy armed soldiers on the level ground.

In the red morning light they set out for the Bœotian plain—columns of bright-faced men well rested after battle, with spear a-quiver and burnished shields taking the sun.

To Aristodemos all life seemed as new as this blessed morning, all effort possible after the night of rest.

THE SPARTAN

The fragrant air—how fresh it met his nostrils! And the sunny hills, the bright, rolling plain, never to be soiled henceforth by Persian feet! The poet in him was uppermost and singing.

By noon they reached the spring Gargaphia, not far from the burned faithful city of Platæa. Here, to Aristodemos's great satisfaction, the battle line began immediately to form. In a moment they would be marching over the low ridge which was now their concealment. Then they would ford the narrow river and wheel eastward upon the unready Persian camp.

"What now, in Hermes's name!" exclaimed Sophanes impatiently. For the columns had halted. Loud talking was heard ahead.

"It's the Tegeans!" he said, as his keen ear caught the talk. "I knew they wanted the left flank!"

This was the second post of honour in the battle line, after the Spartan right.

"Faugh," grumbled on Sophanes, "see the captain point as he argues Tegean merits! Now hath Pausanias the precious opportunity of hearing the whole Tegean ancestry! Aye, back to Troy—back to Troy it is, I, warrant!"

"No," groaned another Athenian, "he's only as far back as Echemos, son of Asopos, son of Phegeus yet! Wait a day or two, Sophanes! No hurry about the battle!"

"Hush—listen!" cried Aristodemos eagerly. "It's Aristides now!"

"I thought," came the tolerant, amused voice of the Athenian statesman, "that we came out for battle with the Barbarian, not for oratory."

The Athenian soldiers listened with a sudden ardent quiet as he began to mention great Athenian deeds of old. One's own ancestors are a different matter.

"But," broke off Aristides, "what profit to talk of ancestors? We ourselves be ancestors enough. We fought Marathon!"

Here the Athenians, and Spartans too, began to

shout, "Marathon!"

"Nevertheless," Aristides went on quietly, "this is no time to contend for a post. Put us where ye will, O Spartans. Wherever we stand, ye shall find us steadfast."

"Athenians—Athenians!" came the instant Spartan shout.

Truly, "children," always "children," as the Egyptian said.

And now up the Asopos ridge in battle order marched the united armies.

They were too late!

With fine strategic insight the enemy had divined their move and had forestalled them. There, just across the little stream, was the freshly fortified camp of the full Persian army, alert and ready.

This was a shock to sober the Greeks. Yet they marched in silence down to the river and pitched their own camp on the bank opposite the great Persian force.

And now began the long disaster of waiting days. Day after day the armies sat glowering at each other on the two sides of the little stream. Day after day they made their anxious sacrifices, but neither Greek nor Persian was able to get the sanction of his gods for an attack.

Aristodemos chafed and fretted. The *impasse* was dangerous. And they had seemed so near the finish! As far as the eye could reach he could see the gorgeous tents of the enemy. Their battle line would be easily four times as deep as the Greek, by so much did the Persians outnumber them. What event could possibly break the locked horns of these two armies?

"Cheer up, thou bloodthirsty son of Ares!" said Sophanes, as they sat one evening at their supper; "thou canst not kill a Masistios every day!"

"Masistios! What's Masistios! Oh, this delay! This delay! Dost thou not see the outcome?"

"Not I. That's Plympiodoros's business. Nay, eat thy cheese in peace. We profit the most by delay. Look yonder."

He pointed to a dusty company of new arrivals. The Greek army was indeed filling hourly from the Corinthian Gulf, from Peloponnese, from Attica, by ones, dozens, fifties. But Aristodemos was not greatly reassured. Sophanes snapped his fingers. What did the "Bloodthirsty" want, anyway?

That night—the ninth of their waiting—Persian Mardonios sent a cavalry troop around and ambushed a Greek provision train as it came through a Kithairon pass, "slaughtering beast and man," as the plain old historian says, "until they were satisfied with killing." Then they drove the rest into their camp. The Greeks had allowed more than two miles of space between them and their hills.

This revealed in a flash the masterly advantage of the Persian position—aye, and showed it to the Persians themselves. For next morning they began an intermittent fighting with the Greeks. It was not actual battle—no such satisfaction as that. It was only a terrible harassment by the cavalry bowmen, little companies at a time crossing the river in sudden sallies, shooting their whizzing flights of death among the Greeks, then fleeing bird-swift away. Thus they occupied the attention of the Greek army.

Meanwhile—with what appalling ease!—they seized all the passes of Kithairon in the rear of the Greeks, and cut off their supplies of provisions.

The men grew silent in the Athenian camp, with set jaws and anxious eyes. Aristodemos saw on their faces a look that gave him a new fear for Greece. Thermopylæ had been her first stand. This would be her last. And the Greeks knew it.

The armies had now been a fortnight on this futile field. One evening Aristodemos was detailed to sentry duty. He took his watch wearily. When one has not eaten a full meal for three days one does not see the bright colours. He could not put from his mind his Phokian journey after Thermopylæ—those charred villages, deserted highways, that ghastly lift of black hair, the dead girl on the hillside. Like that all Greece would be soon—soon!

Night deepened as he paced his beat on the soft grass, exchanging from time to time the low salutation as he met his neighbour sentry.

Suddenly he heard a plash in the river, then a swift thud of hoofs. Nearer, nearer! A night attack? A single horseman could not be coming thus! Now horse and man loomed in the darkness before him.

"I have a message!" The man spoke good Greek. "Important! I must see the generals in haste!"

Aristodemos called the guard. Men were sent for Aristides and Pausanias. In a few moments both generals were there. The three men stood awhile in low, anxious talk. Then the rider galloped off to the dim river.

Aristides caught sight of Aristodemos's remembered, eager face.

"The Persians will give battle to-morrow," he vouchsafed.

"Then all the gods be thanked!" flashed back Aristodemos fervently.

When his watch was done he ran toward his tent laughing aloud. But already the news had spread from tent to tent.

"The Persians have no food. They must give battle whether the gods will or no! They hoped to surprise us, but Alexander of Macedon came over and told us."

Aristodemos rushed into his tent just as Sophanes was coming out and caught the astonished fellow in his arms.

"Oho!" cried Sophanes. "So thou hast heard the news. Is battle thy banquet wine?"

"No—no!" answered Aristodemos, laughing again at the fierce character which Sophanes gave him, "but we could not endure longer. It was a very couragaletting. Didst thou not see it? Hellas was nearer lost than she hath ever been! But now, Zeus save us, the fight is on! The fight is on!"

THE SPARTAN

Sophanes laughed in reply; yet even with his careless laughter came a flash of that divine faith which at this time every true Greek seemed to have.

"Lost! Hellas can not be lost!" And he made off about his business.

Sophanes's word, "Hellas can not be lost," stuck by Aristodemos, whose courage thereby took on a quality of joy that henceforth never left him. In the dark hours that followed the fighters at his side saw in his face a steady shining beneath its sweat and blood and effort— a kind of high absorption and repose.

The rest of the night the Athenian camp was in eager, hushed confusion. Men were hastily rubbing shields, whetting swords already keen, overhauling and putting on armour. Then, softly in the dark, the troops marched and countermarched, taking their positions.

Dawn and the astonished Persians found them ready in battle array.

Nevertheless, the Persians at once began. Their full cavalry force came pounding to the river brink and let fly their deadly mass of arrows. The Greeks quailed under the death rain, though they held steady, and quickly began to fill the places of the fallen. But, before they could recover, the cavalry had dashed across the fords and was charging upon them.

Then did the close-knit brazen phalanx of the Greeks seem like some slow, confused monster at the mercy of its clever-moving foe. The swift Persian squadrons broke over their shielded fronts before the long-spear defence was ready; then wheeled and galloped away, screaming back with scornful laughter—"Women! Ah, women! "

And this taunt went home deeper than the Persian arrows to the suffering, bleeding Greeks. They wept aloud as they fought. It was the supreme disgrace of this disastrous day.

That afternoon the Persians forced the Athenian army back from its position on the river and even drove the Spartans back from the Gargaphian Spring, which they choked up and ruined, completely cutting the Greeks off from water.

It was a tired, thirsty lot of men that fell asleep that night in the new Greek bivouac. And the Persians renewed the attack before dawn. Through this long day the Greeks fought with parched throats and dizzy heads, every hour of dust and exertion adding to their misery.

And now Aristodemos as he fought began to thank the gods for his Spartan training. He saw Athenians falling all about him, unwounded, but done to death with long thirst and strength-spending. But he fought on with the best, feeling that he must fight so, endlessly, as though he were made of brass.

Yet with all his endurance, Aristodemos was not fighting to advantage. He missed the Spartan ways, the sure, united action of the phalanx, the instinctive response to the commands—aye, and the commands themselves to which through the long years he had been drilled. Under the unaccustomed conditions he was not fighting to good purpose, and he knew it, all the wearing day.

At last he saw the sunlight slanting low and felt the cool breath across the hot mass of the fight. Then, with a last derisive yell, the Persians galloped off. Once more blessed night had fallen. It had fallen upon a beaten army, an army without food or water, and well nigh surrounded. But Aristodemos was too tired to sense this fact. He dropped down where he stood and passed instantly into fathomless slumber.

It was after midnight when he became aware of general, hurried movements all about him. He staggered sleepily to his, feet. What was it? They were striking tents, packing wagons, putting on armour. All was anxious hurry.

"What are we doing?" he asked, stopping a hurrying form.

"Going to a hill south of here, called 'The Island,' close to Kithairon and the Megara Pass. They say it is a place surrounded with streams. Great gods, but we need the water!"

It was a move of extremity. The Greeks were preparing to withdraw under cover of the night and while they yet could. They had learned their lesson. They could fight only on the hills.

He found Sophanes trying vainly in the darkness to fasten on his armour.

"My cursed fingers slip so!" he complained.

Aristodemos thrust him down to the ground. "Lie there," he commanded. "I'll fasten thy greaves—Great Zeus, I thought so!" he exclaimed as he knelt by him. "A wound here in thy leg—losing blood. That's what makes thy slippery fingers."

"Oh, that," said the great fellow sheepishly. "That's nothing. Only one of their sickle cuts." But he stretched out with a sigh as Aristodemos tore a strip from his own tunic and bound up the mighty iron-knotted calf.

"Why, Demos, thou'rt fresh even now!" said Sophanes enviously.

"Yes. But thou didst carry thy anchor. Dost know, Sophanes, I believe that that anchor-fighting is going to make thee famous!"

"Oh, I don't believe so," said Sophanes. But he smiled with pleasure in the dark.

The comradeship with Sophanes was a constant refreshment to Aristodemos. He went on with his own preparations, absently answering Sophanes's jests, and feeling a wonderful sense of being in the world again.

Yet all this while he was coming to an inevitable decision. He must get back among his Spartans. Only in his own place in the Spartan phalanx to which he had been trained for fourteen years could he do his best work. To-day would see the final issue. By to-day's fortune Hellas would stand or fall. To-day he dare give nothing but his best.

Together with this conviction Aristodemos had a sudden fervent desire to fight in the place where Leonidas had set him, and in the peculiar fashion which Leonidas had taught. Leonidas the living had once led him back to Sparta; Leonidas the dead was calling him thither again.

He did not hesitate, these days, in his decisions. He said nothing to Sophanes, but quietly shut his helm over his face; took shield and spear, and walked away.

He had scarce passed within the Spartan lines when he was aware of a different atmosphere. Among the Athenians he had seen hunger, suffering, discouragement. Nevertheless every Athenian had been ardent to do the next duty, and they were even now burying their dead without complaint. These Spartans had not been nearly so hard hit; yet Aristodemos found them quarrelsome and full of complaints. He heard angry voices and passed knots of men who talked excitedly.

He passed quickly among the half-packed tents to his old place in the Pitanate Division. Here too the men were fuming.

"This going to The Island," said one, "is all a blunder. It will bring the whole Persian force upon us at once with a crash. Ye'll see it will!"

"Yes, at last, thanks be to the gods!" said Aristodemos fervently and almost unawares.

"Thou'lt not say that when the fight is on!" growled the man, turning at him. "It's the Immortals we Spartans have to deal with. We don't know their fighting ways. How can we meet such fighters, ten to one in open field?"

"Their fighting ways are simple, for all their high sounding name," said Aristodemos, eager to hearten the group, and remembering the grapple with the Immortals at Thermopylæ. "They are no match for Spartan skill."

"By Zeus, but who art thou?" demanded the grumbler.

"I am Aristodemos, son of Lykos," said Aristodemos readily.

"Son of Gylippos, rather! I thought I knew thy damned voice!"

Aristodemos lifted his helm, and his steady face looked out in the flickering torchlight.

THE SPARTAN

"Yes—ha, ha!" sneered the man. "Aristodemos the Coward! Why, I thought thou'dst hung thyself long ago! Of course thou art not afraid of the Immortals! Death'd be a blessing to thee!"

"Death would be no blessing to me," said Aristodemos. "Is not my life—" Then in his sudden, deep voice of anger, "Thou Spartan brute! Canst never see beyond the rooting of thine own snout? What is my death, or thine, or any thousand deaths, to the death of Hellas? All Hellas hangs in the balance. If thou never thought'st of Hellas before, by all the gods thou shouldst think of Hellas now!"

Without reply the man sprang at his throat. Aristodemos flung him off, but the man came up at him again. Then an elder struck between them with his lance-butt.

"Stop, thou fool!" he roared. "The Coward is right. This is no time to kill one of our fighting men. Is he not one more against the Persian? And 'twas Leonidas taught him the sword."

"The man is accursed!" cried the other angrily.

"Apollo hath lifted my curse," said Aristodemos. And they knew that in such a matter he would not dare to lie.

Panting with disgust and anger, he strode away to a less crowded part of the camp. There he paced up and down, trying to compose himself. The brawl was so base and unbelievable in this noble hour. He heard no step behind him; but quietly a hand was thrust into his. He looked and saw in the twilight a most gracious, godlike youth.

"Kallikrates!" he said, recalling him as a boy from Spartan days.

"Yes. I was glad to hear thee speak that good word. It was good on the eve of battle!"

Aristodemos bent and kissed the lad on the mouth because his Doric speech was like that of Leonidas, and also because to see him was to love him. For Kallikrates had grown to be the most beautiful youth of all Hellas. There were men in Sparta who would have given a fortune for his handclasp and his praise.

Aristodemos kept the hand in his, and they walked together.

"Dost think it will be a great battle to-morrow?" asked the youth.

"Yes, dear lad."

And later, as they paced in silence, Kallikrates asked: "Thou art disquiet for the morrow, Aristodemos?"

"I am not disquiet," said Aristodemos, turning upon him a lighted face of faith. "I was even thinking how Greece will act when she is free of the Persian."

"Hark!"

It was the hushed signal for the march. Aristodemos hurried to his old place in the ranks. Then he noted that the young Kallikrates was stationed very near him. It was still dark, and favourable for the retreat. But morning was at hand and they must march at once. They were ready.

A herald arrived from the Athenians asking for final orders from the Spartan general, Pausanias.

Then, through the darkness, Aristodemos heard a strife of voices. He could not believe his ears. Amompharetos, his own commander, was refusing to move.

"No," he was saying, "I will not flee from the Barbarians! I will not disgrace Sparta!"

"But we must move from here at once!" urged Pausanias. "Our men can not fight longer without water."

"Let 'em fight with valour!"

The strife momently grew higher. The Pitanate Division under Amompharetos was an important one. Pausanias did not dare to leave it behind. Yet he dared not wait. Meanwhile the Athenian herald stood by with respectful contempt, awaiting orders. The strife grew absurd.

The burly Amompharetos lifted up a great stone in both hands.

"There!" he cried, casting it at the feet of his general. "With this pebble I give my vote not to flee from the strangers!"

"Thou madman! Thou fool!" cried Pausanias.

"And what commands to the Athenians?" put in the waiting herald.

Pausanias clasped his head in his hands. Leon, the captain of another division, began to persuade and threaten Amompharetos. Military authority and obedience, as we understand them, were unknown in an ancient army.

The faint gray of morning was in the air. If the Persians should discover their movement, the Greeks were lost. Finally great streaks of dawn began to show across the rolling country. Pausanias, in despair, gave over the stupid contest. With a flash of his sword he turned to his army.

"March!" he commanded. And the Spartan army and the Tegeans with them shouldered their spears and marched off. But the Pitanate Division remained standing in its place.

Aristodemos, with breaking heart, saw them go, rank after rank, across the brightening plain to the battle place, while he stood silent with his division in that wrong and helpless station by the river—a place that could become nothing but a shambles. Spartan stupidity had caught him again! Here and at the very last moment he was being cheated of his chance! His dry lips parted. Should he leave the ranks? But that would be instant death.

A loud cry sounded from across the Asopos. The Persians were rushing to battle. They had seen the vacant camp and knew that the Greeks were gone.

Amompharetos turned his stupid head. He had hoped to keep the whole Spartan army with him. Now his small division stood full in the Persian way. It would be annihilated. Grudgingly he lifted his sword. But before he could speak the word his men were bounding forward at a quickstep the way the Spartan army had gone. The Persians had already leaped through the river. Far and near went up their diverse battle cries as nation after nation joined in the pursuit of the Pitanate.

They poured up the near bank and over, yelling wild derision. They did not doubt that the whole Greek army was in full flight. The Pitanate quickened to a hard run. The Persian cavalry was overtaking them by leaps and bounds.

But now, a little way up the slope ahead of them, they saw the Spartans and Tegeans drawn up and awaiting them. They could hear the clamorous encouragement of their comrades. Then, with a final rush and a shout, the Pitanate swept into its place, and under the first discharge of Persian arrows completed the hasty battle line. The Persian archer-cavalry was not a hundred steps behind.

At that interval the enemy halted. The Spartans saw them lift their heavy bows. Their arrows soared up high in air, then, curving over, struck down like voiceless lightning upon the unsheltered Greeks.

"Steady in your places!" cried the captains. And the silent Spartans and the Tegean three thousand beside them, lifted their shields to mitigate the falling death and stood firm. But Pausanias hurriedly sent his mounted herald to the Athenians for aid. Not even Spartans could stand such a storm. And now, just over the little temple-crowned hill opposite them, they could see all the Persians and Median infantry coming on.

The Helots set up the Spartan battle altar. The priest slew the victim, bent close, and peering, shook his head. The omens were unfavourable. The Spartans were not permitted to attack.

Now the Medes and Persians spread out their huge, bright battle line. Aristodemos saw that the Immortals themselves were in the forefront, and thought that they would surely charge at once. But they, too, halted and he could see them with a great clatter drive deep into the ground the stakes of their heavy bull-covered shields as tall as themselves, and lock them into a solid palisade. Then a swift cloud darkened for a moment the air above. The Greeks heard a terrible wide humming. Then came a pattering all about, the sharp impinging of the thousands of arrows, followed by a wild confusion of death-cries.

Such archery as this the Greeks had never known. The large, powerful bows were drawn at close range and with consummate skill. The arrows were like very spears for sharpness and weight. Some of the bow-men shot high and struck the Greeks from above. Others shot straight across.

This was no time for pause. Nothing but an instant phalanx-charge could quench that arrow-storm. Yet—Merciful Zeus!—Pausaruas was delaying to sacrifice again! He did not dare to move without his gods.

But oh, the falling-men! The death-strokes every-where! Flesh and blood could not endure this! The Spartans were dropping like logs or staggering wildly, drawing out the arrows from their flesh to stand pale and reeling in the ranks. And still unceasing fell the rain of death; and there was no protection, and no action!

Fear began to grow.

Then amid the noise and confusion Aristodemos heard just behind him a wild, sweet cry of anguish, and turning he saw the beautiful youth, Kallikrates, fall with one of the heavy Persian shafts buried deep in his side. The soldiers caught him with ready, outstretched arms. But his lovely body stretched and stiffened with pain, and they dared not draw out the buried arrow. It was a death stroke. The men glanced the fatal intelligence into each other's stricken faces.

They bore him away with infinite tenderness. How bitterly the poor lad wept, "Oh, Paian! Paian!" But the cry was not for himself. "No deed done—no deed for Hellas! And I was so strong—I was so ready to—do great deeds! No deed! No deed! No deed!"

His lessening voice died away across the field.

The effect in the ranks was immediate. They had endured inactive as long as men could endure. And now this death of Kallikrates had stricken the heart of every man. Aristodemos saw a horror come over the soldier faces, the wild, uneasy look that precedes the

Panic-god. And he knew that they must break.

Toward the enemy they still could break. But break they must. Aristodemos saw that in a moment more they would break the other way and run like maddened sheep. Yet he knew that they would charge the enemy only at Pausanias's command.

But Pausanias was still awaiting his omens! Appalling dilemma! The Spartans were helpless. But the Tegeans?

Aristodemos looked over toward them. Their horror-shaken ranks were already shifting. The Tegeans! Yes the Tegeans might be tempted to a sudden charge. They were not so routine bound. And once the break were started, nothing could prevent a Spartan charge.

— A single man might do it at this crisis-edge! Yes—Yes! A single man!

Then Aristodemos flung away all discipline. His single battle-shout suddenly shattered the noise. He leaped like a meteor from the Spartan line to the Tegean front. The Tegeans thought they saw a god! The god light surely was in his face.

"Alala!"

With lifted sword and bright, streaming hair he rushed toward the foe. The whole Tegean phalanx plunged forward with him. He seemed to lift it bodily from its place. The backward glance of his lighted face swept courage into them. "Alala! Alala!" His voice rang to them like the note of a clarion.

At this moment Pausanias promptly got his omens right. For the Spartans, even as Aristodemos hoped, had broken restraint and were leaping toward the foe in battle joy, their line near-even with the Tegeans.

Aristodemos reached the Persian shield-wall, behind him the thunder-roar of the Tegean phalanx. Against the tough wattled wall they crashed, splintered it back and broke in among those terrible, splendid fighters, wild faces, flashing daggers—the hot, heaving cauldron of battle. The crash of their impact was instantly followed farther up the line, by Sparta's resistless plunge into the heart of the Persian Immortals.

Now the fight was everywhere, man to man. Aristodemos seemed struggling in some hot, engulfing surge, raging still forward and drawing his Tegeans after him, slaying with unwearied strength, and with a kind of suspended joy—a prophecy of victory.

It seemed as if the gods who had taken away his opportunities at Thermopylæ were restoring them now ten-fold. Where it quick deed was to be done, there was he. Again and again in some dose struggle of failing men it was Aristodemos, bright eyed and strong, who with those wonderful sword strokes swept the Greeks through their crisis. Tegeans and Spartans alike began to look for his flying Athenian crest, at first so white and then so terribly red. "He put strength out of himself into us!" said the adoring Tegean soldiers afterward.

How he praised now that unsparing sword-practice of Leonidas! Not a man of Sparta could wield such a blade or deal such death as Aristodemos dealt that day.

It was a heart breaking, doubtful battle. The Persians fought with mad valour. They were truly of wonderful strength and bravery, though they were destitute of heavy armour. They would mass themselves by dozens and mightily fling themselves at points among the brazen shields, striving, furiously so, to force a breach in the Greek line for their comrades to push through. They would make sudden rushes to break up with their hands in desperation that bitter Greek advantage of long spears.

But, for all their courage, they gave way at last. They went to pieces all at once, as melts the whole river-dam when once the rift has let the waters through. They fled back past the little hill-temple of Demeter, and on over hill and plain toward their camp beyond the Asopos.

The Spartans pursued them, killing them in the hollows, killing them on the heights. It was a rout complete.

Only the Persian cavalry kept free. They hovered

and darted about on the outskirts of battle, harassing the Greek pursuers with many a sharp-set shaft. It was one of these arrows that struck Aristodemos as he was giving chase with the others toward the Persian camp. It struck through his corselet, piercing his side—much as Kallikrates had been wounded, but not so deep. Aristodemos paused in his running and drew it out. The plentiful blood spilled after it over his thigh and knee. But he ran on again, scarce conscious of weakness and, wholly unconscious of pain. The wondrous actuality of Greek Freedom was buoying him. He was trying to believe it. He was singing within. His whole being was an uplift of joy and praise.

He reached the Persian camp just in time to see the Persian remnant get within and bang to the heavy wooden gates in the faces of the Spartans and Tegeans.

The Spartans were not skilled in the assault of fortified places, and they made but little progress until the Athenians arrived. These presently came up, a joyous, noisy rout, fresh from conquering their own separate battle with the Medized Greeks nearer Platæa.

Aristodemos set to work exultantly with the rest at breaching the high, wooden, wall. But suddenly, whether from loss of blood or perhaps because he saw his life's desire accomplished, he reeled and fell.

Teleklos, a Spartan captain, paused to support him. But Aristodemos motioned him on, smiling absently. — "Just as he used to smile," said Teleklos afterward, "when he had finished a song, or when the evening games were done and he had overleaped me in the Dromos."

Sophanes broke away from the Athenian company which was working at the breach and ran to him.

"Why, Demos, old fellow," he said rallyingly, "it's not so bad as that. Thou wouldst not die now—not now!"

But Aristodemos could no longer see him. He was seeing elsewhere.

He lifted his golden head, all battle stained. His eyes widened with a look of surprise and unutterable love.

"Hellas," he spoke; not a call, but a low greeting, as if he had recognized a goddess very near.

Sophanes laid him back tenderly upon the ground, and so doing, felt a sigh brush his cheek, with which the swift soul took flight.

He hurried back to the breach. The wall was broken through. The gates were down. Already terrible shrieks were heard within. The slaying did not cease until the last stranger was ridded from the land.

CHAPTER THIRTY-FIVE

Epilogue

The next day two men were walking together upon the battle-field, one with the joy of emancipated Greece radiant upon his face, the other with bent head, as if in a kind of shame. About them were the great mounds of spoil, glittering with rich shields, jewelled swords and spears whose butts were gold and silver pomegranates. The torn and bloody turf on which they walked was already sacred ground.

"Yet why, Pindar, dost thou grieve?" said the elder man. "Thou art a true lover of Greece. All the world knows thy love."

"I am a Theban," answered the other. "And Thebes's shame is my shame."

For Thebes in the great hour of Greece had sided with the Persian and fought against her own flesh and blood.

"Yes," said Aristides, "Thebes gave thee birth, but Athens gave thee song. Hast any dream how Athens loves thee?"Pindar laid his hand gratefully on Aristides's shoulder.

"Thou giv'st me heart," he said. "Yes, I will go with thee and look on the dead."

The Platæan dead!

Greece was presently to institute the great festival, "Freedom," with games and sacrifices in their honour. They were accounted as gods.

The two men passed along the row of Athenian dead, soon to be buried in one mound. Then they came to the older Spartans, and finally to that wonderful line of younger Spartan warriors—those trained bodies, newly perfect, yet already harvested for the grave.

Perhaps it was because the lithe young bodies of the Greeks were browned all over to rich bronze that they looked so beautiful in death; not deathlike, but statue-like, with the added mystery of Thanatos's touch upon them. They lay there upon the ground in wonderful, appealing silence, each upon his battle cloak and in armor, though Kallikrates, because of his beauty, was left naked.

It was no sad duty, this, to a Greek—to gaze on the heroic dead.

"They lie so straight and strong," said Pindar. "Ah, happy fellows!"

Aristides stopped.

"Saviour Zeus!" he exclaimed, "here is that young, beautiful stranger who came to me at Eleusis. I thought he was an Athenian. But he lies here among the Spartans."

Pindar looked and with a glad cry fell on his knees beside the quiet body.

"My friend! My friend!" he cried. "Art thou even here? Oh, this is as thou wouldst wish!"

He laid his hand upon the cold forehead, put back the golden hair and lost himself in contemplation of the fair young face.

"How he smiles! Even more beautiful than I thought. Oh, now thou art Lykos's very self!"

Then, looking up, "Aristides, I would to the gods thou couldst tell me something of this young man!"

"He told me his name," said Aristides. "—What was it? He said it somewhat proudly, too." Then, as the word came back "Aristodemos," he said, "that was it! Son of—

"Gylippos?" suggested Pindar keenly.

"No—no. It was a name I knew in Athens, but the man died long ago. 'Lykos'—thou saidst the name just now thyself!"

EPILOGUE

"Aye; and have said it long years, long years!" said Pindar, turning with new love to the dead youth.

"But," went on Aristides suddenly, "this then must be the man—that Aristodemos who hath been so much argued since the battle. They say he fought most gloriously of all, deed overtopping deed. Yet the Spartans will not give him any honour. They say he is that man who came back from Thermopylæ—the only one of the 'Three Hundred'."

Pindar leaped to his feet in astonishment.

"And," added Aristides, "they call him 'The Coward', 'Aristodemos the Coward.' And they say he tried to die because his life was of no worth. Yet to me he did not look like a coward."

"Coward? Coward?" Pindar sounded the word. "Elysium is made of such cowards! Ah, now I see! And was it for this thou didst keep silence at Delphi, —for honour of thy dear father's name!—I have heard of that story," Pindar added hotly, "but I did not know—The Spartans wanted thee to die like a fool, and the fool was not in thee! And so thou art he! Ah, but they could not keep thee back. Thou hast died now like thy father's son."

And Pindar knelt again beside the dead, gazing on him in pity and love. Then he rose, plucked a laurel branch, and weaving a crown, crowned the golden head. To Pindar his own praise was a serious and sacred thing. He knew it to be immortal and never gave it without a sort of prayer and a sense of prophetic responsibility. It was his office to honour where honour was due and to sow rebuke on evil-doing.

At length he said:

"Sparta will not honour thee. But she needs must let thee lie with her heroes. Do not grieve, true soul. Pindar hath crowned thee, and Pindar's crowns do not die."

So saying he left him there, smiling still among the dead.

Herodotos's Account of Aristodemos

Herodotos, after describing the struggle at the Pass of Thermopylæ and the heroism of Leonidas and his Three Hundred Spartans, says:

"Of these three hundred there were two named Eurytos and Aristodemos, both of whom, if they had agreed together, might have come safe home to Sparta. For they had both been dismissed from the camp by Leonidas and were lying at Alpenoi suffering extremely with disease of the eyes. Or, if they had not desired to return home, they might both have been slain together with the rest.

"But they could not agree what to do. Eurytos, when he was told that the Persians had got around (by the secret path over the mountain) called for his arms, put them on, and made his Helot lead him (blind as he was) to the fighting. The slave led him in and then fled, while his master plunged into the thick of the fight and perished. Aristodemos was left behind, fainting.

"Now if Aristodemos had been ill alone and so had returned home to Sparta, or if the men had both come back together, I do not think the Spartans would have been angered. But inasmuch as one of them died on the field, which the other, who was in precisely the same condition, refused to do, the Spartans were naturally greatly incensed at Aristodemos.

"Thus is the safe return of Aristodemos to Sparta related and explained.

"There are some, however, who say that he had been dispatched on some business from the camp, and that he could, if he had desired, have come up in time for the fighting, but that he lingered on the road and saved his life. They add that his companion reached the battle and was slain.

"Aristodemos on his return home to Lacedæmon was branded with disgrace and infamy. No Spartan would speak with him. No one would give him light for his fire. And they continually reproached him, calling him always, 'Aristodemos the Coward.'

"Afterwards, however, in the Battle at Platæa, he amply repaired all the guilt that was charged against him."

(Book VII, 229-282).

Later, having described the events following Thermopylæ and Salamis, and especially the freeing of Greece in the conclusive battle at Platæa, Herodotos says:

"Of the Hellenes, while both the Tegeans and the Athenians proved themselves good men, yet the Lacedæmonians surpassed them in valour. Though I have no other proof of it but this (for all the Hellenes were victorious over their several opponents) that it was they who fought against the strongest part of the enemy's force and overcame it.

"And the man who in my opinion proved himself by far the bravest of the Spartans was that same Aristodemos who alone out of the Three Hundred, came back safe from Thermopylæ and suffered such reproach and dishonour.

"After him the best were Poseidonios and Philokyon and Amompharetos the Spartan.

"But when it was debated which of them had on that day proved himself the most valorous, the Spartans present gave it as their opinion that Aristodemos had evidently wished to be slain in consequence of the charge that lay upon him, and that in an emotion of frenzy he had left his place in the phalanx and performed extraordinary exploits.

"This, however, the Spartans may have said from some ill will.

THE SPARTAN

"All those whose names I have mentioned among the men who were killed in this battle were especially honoured, excepting Aristodemos. To him, for the reason mentioned, no respect was paid. 'Because,' they said, 'he willingly sought death'."

(Book IX, 71).

THE SPARTAN